College Algebra Made Easy

Study Guide to Ace your Test With Key Points, Examples, and Practices

Dr. Abolfazl Nazari

Copyright © 2024 Dr. Abolfazl Nazari

PUBLISHED BY EFFORTLESS MATH EDUCATION

EFFORTLESSMATH.COM

All rights reserved. No part of this publication may be reproduced, distributed, or transmitted in any form or by any means, including photocopying, recording, or other electronic or mechanical methods, without the prior written permission of the author, except in the case of brief quotations embodied in critical reviews and certain other noncommercial uses permitted by copyright law, including Section 107 or 108 of the 1976 United States Copyright Act.

Copyright ©2024

Welcome to College Algebra Made Easy

2024

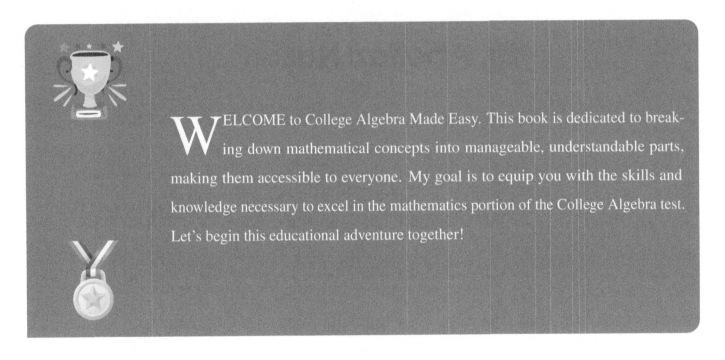

WELCOME to College Algebra Made Easy. This book is dedicated to breaking down mathematical concepts into manageable, understandable parts, making them accessible to everyone. My goal is to equip you with the skills and knowledge necessary to excel in the mathematics portion of the College Algebra test. Let's begin this educational adventure together!

College Algebra Made Easy provides comprehensive coverage of the key mathematical topics needed for the College Algebra test. The book is structured into detailed chapters on Fractions and Mixed Numbers, Decimals, Integers and Order of Operations, Ratios and Proportions, Percentages, and much more. Each chapter starts with basic concepts and gradually moves to more complex ones, ensuring you gain a complete understanding of each topic. The content is tailored to not only prepare you for the College Algebra test but also to apply these skills in real-life situations.

In keeping with the *Math Made Easy* series' philosophy, this book adopts an interactive and practice-oriented approach to learning. Each mathematical concept is introduced in a clear and straightforward manner, accompanied by examples to help illustrate its application. A variety of practice problems are provided to mirror the style and challenges of the College Algebra test, enabling you to test your knowledge and strengthen your understanding. I am excited to show you what the book contains.

What is included in this book

- ☑ Online resources for additional practice and support.
- ☑ A guide on how to use this book effectively.
- ☑ All College Algebra concepts and topics you will be tested on.
- ☑ End of chapter exercises to help you develop the basic math skills.
- ☑ College Algebra test tips and strategies.
- ☑ 2 realistic and full-length practice tests with detailed answers.

Effortless Math's College Algebra Online Center

Effortless Math Online College Algebra Center offers a complete study program, including the following:

- ☑ *Step-by-step instructions on how to prepare for the College Algebra test*
- ☑ *Numerous College Algebra worksheets to help you measure your math skills*
- ☑ *Complete list of College Algebra formulas*
- ☑ *Video lessons for all College Algebra topics*
- ☑ *Full-length College Algebra practice tests*

Visit EffortlessMath.com/PreAlgebra to find your online College Algebra resources.

Scan this QR code

(No Registration Required)

Tips for Making the Most of This Book

This book is all about making mathematics easy and approachable for you. Our aim is to cover everything you need to know, keeping it as straightforward as possible. Here is a guide on how to use this book effectively:

First, each math topic has a core idea or concept. It's important to understand and remember this. That's why we have highlighted key points in every topic. These are like mini-summaries of the most important stuff.

Examples are super helpful in showing how these concepts work in real problems. In every topic, we've included a couple of examples. If you feel very smart, you can try to solve them on your own first. But they are meant to be part of the teaching; They show how key concepts are applied to the problems. The main thing is to learn from these examples.

And, of course, practice is key. At the end of each chapter, you will find problems to solve. This is where you can really sharpen your skills.

To wrap it up:

- *Key Points*: Don't miss the key points. They boil down the big ideas.
- *Examples*: Try out the examples. They show you how to apply what you're learning.
- *Practices*: Dive into the practice problems. They're your chance to really get it.

In addition to the material covered in this book, it is crucial to have a solid plan for your test preparation. Effective test preparation goes beyond understanding concepts; it involves strategic study planning and practice under exam conditions.

- **Begin Early.** Start studying well before the exam to avoid rushing, allowing for a thorough review.
- **Daily Study Sessions.** Study regularly for 30 to 45 minutes each day to enhance retention and reduce stress.
- **Active Note-Taking.** Write down key points to internalize concepts and improve focus. Review notes regularly.
- **Review Challenges.** Spend extra time on difficult topics for better understanding and performance.
- **Practice.** Engage in extensive practice using end-of-chapter problems and additional workbooks.

Explore other guides, workbooks, and tests in the series to complement your study, offering extra practice and enhancing understanding, problem-solving skills, and academic preparation.

Contents

1. Fundamentals and Building Blocks

1.1   Order of Operations

The order of operations (such as addition or multiplication) in a mathematical expression is governed by the acronym "PEMDAS" which stands for Parentheses, Exponents, Multiplication, and Division (from left to right), and Addition and Subtraction (from left to right). The mnemonic "Please Excuse My Dear Aunt Sally" aids in remembering this sequence.

🔔 Key Point

PEMDAS, the acronym for the order of operations, stands for Parentheses, Exponents, followed by Multiplication and Division (left to right), and then Addition and Subtraction (left to right).

Example: Evaluate the expression $7 - 1 \times 3 + 2$.

   Solution: Following PEMDAS, we first carry out the multiplication: $1 \times 3 = 3$. The expression becomes $7 - 3 + 2$. Then, we perform the subtraction and addition from left to right: $7 - 3 = 4$, then $4 + 2 = 6$. Therefore, the solution is 6.

Example: Evaluate the expression $5(2^2 + 3 - 1)$.

   Solution: According to PEMDAS, start with operations inside the parentheses. Within that, follow the rules for exponents first: $2^2 = 4$. The expression becomes $5(4 + 3 - 1)$. Then add and subtract within the parentheses: $4 + 3 - 1 = 6$. This makes the expression 5×6. Finally, carry out the multiplication operation: $5 \times 6 = 30$. Hence, the solution is 30.

1.2   Scientific Notation

There are situations in science and mathematics where we encounter very large or very small numbers. This is where scientific notation comes into play.

🔔 Key Point

Scientific notation is a method used to represent very large or very small numbers in a simplified manner. It is written as $m \times 10^n$ where m is a number greater than 1 and less than 10, and n is an exponent.

To convert a number from standard form to scientific notation, locate the decimal point and move it to the right or left to obtain a number between 1 and 10. The number of places you moved the decimal point will be the exponent n. If the decimal point is moved to the left, the exponent n is positive; if it is moved to the right, the exponent n is negative.

🔔 Key Point

To convert a number from scientific notation to standard form, move the decimal point n places to the right if n is positive, moving it to the left if n is negative.

Example: Convert 5000 to scientific notation.

   Solution: Moving the decimal point three places to the left gives us 5 which falls between 1 and 10. Thus, 5000 in scientific notation is 5×10^3.

Example: Convert 2.6×10^{-3} back to standard form.

   Solution: The exponent -3 indicates that we have to move the decimal point three places to the left. So, 2.6×10^{-3} is converted to 0.0026 in standard form.

1.3   Rules of Exponents

When you are directed to multiply $2 \times 2 \times 2 \times 2$ for example, rather than repeatedly writing 2 multiplied by itself, we can simplify this as 2^4. Here, 2 is known as the base and 4 is the exponent.

🔔 Key Point

An exponent is simply a shorthand way for repeated multiplication of the same number by itself. It is written as x^n, where x is the base and n is the exponent.

When performing operations with exponents, it is essential to follow specific rules tailored to simplify your mathematical calculations. These rules include:

- Rule 1 (Product of Powers Rule): Adding the exponents when multiplying terms with the same base, $x^m \times x^n = x^{(m+n)}$.

- Rule 2 (Quotient of Powers Rule): Subtract the exponents when dividing terms with the same base, $\frac{x^m}{x^n} = x^{(m-n)}$.

- Rule 3 (Power of a Power Rule): Multiply the exponents when raising a power to another power, $(x^m)^n = x^{mn}$.

- Rule 4 (Power of a Product Rule): Apply the exponent to each base in the product, $(xy)^n = x^n y^n$.

- Rule 5 (Power of a Quotient Rule): Apply the exponent to both numerator and denominator, $\left(\frac{x}{y}\right)^n = \frac{x^n}{y^n}$.

🔔 Key Point

Exponent rules simplified:

Rule 1, Product Rule: $x^m \times x^n = x^{(m+n)}$.

Rule 2, Quotient Rule: $\frac{x^m}{x^n} = x^{(m-n)}$.

Rule 3, Power of Power: $(x^m)^n = x^{mn}$.

Rule 4, Product to Power: $(xy)^n = x^n y^n$.

Rule 5, Quotient to Power: $\left(\frac{x}{y}\right)^n = \frac{x^n}{y^n}$.

Example: Simplify the expression $x^3 \times x^5$.

    Solution: Using Rule 1, we add the exponents. Thus, $x^3 \times x^5 = x^{(3+5)} = x^8$.

Example: Simplify the expression $\frac{x^7}{x^2}$.

    Solution: Using Rule 2, we subtract the exponents. Thus, $\frac{x^7}{x^2} = x^{(7-2)} = x^5$.

Example: Simplify the expression $(x^3)^2$.

    Solution: Using Rule 3, we multiply the exponents. Thus, $(x^3)^2 = x^{(3\times 2)} = x^6$.

1.4   Evaluating Expressions

The process of evaluating expressions is straightforward. Substitute the number you are given for each variable, then perform the arithmetic operations. An important rule to remember: always follow the order of operations—Parentheses, Exponents, Multiplication, Division, Addition, Subtraction (PEMDAS)—when performing arithmetic operations.

🔔 Key Point

> To evaluate an algebraic expression, substitute a number for each variable and perform the arith-
> metic operations.

Example: Evaluate the expression $3x + 2y$ for $x = 4$ and $y = 5$.

  Solution: Substitute the given values of x and y into the expression:

$$3(4) + 2(5) = 12 + 10 = 22.$$

Hence, the value of the expression for $x = 4$ and $y = 5$ is 22.

Example: Evaluate the expression $4a^2 - 3b$ for $a = 3$ and $b = 2$.

  Solution: Substitute the given values of a and b into the expression:

$$4(3^2) - 3(2) = 4(9) - 6 = 36 - 6 = 30.$$

Hence, the value of the expression for $a = 3$ and $b = 2$ is 30.

Example: Evaluate the expression $2x^3 - 6x^2 + 4x - 1$ for $x = -1$.

  Solution: Substitute the given value of x into the expression:

$$2(-1)^3 - 6(-1)^2 + 4(-1) - 1 = -2 - 6 - 4 - 1 = -13.$$

Hence, the value of the expression for $x = -1$ is -13.

1.5   Simplifying Algebraic Expressions

Simplifying an expression means performing all possible operations and combining like terms to bring the expression to its simplest form.

Here, *like terms* refer to terms that have the same variables and powers. For instance, $7x$ and $3x$ are like terms because they both represent multiples of x; similarly, $4y^2$ and $-9y^2$ are like terms because they are multiples of y^2.

🔔 Key Point

Like terms are those with both the same variable and the same exponent. Combining these terms allows for the simplification of an algebraic expression.

Simplifying algebraic expressions reduces them into a more manageable form while preserving the initial meaning of the expression. This condensed form is much easier to handle in further operations or equations.

Example: Simplify the expression $7x + 3x + 4y^2 - 9y^2$.

Solution: We combine the like terms, $7x$ and $3x$, as well as $4y^2$ and $-9y^2$:

$$(7x + 3x) + (4y^2 - 9y^2) = 10x - 5y^2.$$

Hence, the simplified expression for $7x + 3x + 4y^2 - 9y^2$ is $10x - 5y^2$.

Example: Simplify the expression $4n^3 + 7n - 3n^3 + 2n$.

Solution: We combine the like terms, $4n^3$ and $-3n^3$, as well as $7n$ and $2n$:

$$(4n^3 - 3n^3) + (7n + 2n) = n^3 + 9n.$$

Hence, the simplified expression for $4n^3 + 7n - 3n^3 + 2n$ is $n^3 + 9n$.

Example: Simplify the expression $6a^2 - 4a + 5 - 2a^2 + 3a - 3$.

Solution: We combine the like terms, $6a^2$ and $-2a^2$, $-4a$ and $3a$, as well as 5 and -3:

$$(6a^2 - 2a^2) + (-4a + 3a) + (5 - 3) = 4a^2 - a + 2.$$

Hence, the simplified expression for $6a^2 - 4a + 5 - 2a^2 + 3a - 3$ is $4a^2 - a + 2$.

1.6   Sets

A set is a collection of distinct objects known as elements or members of the set. These elements share a common feature that can be easily defined or determined. Sets are typically represented by capital English letters, such as A, B, C, and so on. The elements of a set are listed inside curly braces '{}'. Consider, for example, a set B which contains the first five natural numbers: $B = \{1, 2, 3, 4, 5\}$.

🔔 Key Point

Each object in a set is unique. If an object appears more than once in a set, it is still considered as a single entry. The order of elements in a set does not matter.

The concept of set membership is denoted by '$\in$'. For example, $1 \in B$ means 1 is in set B, while $6 \notin B$ indicates 6 is not in B. Sets are classified as *finite* (countable elements) or *infinite*. A set with no elements is termed an *empty* or *null set*, represented by $\varnothing$ or {}.

Example: Let us define a set A which contains lowercase vowels of the English alphabet: $A = \{a, e, i, o, u\}$. Is r an element of set A?

Solution: We clearly see that r is not a lowercase vowel, so it is not listed in set A. Therefore, we can say that $r \notin A$.

Example: Given sets $P = \{2, 4, 6, 8, 10\}$ and $Q = \{3, 6, 9\}$, determine whether $6 \in P$, $6 \in Q$, $4 \in Q$, and $9 \in P$.

Solution: The number 6 is an element of both sets P and Q, so $6 \in P$ and $6 \in Q$. The number 4 is not an element of set Q, so $4 \notin Q$. The number 9 is not an element of set P, so $9 \notin P$.

1.7   Practices

📇 Solve:

1) $9 - 2 \times (4 + 1)$.

2) $6 + 4 \times 2^2 - 8$.

3) $7 \times 2 + 3^2 - 1$.

4) $4(5 - 3^2) + 6$.

5) $(3 + 2)(2^2 + 5)^2 - 4 \times 2$.

Fill in the Blank:

6) Write 7000 in scientific notation: _____

7) Write 4.9×10^{-3} in standard form: _____

8) Write 309 in scientific notation: _____

9) Convert 2.1×10^4 to standard notation: _____

10) Write 0.00012 in scientific notation: _____

Simplify Each Expression:

11) Simplify the expression $x^4 \times x^6$.

12) Simplify the expression $(xy)^3$.

13) Simplify the expression $\frac{y^5}{y^2}$.

14) Simplify the expression $(x^3)^4$.

15) Simplify the expression $\left(\frac{x}{y}\right)^4$.

Solve:

16) Evaluate the expression $2m + 3n$ for $m = 5$ and $n = 3$.

17) Evaluate the expression $5x^2 - 4y$ for $x = 2$ and $y = 1$.

18) Evaluate the expression $6x^3 - 3x^2 + 2x - 1$ for $x = 1$.

19) Evaluate the expression $6p - 4q + 2$ for $p = 3$ and $q = 2$.

20) Evaluate the expression $9a^2 - 3b + 1$ for $a = 2$ and $b = 1$.

Simplify Each Expression:

21) Simplify the expression $5m + 8m^2 - 3m + 7 - 2m^2 + 4$.

22) Simplify the expression $4b - 2b^3 + 7b - 5 + 3b^3 + 6$.

23) Simplify the expression $9c - 6 - 3c^2 + 5c - 2 + 2c^2$.

24) Simplify the expression $7d^2 + 3d - 2d^2 + 5d + 9 - 3$.

25) Simplify the expression $6e + 4 - 3e^2 + 7e - 5 + 2e^2$.

True or False:

26) The order of elements in a set matters.

27) If an object appears more than once in a set, it is still considered as a single entry.

28) A finite set has uncountable elements.

29) The set $Q = \{2, 4, 6, 8\}$ and the set $Q = \{8, 6, 4, 2\}$ are different.

30) Consider the set $A = \{\varnothing\}$. The set A is an empty set.

Answer Keys

1) -1

2) 14

3) 22

4) -10

5) 397

6) 7×10^3

7) 0.0049

8) 3.09×10^2

9) 21000

10) 1.2×10^{-4}

11) x^{10}

12) $x^3 y^3$

13) y^3

14) x^{12}

15) $\frac{x^4}{y^4}$

16) 19

17) 16

18) 4

19) 12

20) 34

21) $6m^2 + 2m + 11$

22) $b^3 + 11b + 1$

23) $-c^2 + 14c - 8$

24) $5d^2 + 8d + 6$

25) $-e^2 + 13e - 1$

26) False

27) True

28) False

29) False

30) False

Answers with Explanation

1) First, evaluate the operation within the parentheses, $4 + 1 = 5$. Then multiply $2 \times 5 = 10$, and finally subtract $9 - 10 = -1$.

2) First perform the exponentiation, $2^2 = 4$. Then carry out the multiplication, $4 \times 4 = 16$. The expression becomes $6 + 16 - 8$. Perform the addition and subtraction from left to right: $6 + 16 = 22$, and then $22 - 8 = 14$.

3) First perform the operation of exponentiation, $3^2 = 9$. The expression becomes $7 \times 2 + 9 - 1$. Perform the multiplication: $7 \times 2 = 14$. The expression then becomes $14 + 9 - 1$. Finally, add and subtract $14 + 9 = 23$, then $23 - 1 = 22$.

4) First evaluate the exponent, $3^2 = 9$. The expression becomes $4(5 - 9) + 6$. Then perform the operation inside the parentheses, $5 - 9 = -4$. This makes the expression $4(-4) + 6$. Perform the multiplication of $4(-4) = -16$. The expression becomes $-16 + 6$. Finally, add and subtract from left to right $-16 + 6 = -10$.

5) First, solve inside the inner parentheses: $2^2 = 4$. This makes the expression $(3 + 2)(4 + 5)^2 - 4 \times 2$. Then evaluate the operations inside the parentheses. First, $3 + 2 = 5$ and $4 + 5 = 9$. The expression becomes $5 \times 9^2 - 4 \times 2$. Then calculate the square $9^2 = 81$, and multiply $5 \times 81 = 405$. The expression becomes $405 - 4 \times 2$. Finally, subtract and multiply from left to right $405 - 8 = 397$.

6) Moving the decimal point three places to the left of 7000 gives us 7 which is greater than 1 and less than 10. Therefore, 7000 in scientific notation is 7×10^3.

7) A negative exponent suggests moving the decimal point to the left three places. Hence, 4.9×10^{-3} in standard form is 0.0049.

8) Shifting the decimal two places to the left of 309 provides us with 3.09. So, the scientific notation for 309 is 3.09×10^2.

9) A positive exponent implies moving decimal point to the right four places. Hence, 2.1×10^4 in standard form is 21000.

10) Moving the decimal four places to the right of 0.00012 gives us 1.2 which is greater than 1 and less than 10. Therefore, 0.00012 in scientific notation is 1.2×10^{-4}.

11) Using Rule 1 (Product of Powers Rule), we add the exponents. Thus, $x^4 \times x^6 = x^{(4+6)} = x^{10}$.

12) Using Rule 4 (Power of a Product Rule), we apply the exponent to each base in the product. Thus, $(xy)^3 = x^3 y^3$.

13) Using Rule 2 (Quotient of Powers Rule), we subtract the exponents. Thus, $\frac{y^5}{y^2} = y^{(5-2)} = y^3$.

14) Using Rule 3 (Power of a Power Rule), we multiply the exponents. Thus, $(x^3)^4 = x^{(3 \times 4)} = x^{12}$.

15) Using Rule 5 (Power of a Quotient Rule), we apply the exponent to both the numerator and denominator. Thus, $\left(\frac{x}{y}\right)^4 = \frac{x^4}{y^4}$.

16) Substitute the given values of m and n into the expression:

$$2(5) + 3(3) = 10 + 9 = 19.$$

17) Substitute the given values of x and y into the expression:

$$5(2)^2 - 4(1) = 5(4) - 4 = 20 - 4 = 16.$$

18) Substitute the given value of x into the expression:

$$6(1)^3 - 3(1)^2 + 2(1) - 1 = 6 - 3 + 2 - 1 = 4.$$

19) Substitute the given values of p and q into the expression:

$$6(3) - 4(2) + 2 = 18 - 8 + 2 = 12.$$

20) Substitute the given values of a and b into the expression:

$$9(2)^2 - 3(1) + 1 = 9(4) - 3 + 1 = 36 - 3 + 1 = 34.$$

21) Combine like terms: $(8m^2 - 2m^2) + (5m - 3m) + (7 + 4) = 6m^2 + 2m + 11.$

22) Combine like terms: $(4b + 7b) + (-2b^3 + 3b^3) + (-5 + 6) = 11b + b^3 + 1.$

23) Combine like terms: $(9c + 5c) + (-3c^2 + 2c^2) + (-6 - 2) = 14c - c^2 - 8.$

24) Combine like terms: $(7d^2 - 2d^2) + (3d + 5d) + (9 - 3) = 5d^2 + 8d + 6.$

25) Combine like terms: $(6e + 7e) + (-3e^2 + 2e^2) + (4 - 5) = 13e - e^2 - 1.$

26) The order in which elements are listed in a set does not matter.

27) Each object in a set is unique. If an object appears more than once in a set, it is still considered as a single entry.

28) A finite set has a countable number of elements.

29) The order in which elements are listed in a set does not matter. Thus, the two sets are the same despite the different ordering of the elements.

30) The set A is not empty, as it contains one element, which is the empty set itself ($\varnothing$). An empty set would be denoted as $\{\}$, containing no elements at all.

2. Equations and Inequalities

2.1 Solving Multi–Step Equations

To solve multi-step equations, we reverse operations in a specific order to isolate the variable, typically x. Start by undoing addition or subtraction, followed by reversing multiplication or division. This process simplifies the equation step by step, leading to the value of x.

🔔 Key Point

In multi-step equations, it is essential to maintain balance by applying identical operations to both sides. This principle forms the cornerstone of equation solving.

Example: Solve the multi-step equation $3x + 4 = 19$.

Solution: First, subtract 4 from both sides: $3x + 4 - 4 = 19 - 4$, which gives: $3x = 15$. Next, divide both sides by 3: $x = \frac{15}{3}$. So, the solution is $x = 5$.

Example: Solve the multi-step equation: $3x + 5 = x + 9$.

Solution: First, we subtract 5 and x from both sides: $3x + 5 - 5 - x = x + 9 - 5 - x$, which yields: $2x = 4$. Then, we divide both sides by 2: $x = \frac{4}{2}$. So, the solution is $x = 2$.

2.2   Slope and Intercepts

The slope of a line reflects its direction and steepness. To determine the slope of a line that passes through the points $A(x_1, y_1)$ and $B(x_2, y_2)$, the formula $\frac{y_2 - y_1}{x_2 - x_1}$ is used.

🔔 Key Point

The slope m of a line through points $A(x_1, y_1)$ and $B(x_2, y_2)$ is the ratio of vertical to horizontal change: $m = \frac{y_2 - y_1}{x_2 - x_1}$.

Meanwhile, intercepts provide information about where the line crosses the x and y axes. This is captured in the general linear equation $y = mx + b$, where m is the slope and b is the y-intercept.

🔔 Key Point

A linear function is represented by $y = mx + b$, where m is the slope and b is the y-intercept. Such a linear equation is called slope-intercept form.

Example: Determine the slope and y-intercept of the line whose equation is $y = 3x + 2$.

Solution: The given equation is already in slope-intercept form, which is $y = mx + b$. Here, $m = 3$ is the slope and $b = 2$ is the y-intercept. Hence, the slope of the line is 3 and it intersects the y-axis at 2.

Example: Find the slope of the line passing through the points $A(3, 4)$ and $B(2, 1)$.

Solution: We can find the slope using the formula, $m = \frac{y_2 - y_1}{x_2 - x_1}$. Substituting the provided values into the formula, we get, $m = \frac{1-4}{2-3} = 3$. Hence, the slope of the line is $m = 3$.

2.3   Using Intercepts

In a given linear equation, each term holds a particular significance. Recall the equation $y = mx + b$, where m is the slope and b is the y-intercept. Similarly, in $cx + dy = f$, the x-intercept is found by setting $y = 0$ and solving for x, and similarly, we find the y-intercept by setting $x = 0$ and solving for y.

🔔 Key Point

The x-intercept, where $y = 0$, is the x value where the line crosses the x-axis, and the y-intercept, where $x = 0$, is the y value where the line crosses the y-axis.

Identifying the x and y intercepts allows for quick sketching of a line's graph. Since a straight line is defined by any two points on it, the intercepts provide these crucial points, precisely representing the line's equation.

Example: Find the x-intercept and y-intercept for the equation $5x + 2y = 10$, and graph the line.

Solution: To find the x-intercept, set $y = 0$, reducing the equation to $5x = 10$, so $x = 2$. For the y-intercept, set $x = 0$, simplifying the equation to $2y = 10$, yielding $y = 5$. The intercepts are found to be:

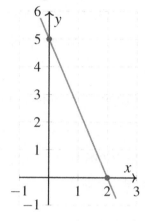

x-intercept $= 2$ and y-intercept $= 5$. These intercepts are the points $(2,0)$ and $(0,5)$ in the Cartesian coordinates. Connect these points with a straight line to graph the given equation, as represented in the following figure.

Example: Solve the equation $3x - 6y = 12$ for its intercepts and draw its graph.

Solution: The x-intercept can be found by setting $y = 0$. This simplifies the equation to $3x = 12$, thus $x = 4$. To find the y-intercept, set $x = 0$. The equation simplifies to $-6y = 12$, thus $y = -2$. The intercepts for this equation are:

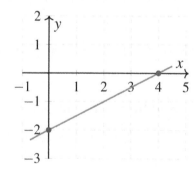

x-intercept $= 4$ and y-intercept $= -2$. This corresponds to points $(4,0)$ and $(0,-2)$ on the Cartesian coordinate plane. By connecting these points, we obtain a clear graph.

2.4 Transforming Linear Functions

Linear functions can transform, altering their position, size, or steepness on a graph. Note that these transformations do not alter the shape of the graph.

The equation $y = mx + b$ represents a linear function, where m is the slope and b is the y-intercept. Small changes in these values can lead to translation, rotation, or reflection of the line.

🔔 **Key Point**

> Three basic transformations for linear functions include translation (shifting the line up or down), rotation (altering the steepness), and reflection (reflecting across the y-axis).

Let us discuss these transformations in detail:

1) Translation: When you alter the y-intercept b in the function $y = mx + b$, this results in the line vertically translating (shifting) up or down. A higher value of b moves the graph up, while a lower value of b moves it down.

2) Rotation: The slope m in the function, $y = mx + b$, determines the line's steepness. Any change in m results in a rotation of the line. This rotation pivots around the point $(0, b)$.

3) Reflection: By negating the slope (i.e., $-m$), we achieve a reflection of the function across the y-axis.

🔔 **Key Point**

> Linear function $y = mx + b$ can undergo three transformations:
>
> *1) Translation*: Changing b shifts the graph vertically.
>
> *2) Rotation*: Modifying m alters steepness and causes rotation around $(0, b)$.
>
> *3) Reflection*: Negating m reflects the function across y-axis.
>
> These do not change the graph's shape but affect position, size, and steepness.

Example: Consider the function $y = 2x + 3$. How does the graph change if we transform this to $y = 2x + 5$?

Solution: The functions $y = 2x + 3$ and $y = 2x + 5$ have the same slope, therefore, the steepness stays the same. However, we can clearly see that the y-intercept has increased from 3 to 5.

Hence, this transformation translates the original graph upwards by 2 units along the y-axis, as demonstrated.

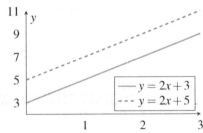

Example: Examine the changes involved in transforming the linear function $y = 3x + 2$ into $y = -3x + 2$

Solution: In our original function, $y = 3x + 2$, the slope is 3.

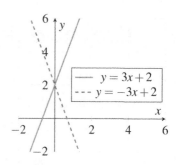

However, in the transformed function, the slope is -3. The y-intercept remains the same. This means we have reflected our function across the y-axis, as presented in the figure.

2.5   Solving Inequalities

Solving inequalities, much like multi-step equations, involves a step-by-step approach. The key difference lies in the solution interpretation: inequalities often yield a range of solutions, rather than a single value.

🔔 Key Point

> When you multiply or divide both sides by a negative number while solving inequalities, remember to flip the inequality sign.

The process of solving one-step inequalities often involves finding the inverse (or opposite) operation to what is used in the inequality. The goal is to isolate the variable.

Example: Solve the inequality $2x > 8$.

Solution: First, identify the inverse operation. In this case, the operation performed on x is multiplication by 2, so the inverse operation will be division by 2. Divide both sides by 2 to isolate x. This gives us: $x > \frac{8}{2}$. Hence, the solution is $x > 4$.

Example: Solve the inequality $x + 7 \leq 10$.

Solution: The inverse operation of adding 7 is subtracting 7. By subtracting 7 from both sides, we can isolate x. This gives us: $x \leq 10 - 7$. So, the solution is $x \leq 3$.

Example: Solve the inequality $-3x \geq 9$.

Solution: The inverse operation of multiplying by -3 is dividing by -3. Remember, dividing or multiplying by a negative number reverses the inequality. So, when we divide both sides by -3, the inequality sign turns from greater than or equal to $\geq$, to less than or equal to $\leq$. This gives us: $x \leq \frac{9}{-3}$. So, the solution is $x \leq -3$.

2.6   Graphing Linear Inequalities

Graphing linear inequalities is akin to graphing linear equations, with an extra step to mark the solution region.

1. Convert the inequality to an equation (equal sign) and graph the line accordingly.

2. Use a dotted or solid line based on whether the inequality includes equality.

3. Select a test point, substitute its coordinates into the inequality, and shade the region where the inequality is true.

🔔 Key Point

> For graphing linear inequalities, use a solid line when the inequality includes equality ($\leq$ or $\geq$), and a dotted line for strict inequalities ($<$ or $>$).

Example: Graph the inequality $2x + y \leq 4$.

Solution: Use the following steps:

Step 1: Treat the inequality as an equation and graph the line $2x + y = 4$. The slope-intercept form of the line is $y = -2x + 4$. This line intercepts the y-axis at 4 and has a slope of -2. So draw a line starting at the y-intercept and moving down 2 units for every 1 unit to the right.

Step 2: As the inequality sign involves equality, draw a solid line.

Step 3: Select the test point. The origin $(0,0)$ is generally a good choice if it does not lie on the line.

Substituting $x = 0$ and $y = 0$ into the inequality results in $2(0) + 0 = 0 \leq 4$, which is true. Therefore, shade the region containing the origin, which in this case, is the region below the line, as represented as follows.

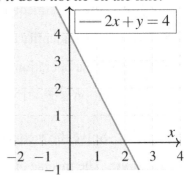

Example: Graph the inequality $y < x + 2$.

Solution: Use the following steps:

Step 1: Treat the inequality as an equation and graph the line $y = x + 2$. This line intercepts the y-axis at 2 and has a slope of 1. So, draw a line starting at the y-intercept and moving up 1 unit for every 1 unit to the right.

Step 2: As the inequality sign does not involve equality, draw a dotted line.

Step 3: Select the test point.

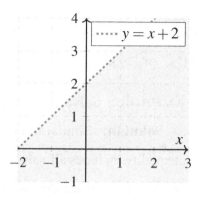

As earlier, let us pick $(0,0)$. Substituting into the inequality, $0 < 0 + 2$, which is valid. So, shade the region containing the origin, or the region below the line, as represented as follows.

2.7   Solving Compound Inequalities

Compound inequalities, combining two inequalities with "and" or "or", vary in solution and graphing methods based on the connector used.

For inequalities connected by "and" (a conjunction), the solution is the intersection of both inequalities' solution sets, representing values satisfying both simultaneously.

🔔 **Key Point**

When solving compound inequalities joined by "and", find the intersection of the individual solutions.

For inequalities connected by "or" (also known as a disjunction), the solution is the union of the solution sets of the two inequalities. This means the solution consists of values that satisfy either inequality. Therefore, "or" inequalities typically have a broader solution than "and" inequalities.

🔔 **Key Point**

When solving compound inequalities, joined by "or", form the union of the individual solutions.

Example: Solve the inequality $1 < x \leq 3$.

Solution: This inequality actually represents two inequalities: $1 < x$ and $x \leq 3$. For $1 < x$, all values of x greater than 1 satisfy this inequality. And for $x \leq 3$, all values of x less than or equal to 3 satisfy this inequality. The solution of the compound inequality is the intersection of these two solutions, i.e., $1 < x \leq 3$.

Closed circles on the number line represent inclusivity ('$\leq$' or '$\geq$'), while open circles represent exclusivity ('$<$' or '$>$').

Example: Solve the inequality $x < 1$ or $x \geq 3$.

Solution: Similar to the previous example, this inequality splits into two: $x < 1$ and $x \geq 3$. The first inequality includes all values of x less than 1 and the second inequality includes all values of x greater than or equal to 3. Since the two inequalities are connected by "or", we form the union of these two solutions. Therefore, the solution of the compound inequality is $x < 1$ or $x \geq 3$.

2.8   Solving Absolute Value Equations

Absolute value, signifying the non-negative distance from zero, is integral to absolute value equations. Solving these equations requires considering that a number's absolute value can result in both positive and negative outcomes, typically leading to multiple solutions.

Key Point

Solving absolute value equations involves creating two related equations without absolute value signs.

Let us start by identifying a structure in these types of equations. For an absolute value equation in the form: $|ax + b| = c$, where a, b, and c are constants, a is not equal to zero, and c is non-negative, we can create two equations: $ax + b = c$, and $ax + b = -c$. We then solve for x in each equation and check the answers.

Key Point

Absolute value equations like $|ax + b| = c$ (with constants $a \neq 0$, b, and $c \geq 0$) lead to two scenarios: $ax + b = c$ and $ax + b = -c$. Solve both for x and verify the solutions.

Example: Solve the equation $|2x - 4| = 6$.

Solution: We can create two equations: $2x - 4 = 6$ and $2x - 4 = -6$. For $2x - 4 = 6$, solving for x gives $x = 5$. And for $2x - 4 = -6$, solving for x gives $x = -1$. To check these solutions, we substitute them back into the original equation:

1) For $x = 5$: $|2(5) - 4| = |6| = 6$.

2) For $x = -1$: $|2(-1) - 4| = |-6| = 6$.

In both cases, the equation is satisfied. Therefore, the solutions to the equation $|2x - 4| = 6$ are $x = 5$ and $x = -1$.

2.9 Solving Absolute Value Inequalities

Understanding absolute value and inequality solving simplifies this topic. Consider the absolute value inequality $|ax + b| \leq c$ or $|ax + b| \geq c$ with constants $a \neq 0$, b, $c \geq 0$. It splits into a compound inequality:

- For $|ax + b| \leq c$, we get $-c \leq ax + b \leq c$, meaning the solution is between $-c$ and c (inclusive).
- For $|ax + b| \geq c$, we have $ax + b \geq c$, or $ax + b \leq -c$, indicating that the solution is not between $-c$ and c (exclusive).

Key Point

When working with absolute value inequalities, the inequality's direction dictates the separation of the absolute value expression into different inequalities. For $|ax + b| \leq c$, the solution falls within the interval $[-c, c]$, whereas for $|ax + b| \geq c$, the solution lies outside the interval $[-c, c]$.

Example: Solve the inequality $|3x + 2| \leq 7$.

Solution: We begin by simplifying the absolute value inequality into a standard inequality as $-7 \leq 3x + 2 \leq 7$. Solving for x in each of these inequalities, we subtract 2 from each side of the inequality so that we get $-9 \leq 3x \leq 5$. Finally, we divide all sides by 3 to discover that $-3 \leq x \leq \frac{5}{3}$. This means the solution for x ranges between and includes -3 and $\frac{5}{3}$ in the real number line.

Example: Solve the inequality $|4x - 1| > 3$.

Solution: Here, we create two inequalities: $4x - 1 > 3$ and $4x - 1 < -3$. For $4x - 1 > 3$, solving for x yields $x > 1$. As for $4x - 1 < -3$, solving for x provides $x < -\frac{1}{2}$. This means the solution for x is less than

$-\frac{1}{2}$ or greater than 1 in the real number line.

2.10   Graphing Absolute Value Inequalities

After solving an absolute value inequality, graphically representing the solutions offers a tangible visualization. This section focuses on converting numerical solutions of absolute value inequalities into number line plots.

🔔 Key Point

The inequality's direction ($\leq$, $\geq$, $<$, $>$) recorresponds to whether a circle on the number line plot should be open (exclusivity) or closed (inclusivity).

Example: Graph the solutions of the inequality $|3x+2| \leq 7$.

  Solution: We previously found the solution for this inequality as $-3 \leq x \leq \frac{5}{3}$. On a number line, we would:

1) Plot closed circles at -3 and $\frac{5}{3}$ as they represent the boundary of our solution, emphasizing that these values are part of the solution due to the use of $\leq$.

2) Shade the region between these points to indicate that all values within this range are solutions to inequality.

Example: Graph the solutions of the inequality $|4x-1| > 3$.

  Solution: We determined the solution for this inequality was $x < -\frac{1}{2}$ and $x > 1$. On a number line, we would:

1) Plot open circles at $-\frac{1}{2}$ and 1 to indicate the boundary of our solution. The values of $-\frac{1}{2}$ and 1 do not satisfy the inequality, as indicated by the directional inequality symbol $>$.

2) Shade the regions that extend outwards from these points to demonstrate that all values less than $-\frac{1}{2}$ and greater than 1 satisfy the inequality.

2.11   Solving Systems of Equations

A system of equations involves multiple equations with the same set of unknowns. For example, in the system $x - y = 1$ and $x + y = 5$, we seek numerical solutions that satisfy all the equations simultaneously.

The method of elimination, the simplest approach, entails adding or subtracting equations to eliminate one variable and solve the system efficiently.

Key Point

The elimination method employs the addition property of equality to systematically eliminate one variable from a system of equations, simplifying the solving process.

Example: Solve the system of equations below using the method of elimination:

$$\begin{cases} x - y = 1 \\ x + y = 5 \end{cases}$$

Solution: We solve this system by adding both equations:

$$x - y + x + y = 1 + 5 \Rightarrow 2x = 6.$$

Solve for x, we get: $x = 3$. Having found the value of x, we can substitute it into the first equation to find y. Substitute $x = 3$ into the equation $x - y = 1$, we get: $3 - y = 1$. From which it follows that $y = 2$. Therefore, the solution to the system is $x = 3$ and $y = 2$. It is always a good idea to check if these values satisfy both original equations. In our case, they do! Our solution, in ordered pair notation, is $(3, 2)$.

Example: Solve the system of equations below using the method of elimination:

$$\begin{cases} x + 3y = 4 \\ 4x - y = 3 \end{cases}$$

Solution: To eliminate one variable, we can first multiply the second equation by 3:

$$3(4x - y) = 3(3) \Rightarrow 12x - 3y = 9.$$

Now, add this equation to the first equation:

$$x + 3y + 12x - 3y = 4 + 9 \Rightarrow 13x = 13.$$

Solve for x, we get: $x = 1$. Now substitute $x = 1$ into the first equation to find y. Substituting $x = 1$ into $x + 3y = 4$ gives: $1 + 3y = 4$. Solving for y, we get:

$$3y = 3 \Rightarrow y = 1.$$

Therefore, the solution to the system is $x = 1$ and $y = 1$.

2.12   Solving Special Systems

A special system of linear equations refers to a system that either has no solution or an infinite number of solutions. This situation arises when the equations in the system produce parallel lines or two lines that overlap.

Key Point

Parallel lines indicate a system of equations with no solution while overlapping lines indicate a system of equations with an infinite number of solutions.

To check if a system is special, we can use three methods: substitution, elimination, and graphical representation.

Substitution Method: In this method, we can represent y in terms of x in one of the equations and substitute it into the other equation.

Graphical Method: In the graphical method, we find the solution to the system of equations by plotting their graphs. If the graph results in parallel lines or straight lines that overlap each other, the system is a special one.

Example: Consider the system of equations:

$$\begin{cases} y = 2x + 3 \\ 2y = 4x + 6 \end{cases}$$

Do these two equations represent the same line, and if so, how does that affect the number of solutions to the system?

   Solution: This system seems like one equation was multiplied by a constant to derive the other. Since these two equations represent the same line, there is an infinite number of solutions. Every point on the line $y = 2x + 3$ is also a point on the line $2y = 4x + 6$, and vice versa.

Example: Using the elimination method on the system of equations:

$$\begin{cases} y = 2x + 3 \implies 2y = 4x + 6 \\ 2y = 4x + 6 \end{cases}$$

Can we deduce the relationship between the two equations and their solutions?

   Solution: Upon applying the elimination method, we notice that the two equations become identical. This reinforces the assumption that the system has an infinite number of solutions because they are essentially the same equation.

Example: If we plot the equations $y = 2x + 3$ and $2y = 4x + 6$, we notice that they overlap completely, which again points to their being an infinite number of solutions. This is because every point on the line $y = 2x + 3$ is also a point on the line $2y = 4x + 6$, and vice versa.

What conclusion can we draw if we plot the equations $y = 2x + 3$ and $2y = 4x + 6$ and observe their relationship?

Solution: The two lines overlap completely, which means that the system has an infinite number of solutions.

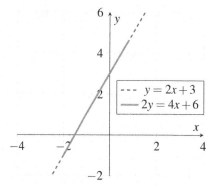

2.13   Systems of Equations Word Problems

Systems of equations can frequently be applied to solve real-world problems. Such problems can be formulated in the language of systems of equations, and hence, provide practical implications of this concept.

🔔 Key Point

> The solution to a system of equations in word problems corresponds to the solution of the problem in the real-world context.

Identifying Variables and Writing Equations: In word problems, we first identify the variables in the problem, assign them algebraic symbols, and then write down the equations that represent the relations as stated in the problem.

Example: Tickets to a movie cost $8 for adults and $5 for students. A group of friends purchased 20 tickets for $115. How many adult tickets did they buy?

Solution: we let x be the number of adult tickets and y be the number of student tickets. We then write two equations, $x + y = 20$ and $8x + 5y = 115$, representing the number of tickets and total cost respectively. The solution involves solving these two equations using the elimination method. The result gives $x = 5$ and $y = 15$, indicating that 5 adult tickets and 15 student tickets were purchased.

2.14   Practices

 Solve:

1) Solve the equation: $4x + 3 = 19$.

2) Solve the equation: $3y - 5 = 10$.

3) Solve the equation: $100 - 2z = 80$.

4) Solve the equation: $5p + 7 = 32$.

5) Solve the equation: $50 - 10a = 20$.

 Fill in the Blank

6) Given a line passing through the points $A(5, -2)$ and $B(9, 10)$, find the slope. The slope is _____ .

7) Given the equation of the line $y = 2x + 4$, the y-intercept is _____ .

8) Given the line passing through $A(-3, 1)$ and $B(1, 4)$, the slope is _____ .

9) Given the equation of a line $y = -3x + 2$, the slope of the line is _____ .

10) Given a line which passes through the points $A(6, 4)$ and $B(2, -1)$, the slope is _____ .

Solve:

11) Find the intercepts for the equation $8x - 4y = 16$.

12) Identify the intercepts for $3x + 6y = 12$.

13) Calculate the intercepts for the given equation $5x - 10y = 20$.

14) Determine the intercepts of the equation $4x + 8y = 16$.

15) Find out the intercepts for the equation $6x - 3y = 12$.

Find the Answer:

16) Consider the function $y = 3x - 1$. By how many units would you translate this function upwards to intersect with the line $y = 3x + 3$?

17) A linear function passes through the origin and the point $(2, 4)$. After reflection on y-axis, what must be the slope of the new function?

18) A linear function is given by $y = 2x + 3$. If the function is rotated to halve its steepness, what would be the new slope?

19) A function is defined as: $y = 4x + 5$. If the function is translated downwards 5 units, what would be the new y-intercept?

20) A linear function passes through the point $(3, 2)$. If the function is reflected on the y-axis, what will be the new point?

Solve:

21) Solve the inequality $5x < 25$.

22) Solve the inequality $2x + 3 > 9$.

23) Solve the inequality $3x - 10 < 5$.

24) Solve the inequality $-2x \geq 4$.

25) Solve the inequality $4x - 7 \leq 5$.

Solve:

26) Solve $x \geq 0$ and $x < 5$.

27) Solve $x \leq 1$ or $x > 3$.

28) Solve $x > -2$ and $x \leq 3$.

29) Solve $x \leq -1$ or $x > 2$.

30) Solve $x < 1$ and $x \geq 5$.

True or False

31) A solution to a system of equations is a set of numerical values for the variables that makes all equations in the system true.

32) In the elimination method, we always need to multiply or divide the equations to align the coefficients before adding or subtracting.

33) The elimination method cannot be used to solve systems of equations with three or more variables.

34) After eliminating a variable using the elimination method, its value can be found by substituting the found value of the other variable into any of the original equations.

35) If a system of equations has no solution, adding or subtracting the equations may result in a false statement, such as $0 = 3$.

Solve:

36) Solve the following system of equations:

$$\begin{cases} y = 6x + 1 \\ 2y = 9x + 2 \end{cases}$$

37) Solve the following system of equations:

$$\begin{cases} 2y = 5x + 4 \\ 4y = 10x + 8 \end{cases}$$

38) Solve the following system of equations:

$$\begin{cases} y = 3x + 2 \\ y = 3x + 3 \end{cases}$$

39) Solve the following system of equations:

$$\begin{cases} y = 4x + 7 \\ 2y = 8x + 14 \end{cases}$$

40) Solve the following system of equations:

$$\begin{cases} y = 5x + 4 \\ 2y = 9x + 6 \end{cases}$$

Answer Keys

1) $x = 4$

2) $y = 5$

3) $z = 10$

4) $p = 5$

5) $a = 3$

6) 3

7) 4

8) 0.75

9) -3

10) 1.25

11) x-intercept = 2, y-intercept = -4

12) x-intercept = 4, y-intercept = 2

13) x-intercept = 4, y-intercept = -2

14) x-intercept = 4, y-intercept = 2

15) x-intercept = 2, y-intercept = -4

16) 4 units

17) -2

18) 1

19) 0

20) $(-3, 2)$

21) $x < 5$

22) $x > 3$

23) $x < 5$

24) $x \leq -2$

25) $x \leq 3$

26) $0 \leq x < 5$

27) $x \leq 1$ or $x > 3$

28) $-2 < x \leq 3$

29) $x \leq -1$ or $x > 2$

30) No solution

31) True

32) False

33) False

34) True

35) True

36) $x = 0, y = 1$

37) Infinite solutions

38) No solution

39) Infinite solutions

40) $x = -2, y = -6$

Answers with Explanation

1) Subtract 3 from both sides: $4x = 16$. Then divide both sides by 4: $x = 4$.

2) Add 5 to both sides: $3y = 15$. Then divide both sides by 3: $y = 5$.

3) Add $2z$ to both sides: $100 = 80 + 2z$. Then subtract 80 from both sides: $20 = 2z$. Finally, divide both sides by 2: $z = 10$.

4) Subtract 7 from both sides: $5p = 25$. Then divide both sides by 5: $p = 5$.

5) Add $10a$ to both sides: $50 = 20 + 10a$. Then subtract 20 from both sides: $30 = 10a$. Finally divide both sides by 10: $a = 3$.

6) The slope is $\frac{y_2 - y_1}{x_2 - x_1} = \frac{10 - (-2)}{9 - 5} = \frac{12}{4} = 3$.

7) The y-intercept is the value of b in the equation $y = mx + b$, here $b = 4$.

8) The slope is $\frac{y_2 - y_1}{x_2 - x_1} = \frac{4 - 1}{1 - (-3)} = \frac{3}{4} = 0.75$.

9) The slope is represented by the coefficient of x in the equation $y = mx + b$, here $m = -3$.

10) The slope is $\frac{y_2 - y_1}{x_2 - x_1} = \frac{-1 - 4}{2 - 6} = \frac{-5}{-4} = 1.25$.

11) For the x-intercept set $y = 0$. Then the equation simplifies to $8x = 16$, thus $x = 2$. For the y-intercept, set $x = 0$. The equation simplifies to $-4y = 16$, thus $y = -4$.

12) Setting $y = 0$, we find that $3x = 12$, thus $x = 4$. Setting $x = 0$, we get $6y = 12$, thus $y = 2$.

13) When $y = 0$, the equation reduces to $5x = 20$, thus $x = 4$. If $x = 0$, we find $-10y = 20$, thereby $y = -2$.

14) For x-intercept, when $y = 0$, the simplified equation is $4x = 16$, thus $x = 4$. For y-intercept, when $x = 0$, we get $8y = 16$, which leads to $y = 2$.

15) To find x-intercept, set $y = 0$. The equation simplifies to $6x = 12$, thus $x = 2$. To find y-intercept, set $x = 0$.

The equation simplifies to $-3y = 12$, thus $y = -4$.

16) To make the two functions intersect, we need to change the y-intercept of the first function to be the same as that of the second. This requires an upward translation of 4 units.

17) After reflection on y-axis, the points $(0,0)$ and $(2,4)$ are transformed to $(0,0)$ and $(-2,4)$, respectively. Using the formula for the slope, we conclude that the slope of the new function has to be -2.

18) Halving the steepness of the line equation $y = 2x + 3$ reduces the slope to half its original value, resulting in a new slope of 1.

19) A downwards translation of 5 units decreases the y-intercept by 5, resulting in a new y-intercept of 0.

20) Reflection of the coordinate point on the y-axis simply changes the sign of the x-coordinate. Therefore, the new point is $(-3,2)$.

21) Divide both sides by 5 to isolate x. This gives $x < \frac{25}{5}$, hence the solution is $x < 5$.

22) Subtract 3 from both sides to find $2x > 6$. Then, divide by 2 to get $x > 3$.

23) First add 10 from both sides, $3x < 15$. Then divide by 3 to get $x < 5$.

24) First, divide both sides by -2. When dividing by a negative number, remember to flip the directional sign. This gives $x \leq -2$.

25) Begin by adding 7 from both sides to get $4x \leq 12$ and then divide by 4 to get $x \leq 3$.

26) The solution is the intersection of the solutions to $x \geq 0$ and $x < 5$. This results in the compound inequality $0 \leq x < 5$.

27) The solution is the union of the solutions to $x \leq 1$ or $x > 3$. This results in the compound inequality $x \leq 1$ or $x > 3$.

28) The solution is the intersection of the solutions to $x > -2$ and $x \leq 3$. This results in the compound inequality $-2 < x \leq 3$.

29) The solution is the union of the solutions to $x \leq -1$ or $x > 2$. This results in the compound inequality

$x \leq -1$ or $x > 2$.

30) There is no intersection between the solutions to $x < 1$ and $x \geq 5$. Therefore, this compound inequality has no solution.

31) True. A solution to a system of equations is a set of values for the variables that satisfy all the equations in the system simultaneously.

32) False. While this is often the case, it is not always necessary. If the coefficients of the variables that we aim to eliminate are already opposite, we can directly add or subtract the two equations.

33) False. While it can be complex and time-consuming, the elimination method can be used to solve systems of equations with any number of variables.

34) True. After one of the variables has been eliminated, and we have found the values of the other variable, the value of the eliminated variable can be found by substitution into any of the original equations.

35) Finally a system of equations has no solution, it is inconsistent. When adding or subtracting the inconsistent system's equations, the result could be an equation that makes no sense, like $0 = 3$.

36) Substituting y from the first into the second equation, we get $2(6x + 1) = 9x + 2$ which simplifies to $x = 0$. Substituting back into the first equation, $y = 1$. Thus, the solution is $x = 0$ and $y = 1$.

37) The second equation is exactly two times the first equation. So, these equations represent the same line, implying that the system of equations has infinite solutions.

38) The lines have the same slope (3), but different y-intercepts, indicating that they are parallel lines. Thus, there are no solutions to this system.

39) The second equation is exactly twice the first equation, indicating that they represent the same line. This means the system of equations has infinite solutions.

40) Using elimination, we align and manipulate the equations:

$$\begin{cases} 2y - 10x = 8 \\ 2y - 9x = 6 \end{cases}$$

Subtracting these, we find $x = -2$. Substituting into the first equation gives $y = -6$. Therefore, the solution is $x = -2$ and $y = -6$.

3. Quadratic Function

3.1   Solving a Quadratic Equation

A quadratic equation, $ax^2 + bx + c = 0$, with given constants a, b, and c (where $a \neq 0$), seeks a value of x satisfying the equation. To solve it, several methods are available: factoring, square roots, and the quadratic formula. The discriminant ($b^2 - 4ac$) plays a crucial role in the nature of the solutions. It determines whether the equation has two distinct real roots, one real root (a repeated root), or no real roots.

Positive Discriminant: In this case, the quadratic formula is used to find two roots: $x = \frac{-b \pm \sqrt{b^2 - 4ac}}{2a}$, the $\pm$ symbol indicates two values: one with a plus and one with a minus.

Zero Discriminant: When the discriminant is zero, the root is given by: $x = \frac{-b}{2a}$, this represents where the parabola touches the x-axis.

Key Point

In a quadratic equation, $ax^2 + bx + c = 0$, the solutions are given by $x = \frac{-b \pm \sqrt{b^2 - 4ac}}{2a}$, where $b^2 - 4ac$ is known as the discriminant.

Key Point

The discriminant determines the nature of the solutions as follows:

1) $b^2 - 4ac > 0$: Two distinct real roots.

2) $b^2 - 4ac = 0$: Exactly one real root (repeated).

3) $b^2 - 4ac < 0$: No real roots.

Example: Solve the quadratic equation $x^2 - 5x + 6 = 0$.

Solution: First, we try to factorize the equation: $(x - 2)(x - 3) = 0$. Now, we set each factor equal to zero and solve for x:

$$x - 2 = 0 \Rightarrow x = 2, \text{ and } x - 3 = 0 \Rightarrow x = 3.$$

So, the solutions of the equation are $x = 2$ and $x = 3$.

Example: Solve the quadratic equation $x^2 + 4x + 5 = 0$.

Solution: The above equation does not have real roots as the discriminant is negative: $b^2 - 4ac = 16 - 20 = -4 < 0$.

Example: Solve the quadratic equation $x^2 - 3x + 2 = 0$.

Solution: To solve this equation, we first calculate the discriminant:

$$b^2 - 4ac = (-3)^2 - 4(1)(2) = 9 - 8 = 1 > 0.$$

Since the discriminant is positive, there are two distinct real roots. We use the quadratic formula: $x = \frac{-b \pm \sqrt{b^2 - 4ac}}{2a}$. Plugging in the values, we get:

$$x = \frac{-(-3) \pm \sqrt{(-3)^2 - 4(1)(2)}}{2(1)} = \frac{3 \pm \sqrt{1}}{2}.$$

This simplifies to two solutions: $x = \frac{3 \pm 1}{2}$. So, the solutions of the equation are $x = 2$ and $x = 1$.

3.2   Graphing Quadratic Functions

A quadratic function is a function that can be written in the standard form $y = ax^2 + bx + c$ or the vertex form $y = a(x - h)^2 + k$. Depending on the value of a, the graph of a quadratic function (called a parabola) opens upwards ($a > 0$) or downwards ($a < 0$).

Key Point

The standard form of a quadratic function is $y = ax^2 + bx + c$, where the vertex of the function is located at $x = -\frac{b}{2a}$.

Key Point

The vertex form of a quadratic function is $y = a(x-h)^2 + k$, where (h,k) represents the vertex of the function. The axis of symmetry is $x = h$.

To graph a quadratic function, first find the vertex, then substitute some values for x and solve for y. Finally, connect the points to obtain a parabola.

Example: Graph the quadratic function $y = x^2 - 2x + 1$.

Solution: First, we need to express the given function in the vertex form. It can be expressed as $y = (x-1)^2$. So, the vertex of the function is at $(1,0)$ and the axis of symmetry is $x = 1$. Now, we will plot some points. For $x = 0$, $y = 1$; and for $x = 2$, $y = 1$, therefore our points are $(0,1)$, $(1,0)$, and $(2,1)$.

Plot these points and the axis of symmetry on the graph. The symmetry of the parabola means that other points continuously mirror across the axis of symmetry. Finally, sketch the graph by joining the points.

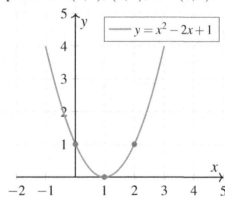

Example: Graph the quadratic function $y = -2x^2 + 4x - 1$.

Solution: The vertex form of the given function is $y = -2(x-1)^2 + 1$. So, the vertex of the function is at $(1,1)$ and the axis of symmetry is $x = 1$. Let us plot some points. For $x = 0$, $y = -1$; and for $x = 2$, $y = -1$, so our points are $(0,-1)$, $(1,1)$, and $(2,-1)$.

Again, plot these points and the axis of symmetry on the graph. The symmetry of the parabola means that points continuously mirror across the axis of symmetry. Join the points to sketch the graph.

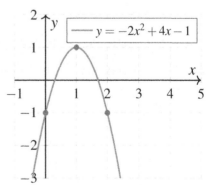

3.3   Axis of Symmetry of Quadratic Functions

A key feature of a quadratic function is its axis of symmetry, a vertical line dividing the parabolic graph into symmetrical halves. This line passes through the vertex, aiding in locating the function's highest or lowest point.

Key Point

In a quadratic function given in the standard form, $y = ax^2 + bx + c$, the axis of symmetry is found using the formula $x = -\frac{b}{2a}$.

Key Point

In a quadratic function given in vertex form, $y = a(x - h)^2 + k$, the axis of symmetry is $x = h$.

These formulas allow us to identify key aspects of the graph of a quadratic function without needing to draw the full graph. However, it is always valuable to visualize these functions in a graph to fully understand their behavior.

Example: Determine the equation of the axis of symmetry for the quadratic function $y = 3x^2 - 18x + 7$.

Solution: Since this function is given in the standard form, we calculate the axis of symmetry using the formula $x = -\frac{b}{2a}$.

Substitute $a = 3$, and $b = -18$: $x = -\frac{(-18)}{(2)(3)} = 3$. So, the equation of the axis of symmetry for this quadratic function is $x = 3$, as illustrated.

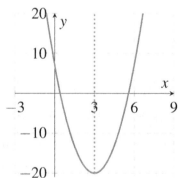

Example: Determine the axis of symmetry for the quadratic function $y = 2(x - 4)^2 - 3$.

Solution: Given that this function is in vertex form, we directly see that the h-value is 4.

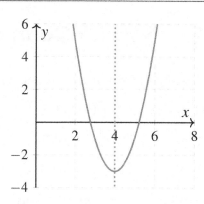

Hence, the equation of the axis of symmetry for this quadratic

function is $x = 4$.

3.4   Solve a Quadratic Equation by Graphing

With our understanding of quadratic functions and their graphs, we can utilize graphing to solve quadratic

equations. This method provides visual intuition and is accessible. A quadratic equation $(ax^2 + bx + c = 0)$

involves constants a, b, and c ($a \neq 0$). In essence, it is an equation dealing with the square of the variable.

Key Point

> To solve a quadratic equation by graphing, create two new equations from the original, graph them,
>
> and find the intersection points, which represent the solutions.

The process of converting the quadratic equation into two equations involves setting y equal to the left side

first, and then the right side of the quadratic equation.

Example: Solve the quadratic equation $x^2 - 4x + 3 = 0$ by graphing.

Solution: The given quadratic equation is in the form $ax^2 + bx + c = 0$.

Step 1: Create two new equations from the original one. Hence, we get $y = x^2 - 4x + 3$ and $y = 0$.

Step 2: Plot these two equations on the same graph. The parabola $y = x^2 - 4x + 3$ intersects the line $y = 0$ at

two points.

Step 3: Identify the intersection points. These are the solutions to the original quadratic equation.

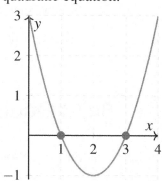

By graphing this equation, we find the intersection points at $x = 1$ and

$x = 3$. Therefore, the solutions to the given quadratic equation are

$x = 1$ and $x = 3$.

3.5   Solving Quadratic Equations with Square Roots

The method of solving quadratic equations using square roots is especially helpful when the equations are in the form $ax^2 = c$ or $(ax+b)^2 = c$.

The steps are straightforward:

1. Rewrite the equation as $ax^2 = c$ or $(ax+b)^2 = c$.
2. For $ax^2 = c$, divide by a to get $x^2 = \frac{c}{a}$ and take the square root: $x = \pm\sqrt{\frac{c}{a}}$. For $(ax+b)^2 = c$, take the square root on both sides: $ax+b = \pm\sqrt{c}$.
3. Solve for x in the obtained equation.

Key Point

To solve $ax^2 = c$, isolate the square term, take the square root on both sides, and include a "$\pm$" sign, representing both the positive and negative roots.

Key Point

To solve $(ax+b)^2 = c$, take the square root on both sides, leading to $ax+b = \pm\sqrt{c}$. Solve for x from this equation.

Example: Solve the equation $x^2 = 25$ using the square root method.

Solution: Given that the equation is $x^2 = 25$, we can take the square root on both sides to solve for x. Hence, $x = \pm\sqrt{25}$. Therefore, our solutions are $x = 5$ and $x = -5$.

Example: Solve the equation $2(x-3)^2 = 18$.

Solution: Given the equation $2(x-3)^2 = 18$, as a first step, divide both sides by 2 to simplify it to $(x-3)^2 = 9$. Now we can take the square root on both sides, resulting in $x-3 = \pm\sqrt{9}$. Simplifying further, we get $x-3 = \pm3$. Our final solutions are then $x = 6$ and $x = 0$.

3.6   Build Quadratics from Roots

Creating a quadratic equation from its roots involves exploring the essential connection between the roots and coefficients of the equation. In a quadratic equation in standard form $ax^2 + bx + c = 0$, if α and β are the roots, the sum and product of roots are as follows:

$$\alpha + \beta = -\frac{\text{coefficient of } x}{\text{coefficient of } x^2} = -\frac{b}{a}, \quad \text{and} \quad \alpha\beta = \frac{\text{constant term}}{\text{coefficient of } x^2} = \frac{c}{a}.$$

Note that the roots of a quadratic equation always occur in conjugate pairs.

🔔 Key Point

To create a quadratic equation from its roots, use the reverse factoring method. The standard equation is $x^2 - (\alpha + \beta)x + \alpha\beta = 0$, where α and β are the roots, and it satisfies the quadratic form with the sum of roots equaling the coefficient of x and the product of roots as the constant term.

Example: Construct a quadratic equation given its roots as 3 and 5.

Solution: Given the roots $\alpha = 3$ and $\beta = 5$, we can substitute these values into the equation $x^2 - (\alpha + \beta)x + \alpha\beta = 0$. We obtain $x^2 - (3+5)x + (3)(5) = 0$, which simplifies to $x^2 - 8x + 15 = 0$. This is the quadratic equation for the given roots.

Example: Construct a quadratic equation, given the roots are in the ratio 7:2.

Solution: Let the roots of the equation be $7k$ and $2k$. Substitute these values into the equation $x^2 - (\alpha + \beta)x + \alpha\beta = 0$. This gives us $x^2 - ((7k) + (2k))x + (7k)(2k) = 0$, which simplifies to $x^2 - 9kx + 14k^2 = 0$. Thus, any quadratic equation having roots derived from the ratio 7:2 will be a multiple of $x^2 - 9x + 14 = 0$.

3.7 Solving Quadratic Inequalities

A quadratic inequality, written as $ax^2 + bx + c > 0$ (or using $<$, $\leq$, or $\geq$ instead of $>$), is solved in a manner similar to quadratic equations. After finding the roots, we identify intervals that satisfy the inequality. By testing a value within each interval, we determine if the inequality is true for all values in that interval.

🔔 Key Point

In solving a quadratic inequality, begin by converting it into an equation and finding its roots. The solutions found will divide the number line into intervals.

Example: Solve the quadratic inequality $x^2 - 5x + 6 > 0$.

Solution: The first step is to rewrite the inequality as an equation: $x^2 - 5x + 6 = 0$. On solving this quadratic equation, we find the roots as $x = 2$ and $x = 3$. These roots divide the number line into intervals: $(-\infty, 2)$, $(2, 3)$, and $(3, \infty)$. We choose a test value from each interval, say $1, 2.5$, and 4, and substitute it into the original inequality:

1. For $x = 1$; we get $1 - 5 + 6 = 2 > 0$. So the interval $(-\infty, 2)$ is part of the solution.

2. For $x = 2.5$; we get $6.25 - 12.5 + 6 = -0.25$, which is not greater than 0. Hence, the interval $(2, 3)$ is not part of the solution.

3. For $x = 4$; we get $16 - 20 + 6 = 2 > 0$. So the interval $(3, \infty)$ is part of the solution.

The solution to the inequality $x^2 - 5x + 6 > 0$ is $x \in (-\infty, 2) \cup$ $(3, \infty)$. The solution region is clearly depicted in the plot.

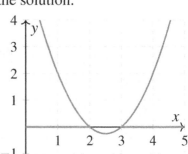

3.8   Graphing Quadratic Inequalities

Quadratic inequalities in the format $ax^2 + bx + c > 0$ (or $\leq, <$, or $\geq$) can be visually represented on graphs using parabolas. Graphs offer a visual grasp of the inequality, simplifying both the solution and interpretation by showing where the quadratic function is positioned relative to the x-axis.

🔔 Key Point

To graph a quadratic inequality, start by plotting the corresponding quadratic equation's graph, the parabola $y = ax^2 + bx + c$. The roots of this equation represent the points where the graph intersects the x-axis, dividing it into intervals. Test a point in each interval.

A positive result represents the region above the x-axis where the parabola exists for $>$ or $\geq$ inequalities; a negative result represents the region below the x-axis for $<$ or $\leq$ inequalities.

Example: Graph the inequality $x^2 - 4 \geq 0$.

Solution: First, you graph the equation $x^2 - 4 = 0$. The roots (where the graph intersects the x-axis) of this equation are $x = -2$ and $x = 2$. These roots divide the x-axis into intervals: $(-\infty, -2)$, $(-2, 2)$, and

$(2, \infty)$. Now to test which solution region to shade, you choose a test point from each interval, like -3, 0, and 3, and substitute it into the original inequality:

1. For $x = -3$; $(-3)^2 - 4 = 9 - 4 = 5$, which is greater than 0. So the interval $(-\infty, -2)$ is part of the solution and we shade it on the graph.

2. For $x = 0$; $0^2 - 4 = -4$, which is not greater than or equal to 0. So we do not shade the interval $(-2, 2)$.

3. For $x = 3$; $3^2 - 4 = 9 - 4 = 5$, which is greater than 0. Therefore, we shade the interval $(2, \infty)$ in the graph.

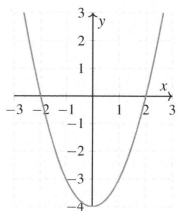

The solution to the inequality $x^2 - 4 \geq 0$ is $x \in (-\infty, -2] \cup [2, \infty)$.

3.9 Factoring the Difference of Two Perfect Squares

We frequently encounter perfect squares, and to work with them effectively, we utilize a technique called factoring the difference of two perfect squares. This method is invaluable when dealing with polynomial expressions that involve subtracting two perfect squares, making it a powerful tool for solving equations with perfect squares.

🔔 Key Point

The formula for factoring the difference of two perfect squares is

$$a^2 - b^2 = (a - b)(a + b).$$

To factor expressions involving perfect squares, find the square roots of the perfect squares in the expression and use this formula.

The steps to factor the difference between two perfect squares are straightforward:

1. Apply the difference of squares formula: $a^2 - b^2 = (a - b)(a + b)$, where a^2 and b^2 are the terms of the

perfect squares in your expression, and a and b are the square roots.

2. Find the values for a and b by taking the square roots of the perfect squares in the expression.

3. Substitute the values of a and b into the formula.

4. Double-check the result. If correct, you will obtain the original perfect square difference expression.

Example: Factorize the polynomial $x^4 - 16$.

Solution: The first step is to identify this as a difference of two squares, where x^4 (the square of x^2) and 16 (the square of 4) are the perfect squares. Substituting $a = x^2$ and $b = 4$ into the difference of squares formula $a^2 - b^2$, we get:

$$(x^2)^2 - 4^2 = (x^2 - 4)(x^2 + 4).$$

We can further factorize the term $(x^2 - 4)$, as it again represents a difference of squares, with $a = x$ and $b = 2$: $x^2 - 2^2 = (x - 2)(x + 2)$. Therefore, the factorization of $x^4 - 16$ is $(x - 2)(x + 2)(x^2 + 4)$.

Example: Factorize the polynomial $9y^4 - 16$.

Solution: Recognizing this as a difference of two squares with $9y^4$ (the square of $3y^2$) and 16 (the square of 4) as the perfect squares, we substitute $a = 3y^2$ and $b = 4$ into the difference of squares formula:

$$(3y^2)^2 - 4^2 = (3y^2 - 4)(3y^2 + 4).$$

We can further factorize the term $(3y^2 - 4)$, as it again represents a difference of squares, with $a = \sqrt{3}y$ and $b = 2$: $(\sqrt{3}y)^2 - 2^2 = (\sqrt{3}y - 2)(\sqrt{3}y + 2)$. Therefore, the factorization of $9y^4 - 16$ is $(\sqrt{3}y - 2)(\sqrt{3}y + 2)(3y^2 + 4)$.

3.10   Practices

 Solve:

1) Solve $x^2 - 7x + 10 = 0$.

2) Solve $x^2 + 6x + 13 = 0$.

3) Solve $x^2 - 20 = 0$.

4) Solve $4x^2 - 4x - 7 = 0$.

5) Solve $x^2 + 4x + 4 = 0$.

Graphical Questions:

6) Graph the function $y = x^2 + 2x - 1$.

7) Graph the function $y = -2x^2 + 8x - 3$.

8) Graph the function $y = 3x^2 - 6x + 1$.

9) Graph the function $y = -x^2 + 4x - 1$.

10) Graph the function $y = 2x^2 - 8x + 5$.

Fill in the Blank:

11) If the equation of a quadratic function in standard form is $y = 5x^2 + 10x - 2$, the axis of symmetry is $x = $ _____.

12) The axis of symmetry for the quadratic function $y = 4(x + 7)^2 + 1$ is $x = $ _____.

13) If a quadratic function is given in the form $y = a(x - h)^2 + k$, the equation of its axis of symmetry is _____.

14) For the quadratic equation $y = -3x^2 + 6x - 9$, the axis of symmetry is $x = $ _____.

15) The axis of symmetry of the quadratic function $y = -2(x - 3)^2 + 4$ is $x = $ _____.

Solve:

16) Solve the quadratic equation $2x^2 + 5x - 3 = 0$ by graphing.

17) Solve the quadratic equation $x^2 - 6x + 9 = 0$ by graphing.

18) Solve the quadratic equation $3x^2 - 12 = 0$ by graphing.

19) Solve the quadratic equation $4x^2 = 8x$ by graphing.

20) Solve the quadratic equation $x^2 - 3x - 4 = 0$ by graphing.

Solve:

21) Solve the equation $4x^2 = 64$.

22) Solve for x given that $x^2 = 49$.

23) Solve the equation $(x+2)^2 = 81$.

24) Rewrite and solve the equation $3x^2 = 75$.

25) Solve for x from the equation $(2x - 7)^2 = 64$.

Solve:

26) Construct a quadratic equation, if the roots are -1 and 4.

27) Construct a quadratic equation, if one root is 2.5 and the other root is the double of the first.

28) Construct a quadratic equation, if the roots are in the ratio 4:5.

29) Construct a quadratic equation, if the roots are -3 and -6.

30) Construct a quadratic equation, if the roots are in the ratio 3:7.

True or False:

31) True or False: In order to solve a quadratic inequality, first we find the roots by setting the inequality as an equation equal to zero.

32) True or False: If a test value holds the original inequality, then the test value is the only solution.

33) True or False: The roots of the quadratic inequality are always part of the solution set of the inequality.

34) True or False: The roots of a quadratic inequality divide the number line into equal intervals.

35) True or False: If the quadratic inequality is given in the form $ax^2 + bx + c > 0$, it cannot be rewritten in the form $ax^2 + bx + c = 0$.

Solve Each Inequality:

36) Solve the quadratic inequality $x^2 - 1 < 0$.

37) Graph the inequality $3x^2 + 2x - 1 \leq 0$.

38) Solve the inequality $2x^2 + x - 3 > 0$.

True or False:

39) The expression $9r^2 - 16$ can be factorized as $(3r - 4)(3r + 4)$. True or False?

40) The expression $4s^4 - 9$ can be factorized as $(2s^2 - 3)(2s^2 + 3)$. True or False?

41) The expression $a^2 - b^2$ can be factorized as $(a - b)(a + b)$. True or False?

42) The expression $16t^2 - 25$ can be factorized as $(4t - 5)(4t + 5)$. True or False?

43) The expression $4u^4 - 9$ can be factorized as $(2u^2 - 6)(2u^2 + 6)$. True or False?

Answer Keys

1) $x = 2, x = 5$

2) No real solution

3) $x = 2\sqrt{5}, x = -2\sqrt{5}$

4) $x = \frac{1 \pm \sqrt{8}}{2}$

5) $x = -2$

6) Vertex: $(-1, -2)$, Axis of symmetry: $x = -1$

7) Vertex: $(2, 5)$, Axis of symmetry: $x = 2$

8) Vertex: $(1, -2)$, Axis of symmetry: $x = 1$

9) Vertex: $(2, 3)$, Axis of symmetry: $x = 2$

10) Vertex: $(2, -3)$, Axis of symmetry: $x = 2$

11) -1

12) -7

13) $x = h$

14) 1

15) 3

16) $x = -3, \frac{1}{2}$

17) $x = 3$

18) $x = \pm 2$

19) $x = 0, 2$

20) $x = -1, 4$

21) $x = \pm 4$

22) $x = \pm 7$

23) $x = 7, x = -11$

24) $x = \pm 5$

25) $x = -\frac{1}{2}, x = \frac{15}{2}$

26) $x^2 - 3x - 4 = 0$

27) $x^2 - 7.5x + 12.5 = 0$

28) $x^2 - 9kx + 20k^2 = 0$

29) $x^2 + 9x + 18 = 0$

30) $x^2 - 10kx + 21k^2 = 0$

31) True

32) False

33) False

34) False

35) False

36) $x \in (-1, 1)$

37) $x \in [-1, \frac{1}{3}]$

38) $x \in (-\infty, -1.5) \cup (1, \infty)$

39) True

40) True

41) True

42) True

43) False

Answers with Explanation

1) This equation can be factored to $(x-2)(x-5) = 0$. After setting each factor equal to zero, $x = 2$ and $x = 5$ are obtained.

2) As the discriminant $b^2 - 4ac = 36 - 52 = -16 < 0$, implying that the equation has no real roots.

3) The equation can be solved as follows: $x^2 = 20$, then $x = \pm\sqrt{20}$. After that, $x = 2\sqrt{5}, x = -2\sqrt{5}$ are obtained.

4) Using the quadratic formula, the solution can be obtained: $x = \frac{1 \pm \sqrt{8}}{2}$.

5) This equation is a perfect square trinomial. It can be factored to $(x+2)^2 = 0$. Setting this factor to zero gives the solution, $x = -2$.

6) The vertex is at $(-1, -2)$ and the axis of symmetry is $x = -1$.

The graph is a parabola that opens upwards.

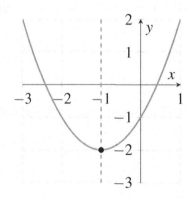

7) The vertex is at $(2, 5)$ and the axis of symmetry is $x = 2$.

The graph is a parabola that opens downwards.

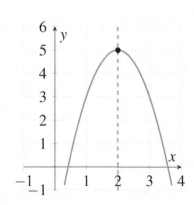

8) The vertex is at $(1, -2)$ and the axis of symmetry is $x = 1$.

The graph is a parabola that opens upwards.

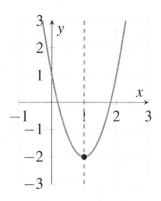

9) The vertex is at $(2, 3)$ and the axis of symmetry is $x = 2$.

The graph is a parabola that opens downwards.

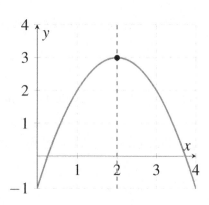

10) The vertex is at $(2, -3)$ and the axis of symmetry is $x = 2$.

The graph is a parabola that opens upwards.

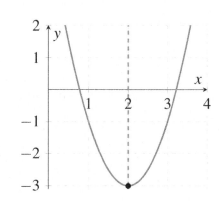

11) Using the formula $x = -\frac{b}{2a}$, we get $x = -\frac{10}{2(5)} = -1$.

12) For a quadratic function in vertex form of $y = a(x - h)^2 + k$, the axis of symmetry is $x = h$. In this case $h = -7$.

13) For a quadratic function in vertex form, the equation of its axis of symmetry is $x = h$.

14) Using the formula $x = -\frac{b}{2a}$, we get $x = -\frac{6}{2(-3)} = 1$.

15) As the function is in vertex form, its axis of symmetry is $x = h$ where $h = 3$.

16) Create the two equations $y = 2x^2 + 5x - 3$ and $y = 0$. Graph these equations.

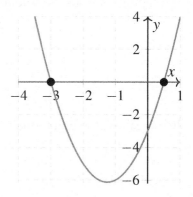

The intersection points reveal the solutions: $x = -3$ and $x = \frac{1}{2}$.

17) By constructing the equations $y = x^2 - 6x + 9$ and $y = 0$.

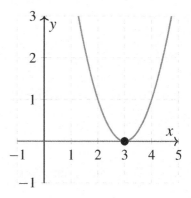

We can graph these to find the intersection points, which yield the solution: $x = 3$.

18) The equations $y = 3x^2 - 12$ and $y = 0$,

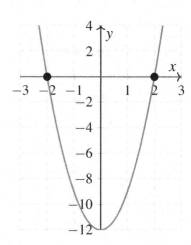

when graphed, intersect at the points $x = -2$ and $x = 2$, thereby providing the solutions.

19) After creating the two equations $y = 4x^2$ and $y = 8x$,

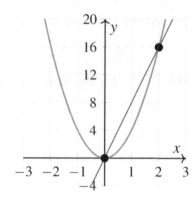

graphing reveals the solutions as the intersection points: $x = 0$ and $x = 2$.

20) Forming the equations $y = x^2 - 3x - 4$ and $y = 0$,

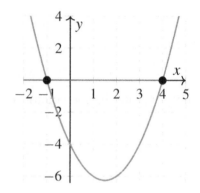

we find the solutions as the points of intersection when graphed: $x = -1$ and $x = 4$.

21) To solve for x, we first divide both sides by 4 to get $x^2 = 16$. Taking the square root of both sides, we find $x = \pm 4$.

22) Taking the square root on both sides of the equation $x^2 = 49$, we get $x = \pm 7$.

23) Taking the square root on both sides of the equation $(x + 2)^2 = 81$, we get $x + 2 = \pm 9$. This gives us two solutions: $x = 7$ and $x = -11$.

24) Dividing both sides by 3, we get $x^2 = 25$. Taking the square root of both sides, $x = \pm 5$.

25) Taking the square root of both sides, we get $2x - 7 = \pm 8$. This gives us two equations to solve, namely $2x - 7 = 8$ and $2x - 7 = -8$. Solving these gives $x = \frac{15}{2}$ and $x = -\frac{1}{2}$, respectively.

26) Given the roots $\alpha = -1$ and $\beta = 4$, we substitute these values into the equation

$$x^2 - (\alpha + \beta)x + \alpha\beta = 0.$$

We get $x^2 - ((-1) + 4)x + ((-1)(4)) = 0$, which simplifies to $x^2 - 3x - 4 = 0$.

27) Given the roots $\alpha = 2.5$ and $\beta = 2(2.5) = 5$, we substitute these values into the equation $x^2 - (\alpha + \beta)x + \alpha\beta = 0$. We get $x^2 - (2.5 + 5)x + (2.5)(5) = 0$, which simplifies to $x^2 - 7.5x + 12.5 = 0$.

28) Let the roots of the equation be $4k$ and $5k$. Substitute these values into the equation $x^2 - (\alpha + \beta)x + \alpha\beta = 0$. This gives us $x^2 - ((4k) + (5k))x + (4k)(5k) = 0$, which simplifies to $x^2 - 9kx + 20k^2 = 0$. Thus, any quadratic equation having roots derived from the ratio 4:5 will be a multiple of $x^2 - 9x + 20 = 0$.

29) Given the roots $\alpha = -3$ and $\beta = -6$, we substitute these values into the equation $x^2 - (\alpha + \beta)x + \alpha\beta = 0$. We get $x^2 - ((-3) + (-6))x + ((-3)(-6)) = 0$, which simplifies to $x^2 + 9x + 18 = 0$.

30) Let the roots of the equation be $3k$ and $7k$. Substitute these values into the equation $x^2 - (\alpha + \beta)x + \alpha\beta = 0$. This gives us $x^2 - ((3k) + (7k))x + (3k)(7k) = 0$, which simplifies to $x^2 - 10kx + 21k^2 = 0$. Thus, any quadratic equation having roots derived from the ratio 3:7 will be a multiple of $x^2 - 10x + 21 = 0$.

31) The roots of a quadratic are found by solving the corresponding equation, which is a key step in solving a quadratic inequality.

32) If a test value from an interval makes the inequality true, it means all the values in that interval are part of the solution.

33) Whether or not roots are included in the solution set depends on the inequality sign: $<$ or $>$ excludes the roots, while $\leq$ or $\geq$ includes the roots.

34) The roots of a quadratic inequality divide the number line into intervals, however, these intervals are not necessarily equal.

35) Yes, it can be rewritten. This is the first step in solving a quadratic inequality, where we find the roots.

36) The roots of $x^2 - 1 = 0$ are $x = -1$ and $x = 1$. Testing the intervals $(-\infty, -1)$, $(-1, 1)$, and $(1, \infty)$ with points -2, 0, and 2 respectively gives positive, negative, and positive results. This implies the solution lies between -1 and 1, therefore, $x \in (-1, 1)$.

37) The roots of the equation $3x^2 + 2x - 1 = 0$ are $x = -1$ and $x = \frac{1}{3}$. Testing intervals $(-\infty, -1)$, $[-1, \frac{1}{3}]$, and $(\frac{1}{3}, \infty)$ with points -2, 0, and 1 results in positive, negative, and positive values respectively. This shows that the solution lies in the interval $[-1, \frac{1}{3}]$.

38) The roots of the equation $2x^2 + x - 3 = 0$ are $x = -1.5$ and $x = 1$. Testing intervals $(-\infty, -1.5)$, $(-1.5, 1)$, and $(1, \infty)$ with points -2, 0, and 2 gives positive, negative, and positive values. Thus, the solution is $x \in (-\infty, -1.5) \cup (1, \infty)$.

39) This is a correct application of the difference of squares formula. The expression is indeed factorized as $(3r - 4)(3r + 4)$.

40) This is true. Using the difference of squares formula, the expression $4s^4 - 9$ becomes $(2s^2 - 3)(2s^2 + 3)$.

41) This is the basic difference of squares formula. The statement is true.

42) This is correct. The expression $16t^2 - 25$ factorizes to $(4t - 5)(4t + 5)$ with the difference of squares formula.

43) This is false. The correct factorization using the difference of squares formula would be $(2u^2 - 3)(2u^2 + 3)$.

4. Complex Numbers

4.1 Adding and Subtracting Complex Numbers

A complex number is given by $a + bi$, where a and b are real numbers and i is an imaginary unit defined by $i^2 = -1$.

The process of adding or subtracting complex numbers is straightforward. First, we combine the real parts together, and then we combine the imaginary parts together.

🔔 Key Point

The rule for adding and subtracting complex numbers is given as follows:

Addition: $(a + bi) + (c + di) = (a + c) + (b + d)i$

Subtraction: $(a + bi) - (c + di) = (a - c) + (b - d)i$

Example: Add $3 + 4i$ and $1 + 2i$.

Solution: To add these complex numbers, we add the real parts and the imaginary parts separately:
$(3 + 4i) + (1 + 2i) = (3 + 1) + (4 + 2)i = 4 + 6i$.

Example: Subtract $5 - 6i$ from $2 + 3i$.

Solution: To subtract these complex numbers, we subtract the real parts and the imaginary parts separately: $(2 + 3i) - (5 - 6i) = (2 - 5) + (3 + 6)i = -3 + 9i$.

4.2   Multiplying and Dividing Complex Numbers

Multiplication of complex numbers can be achieved using the rule $i^2 = -1$, which means that any imaginary number squared becomes a negative real number.

🔔 Key Point

The rule for multiplying complex numbers $(a+bi)$ and $(c+di)$ is:

$$(a+bi)(c+di) = (ac-bd) + (ad+bc)i.$$

On the other hand, the division of complex numbers involves finding the conjugate of the denominator.

🔔 Key Point

The conjugate of a complex number $(a+bi)$ is $(a-bi)$, which only changes the sign of the imaginary part.

This process, known as rationalizing the denominator, makes division operations on complex numbers feasible.

🔔 Key Point

The process for dividing complex numbers $\frac{a+bi}{c+di}$ is:

$$\frac{a+bi}{c+di} \times \frac{c-di}{c-di} = \frac{ac+bd}{c^2+d^2} + \frac{bc-ad}{c^2+d^2}i.$$

Example: Multiply $(3+2i)$ and $(1+4i)$.

Solution: Using the multiplication rule, we have:

$$(3+2i)(1+4i) = (3 \times 1 - 2 \times 4) + (3 \times 4 + 2 \times 1)i = -5 + 14i.$$

Example: Divide $(2+3i)$ by $(1-2i)$.

Solution: To divide, multiply the numerator and denominator by the conjugate of the denominator and use the division rule:

$$\frac{2+3i}{1-2i} = \frac{2+3i}{1-2i} \times \frac{1+2i}{1+2i} = \frac{2-6}{1+4} + \frac{3+4}{1+4}i = -\frac{4}{5} + \frac{7}{5}i.$$

4.3 Rationalizing Imaginary Denominators

The rationalizing imaginary denominators in complex fractions procedure removes the imaginary component from the denominator of a fraction.

Consider a complex fraction $\frac{a+bi}{c+di}$. We can simplify this by multiplying both numerator and denominator by the conjugate of the denominator, $(c-di)$.

🔔 Key Point

To rationalize the denominator of a complex fraction $\frac{a+bi}{c+di}$, multiply both numerator and denominator by the conjugate of the denominator, $(c-di)$.

This process results in a denominator that is a real number, which is easier to handle mathematically.

Example: Rationalize the denominator of $\frac{1+2i}{3+4i}$.

Solution: Begin by finding the conjugate of the denominator, which is $3-4i$. Multiply both numerator and denominator of the fraction by this conjugate:

$$\frac{1+2i}{3+4i} \times \frac{3-4i}{3-4i} = \frac{11+2i}{25}.$$

Then, we can write this as $\frac{11}{25} + \frac{2}{25}i$.

Example: Simplify the complex number $\frac{5+6i}{7+8i}$.

Solution: First, find the conjugate of the denominator, $7-8i$. Multiply both the numerator and denominator by this conjugate:

$$\frac{5+6i}{7+8i} \times \frac{7-8i}{7-8i} = \frac{83+2i}{113}.$$

We simplify this expression to get $\frac{83}{113} + \frac{2}{113}i$.

4.4   Practices

Fill in the Blank

1) If $a + bi$ is a complex number, then $a - bi$ is the _____ of the complex number.

2) The real part of the complex number $7 + 9i$ is _____.

3) Subtract $(2 + 5i)$ from $(8 + 3i)$ to get _____.

4) The complex number $(5 - 2i)$ added to $(1 +$ _____ $i)$ gives an imaginary part of 4i.

5) To subtract complex numbers, the real parts and the _____ parts should be subtracted separately.

Solve

6) Multiply $2 - 3i$ and $4 + i$.

7) Divide $3 - 4i$ by $2 + i$.

8) Multiply $-i$ and $4 - 3i$.

9) Divide $-1 + i$ by $2 - i$.

10) Multiply $7 + 2i$ and $-3 + 5i$.

Simplify Each Expression

11) Simplify the complex number $\frac{3+4i}{2-3i}$.

12) Simplify the complex number $\frac{7+5i}{4+2i}$.

13) Simplify the complex number $\frac{2+6i}{3+4i}$.

14) Simplify the complex number $\frac{8+9i}{3-4i}$.

15) Simplify the complex number $\frac{5-3i}{4+2i}$.

Answer Keys

1) Conjugate

2) 7

3) $6 - 2i$

4) 6

5) Imaginary

6) $11 - 10i$

7) $\frac{2}{5} - \frac{11}{5}i$

8) $-3 - 4i$

9) $-\frac{3}{5} + \frac{1}{5}i$

10) $-31 + 29i$

11) $-\frac{6}{13} + \frac{17}{13}i$

12) $\frac{19}{10} + \frac{3}{10}i$

13) $\frac{6}{5} + \frac{2}{5}i$

14) $-\frac{12}{25} + \frac{59}{25}i$

15) $\frac{7}{10} - \frac{11}{10}i$

Answers with Explanation

1) The conjugate of a complex number changes the sign of the imaginary part.

2) The component without i in a complex number is the real part.

3) $(8+3i) - (2+5i) = (8-2) + (3i-5i) = 6-2i.$

4) To get an imaginary part of $4i$, the imaginary part of the second complex number needs to be $(4i+2i)$, thus it is 6i.

5) The subtraction of complex numbers involves subtraction of the real parts and imaginary parts separately.

6) Using the multiplication rule,

$$(2-3i)(4+i) = (2 \times 4 - (-3) \times 1) + (2 \times 1 + (-3) \times 4)i = 11 - 10i.$$

7) To divide, multiply the numerator and denominator by the conjugate of the denominator and use the division rule:

$$\frac{3-4i}{2+i} = \frac{3-4i}{2+i} \times \frac{2-i}{2-i} = \frac{3 \times 2 - (-4 \times -1)}{2^2 + 1^2} - \frac{-4 \times 2 + 3 \times -1}{2^2 + 1^2}i = \frac{2}{5} - \frac{11}{5}i.$$

8) Using the multiplication rule,

$$(-i)(4-3i) = (0 \times 4 - (-1 \times -3)) + (0 \times -3 + (-1 \times 4))i = -3 - 4i.$$

9) To divide, multiply the numerator and denominator by the conjugate of the denominator and use the division rule:

$$\frac{-1+i}{2-i} = \frac{-1+i}{2-i} \times \frac{2+i}{2+i} = -\frac{1 \times 2 + 1}{2^2 + (-1)^2} + \frac{-1 + 2 \times 1}{2^2 + (-1)^2}i = -\frac{3}{5} + \frac{1}{5}i.$$

10) Using the multiplication rule,

$$(7+2i)(-3+5i) = (7 \times -3 - 2 \times 5) + (7 \times 5 + 2 \times -3)i = -31 + 29i.$$

11) Multiply both the numerator and denominator by the conjugate of the denominator, yielding $\frac{-6+17i}{13}$, which simplifies to $-\frac{6}{13} + \frac{17}{13}i$.

12) Multiply both the numerator and denominator by the conjugate of the denominator to obtain $\frac{38+6i}{20}$, which simplifies to $\frac{19}{10} + \frac{3}{10}i$.

13) Multiply both the numerator and denominator by the conjugate of the denominator to get $\frac{30+10i}{25}$, which simplifies to $\frac{6}{5} + \frac{2}{5}i$.

14) Multiply both the numerator and denominator by the conjugate of the denominator to get $-\frac{12}{25} + \frac{59}{25}i$.

15) Multiply both the numerator and denominator by the conjugate of the denominator to get $\frac{14-22i}{20}$, which then simplifies to $\frac{7}{10} - \frac{11}{10}i$.

5. Matrices

5.1 Using Matrices to Represent Data

Matrices are powerful tools for handling multidimensional data, serving as data containers for various real-life applications like social networks, supply chains, and 3D graphics.

🔔 Key Point

Matrix representation is a method to store, sort, and operate data, especially when dealing with multivariate systems.

Matrices can be of any size, and they are usually represented by a capital letter like A, B, C, etc. The general representation of a matrix A is as follows:

$$A = \begin{bmatrix} a_{11} & a_{12} & \cdots & a_{1n} \\ a_{21} & a_{22} & \cdots & a_{2n} \\ \vdots & \vdots & \ddots & \vdots \\ a_{m1} & a_{m2} & \cdots & a_{mn} \end{bmatrix}$$

The dimension of a matrix is given by the number of rows (m) by the number of columns (n), usually expressed as $m \times n$.

🔔 *Key Point*

Matrices come in various sizes, and their dimensions are described as $m \times n$, where m is the number of rows and n is the number of columns.

Example: Say, we are running a café, and we sold 5 cups of coffee and 3 pastries on Monday, and 4 cups of coffee and 7 pastries on Tuesday. Represent this data using a matrix.

  Solution: We can create a 2×2 matrix as follows:

$$Sales = \begin{bmatrix} 5 & 3 \\ 4 & 7 \end{bmatrix},$$

where the first column represents the sales for coffee and the second column represents the sales for pastries. The first row represents Monday's sales and the second row represents Tuesday's sales.

Example: Consider a grocery store that has 3 branches. The store sells apples and oranges. The sales for the week for each branch are as follows:

- Branch 1 sold 20 apples and 15 oranges.

- Branch 2 sold 30 apples and 40 oranges.

- Branch 3 sold 40 apples and 35 oranges.

Represent this data using a matrix.

  Solution: We will create a 3×2 matrix where the rows represent each branch and the columns represent the fruit:

$$Sales = \begin{bmatrix} 20 & 15 \\ 30 & 40 \\ 40 & 35 \end{bmatrix},$$

each entry in the matrix represents the sales of a specific fruit in a specific branch.

5.2   Adding and Subtracting Matrices

Adding and subtracting matrices follows a straightforward procedure. First, the matrices must have the same dimensions. Then, we add or subtract the corresponding elements in the two matrices to form a new matrix with the same dimensions.

For example, if we have two matrices, A and B, both of size $m \times n$, then the sum or the difference $C = A \pm B$ is produced by adding or subtracting the corresponding elements of A and B. The resulting matrix C will also have the same dimension, $m \times n$.

🔔 Key Point

In matrix addition and subtraction, matrices must have the same dimensions, and the operation is performed element-wise.

Example: Given that $A = \begin{bmatrix} 1 & 2 \\ 3 & 4 \end{bmatrix}$ and $B = \begin{bmatrix} 5 & 6 \\ 7 & 8 \end{bmatrix}$ calculate $A + B$ and $A - B$.

Solution: To calculate $A + B$ and $A - B$, we simply add or subtract the corresponding elements of A and B.

For $A + B$:
$$A + B = \begin{bmatrix} 1+5 & 2+6 \\ 3+7 & 4+8 \end{bmatrix} = \begin{bmatrix} 6 & 8 \\ 10 & 12 \end{bmatrix}.$$

For $A - B$:
$$A - B = \begin{bmatrix} 1-5 & 2-6 \\ 3-7 & 4-8 \end{bmatrix} = \begin{bmatrix} -4 & -4 \\ -4 & -4 \end{bmatrix}.$$

Now, let's take a look at a real-world scenario.

Example: Suppose a teacher records the marks of two tests for a class of three students as follows:

- Test 1: Student 1 scored 65, Student 2 scored 75, Student 3 scored 85.

- Test 2: Student 1 scored 70, Student 2 scored 80, Student 3 scored 90.

Mathematically represent the score improvement from Test 1 to Test 2.

Solution: First, we represent the scores of the students in Test 1 and Test 2 using two 1×3 matrices as follows:

$$Test1 = \begin{bmatrix} 65 & 75 & 85 \end{bmatrix},$$

and

$$Test2 = \begin{bmatrix} 70 & 80 & 90 \end{bmatrix},$$

The score improvement from Test 1 to Test 2 can be represented as $Test2 - Test1$:

$$Improvement = Test2 - Test1 = \begin{bmatrix} 70-65 & 80-75 & 90-85 \end{bmatrix} = \begin{bmatrix} 5 & 5 & 5 \end{bmatrix}.$$

So, each student has improved by 5 marks from Test 1 to Test 2.

5.3 Matrix Multiplication

Multiplying matrices, unlike multiplying numbers, is not a straightforward operation. It involves a specific and set process that needs to be strictly adhered to. Most importantly, the number of columns in the first matrix must be equal to the number of rows in the second matrix for multiplication to be possible.

Key Point

Matrix multiplication requires the first matrix to have the same number of columns as the second matrix has rows.

The multiplication process itself involves taking each row of the first matrix, multiplying it element-wise with each column of the second matrix, and adding the resulting products. This is done for each row of the first matrix and each column of the second matrix.

Key Point

In matrix multiplication, each row of the first matrix is multiplied with each column of the second matrix, and the resulting products are summed.

If we have two matrices A and B, where A is a matrix of size $m \times n$ and B is a matrix of size $n \times p$, then the product $C = A \times B$ is a new matrix of size $m \times p$. Each component c_{ij} of C is the sum of the products of the elements of the i-th row of A and the elements of the j-th column of B.

Example: Given that $A = \begin{bmatrix} 1 & 2 \\ 3 & 4 \end{bmatrix}$ and $B = \begin{bmatrix} 5 & 6 \\ 7 & 8 \end{bmatrix}$, calculate $A \times B$.

Solution: To calculate $A \times B$, we take each row of A and multiply it with each column of B and add the results. For $A \times B$:

$$A \times B = \begin{bmatrix} (1 \times 5) + (2 \times 7) & (1 \times 6) + (2 \times 8) \\ (3 \times 5) + (4 \times 7) & (3 \times 6) + (4 \times 8) \end{bmatrix} = \begin{bmatrix} 19 & 22 \\ 43 & 50 \end{bmatrix}.$$

So, the product of A and B is the matrix $\begin{bmatrix} 19 & 22 \\ 43 & 50 \end{bmatrix}$.

Example: A company sells two products P and Q at the prices of £5 and £7 respectively. In January, they sold 10 units of P and 20 units of Q; in February, they sold 15 units of P and 18 units of Q. Represent the total sales for each month using matrix multiplication.

Solution: We let a 2×1 matrix P represent the prices of products P and Q:

$$P = \begin{bmatrix} 5 \\ 7 \end{bmatrix}.$$

We let a 2×2 matrix S represent the quantities sold in January and February:

$$S = \begin{bmatrix} 10 & 20 \\ 15 & 18 \end{bmatrix}.$$

The total sales for each month, T, can be calculated as $T = S \times P$:

$$T = S \times P = \begin{bmatrix} 10 & 20 \\ 15 & 18 \end{bmatrix} \begin{bmatrix} 5 \\ 7 \end{bmatrix} = \begin{bmatrix} (10 \times 5) + (20 \times 7) \\ (15 \times 5) + (18 \times 7) \end{bmatrix} = \begin{bmatrix} 190 \\ 201 \end{bmatrix}.$$

So, the total sales in January were £190 and in February were £201.

5.4   Finding Determinants of a Matrix

The determinant of a matrix A, written as $|A|$ or $\det(A)$, is a special numerical value that is calculated from a square matrix. A matrix where the number of rows is equal to the number of columns is known as a square matrix, and it has a dimension of $n \times n$.

🔔 Key Point

The determinant is a fundamental property of matrices and is defined only for square matrices.

The procedure for calculating the determinant depends on the size of the matrix. We begin with 2×2 matrices. Given matrix A in the form:

$$A = \begin{bmatrix} a & b \\ c & d \end{bmatrix},$$

the determinant is calculated as $ad - bc$.

For 3×3 matrices, there is a slightly more complex formula that involves "traversing" 3×3 matrix A:

$$A = \begin{bmatrix} a & b & c \\ d & e & f \\ g & h & i \end{bmatrix},$$

the determinant is calculated as $|A| = a(ei - fh) - b(di - fg) + c(dh - eg)$.

🔔 Key Point

For 2×2 matrices like $A = \begin{bmatrix} a & b \\ c & d \end{bmatrix}$, the determinant is $ad - bc$.

🔔 Key Point

For 3×3 matrices like $A = \begin{bmatrix} a & b & c \\ d & e & f \\ g & h & i \end{bmatrix}$, the determinant is calculated as

$$|A| = a(ei - fh) - b(di - fg) + c(dh - eg).$$

Example: Evaluate the determinant of the matrix $\begin{bmatrix} 1 & -2 \\ -5 & 0 \end{bmatrix}$.

Solution: To evaluate the determinant of a 2×2 matrix, we employ the formula $|A| = ad - bc$. Plugging in the values from our matrix, we find $|A| = (1)(0) - (-2)(-5) = -10$.

Example: Evaluate the determinant of the matrix $\begin{bmatrix} 2 & 6 & 3 \\ 0 & 5 & 1 \\ 4 & 7 & 4 \end{bmatrix}$.

Solution: For a 3×3 matrix, we use the formula $|A| = a(ei - fh) - b(di - fg) + c(dh - eg)$. Plugging in the values from the matrix, we have

$$|A| = 2((5 \times 4) - (7 \times 1)) - 6((0 \times 4) - (4 \times 1)) + 3((0 \times 7) - (5 \times 4)) = -10.$$

Recognizing how to compute a matrix's determinant is a pivotal tool, as this will be a cornerstone in many subsequent mathematical computations pertaining to matrices. We conclude this section with one more example to reinforce the concept.

Example: Evaluate the determinant of the matrix $\begin{bmatrix} 1 & 2 \\ -1 & -1 \end{bmatrix}$.

Solution: We employ the determinant formula for a 2×2 matrix $|A| = ad - bc$. Thus, $|A| = (1)(-1) - (2)(-1) = 1$.

5.5   The Inverse of a Matrix

Suppose we have a matrix A and we want to find another matrix which, when multiplied with A, produces the identity matrix (An Identity matrix I is a square matrix that has 1 in the elements that are in the same row and column, and 0 in the elements that are in different rows and columns). This matrix is known as the inverse of A.

🔔 **Key Point**

A matrix A has an inverse, denoted as A^{-1}, if and only if it is square (having the equal number of rows and columns) and non-singular (with a non-zero determinant).

🔔 **Key Point**

The inverse of a 2×2 matrix $A = \begin{bmatrix} a & b \\ c & d \end{bmatrix}$ is $A^{-1} = \frac{1}{ad-bc} \begin{bmatrix} d & -b \\ -c & a \end{bmatrix}$.

Example: Find the inverse of the matrix: $A = \begin{bmatrix} 3 & 4 \\ 2 & 1 \end{bmatrix}$.

Solution: First, we calculate the determinant of A: $|A| = (3 \times 1) - (4 \times 2) = -5$. Since $|A| \neq 0$, A is non-singular, so an inverse exists. Apply the previously given formula, where $a = 3$, $b = 4$, $c = 2$, $d = 1$, and $|A| = -5$:

$$A^{-1} = \frac{1}{-5} \begin{bmatrix} 1 & -4 \\ -2 & 3 \end{bmatrix} = \begin{bmatrix} -0.2 & 0.8 \\ 0.4 & -0.6 \end{bmatrix}.$$

Example: Find the inverse of the matrix $A = \begin{bmatrix} 2 & 3 \\ 1 & 1 \end{bmatrix}$.

Solution: We start by finding the determinant: $|A| = (2 \times 1) - (3 \times 1) = -1$. Once again, $|A| \neq 0$, so an inverse exists. We then apply the inverse formula, where now $a = 2$, $b = 3$, $c = 1$, $d = 1$, and $|A| = -1$:

$$A^{-1} = \frac{1}{-1} \begin{bmatrix} 1 & -3 \\ -1 & 2 \end{bmatrix} = \begin{bmatrix} -1 & 3 \\ 1 & -2 \end{bmatrix}.$$

5.6 Solving Linear Systems with Matrix Equations

Systems of linear equations can be written in the form of a matrix equation, as $AX = B$, where A is the coefficient matrix, X is the variable matrix, and B is the constant matrix.

🔔 **Key Point**

A system of linear equations can be represented as a matrix equation of the form $AX = B$, facilitating easier solutions with matrix operations.

Given below is the systematic approach to solving such a matrix equation:

1. Rewrite the system of equations in standard form, i.e., arrange each equation into form $ax + by = c$.

2. Write the system as a matrix equation. The coefficients of the variables are organized into the coefficient matrix A and the constant terms into the constant matrix B.

3. Calculate the inverse of A, if exists, and then solve for X using $X = A^{-1}B$.

⚠ Key Point

The inverse A^{-1} is crucial for solving the matrix equation. To find X, multiply A^{-1} with B.

Note that not all matrices have an inverse and those that do not are called singular or degenerate. A matrix has an inverse only if its determinant is non-zero.

Example: For the system of linear equations:

$$\begin{cases} x + 2y = 5 \\ 3x - y = 1 \end{cases}$$

solve for X using matrix equations.

Solution: Step 1: These equations are already in the standard form.

Step 2: Rewrite this system as $AX = B$:

$$A = \begin{bmatrix} 1 & 2 \\ 3 & -1 \end{bmatrix}, \ X = \begin{bmatrix} x \\ y \end{bmatrix}, \text{ and } B = \begin{bmatrix} 5 \\ 1 \end{bmatrix}.$$

Step 3: Calculate A^{-1} using the formula for the inverse of a 2×2 matrix and multiply it with B to solve for X. We find the determinant of A as $(1 \times (-1)) - (2 \times 3) = -7$, which is non-zero, therefore A has an inverse. Applying the formula for the inverse of a 2×2 matrix, we find:

$$A^{-1} = \frac{1}{|A|} \begin{bmatrix} -1 & -2 \\ -3 & 1 \end{bmatrix} = \begin{bmatrix} \frac{1}{7} & \frac{2}{7} \\ \frac{3}{7} & \frac{-1}{7} \end{bmatrix}.$$

Now, we find $X = A^{-1}B$:

$$X = \begin{bmatrix} \frac{1}{7} & \frac{2}{7} \\ \frac{3}{7} & \frac{-1}{7} \end{bmatrix} \times \begin{bmatrix} 5 \\ 1 \end{bmatrix} = \begin{bmatrix} 1 \\ 2 \end{bmatrix}.$$

So, the solution to the system of equations is $x = 1$, and $y = 2$.

5.7   Practices

   Solve:

1) A fast-food restaurant sells Burgers, Hot Dogs and Fries on three different days. The Packages sold are provided in the table:

	Burgers	Hot Dogs	Fries
Monday	150	175	225
Tuesday	200	215	250
Wednesday	180	215	230

Represent this data in a matrix.

2) A tech store sells Phones, Laptops and Tablets in three different branches. The items sold are as follows:

	Phones	Laptops	Tablets
Branch A	120	180	100
Branch B	150	200	170
Branch C	140	190	150

Create a matrix to represent this data.

3) A grocery store sells Fruit, Dairy and Meat products on four different days. The items sold in pounds are as follows:

	Fruit	Dairy	Meat
Monday	500	700	500
Tuesday	600	800	600
Wednesday	550	750	550
Thursday	650	850	650

Form a matrix to represent this data.

4) A book store sells Fiction, Non-Fiction and Academic books in two different cities. The quantities sold are as follows:

	Fiction	Non-Fiction	Academic
City A	120	150	100
City B	140	170	120

Create a matrix to represent this data.

5) A clothes store sells Shirts, Pants and Jackets in three different outlets. The items sold are provided in the table:

	Shirts	Pants	Jackets
Outlet A	300	350	250
Outlet B	350	400	300
Outlet C	320	370	270

Represent this data in a matrix.

Equivalent Matrices:

6) Identify which of the following two pairs of matrices can be added or subtracted:

$$A = \begin{bmatrix} 2 & 3 \\ 4 & 5 \end{bmatrix} \text{ and } B = \begin{bmatrix} 6 & 7 \\ 8 & 9 \end{bmatrix}, \qquad C = \begin{bmatrix} 1 & 2 \\ 3 & 4 \\ 5 & 6 \end{bmatrix} \text{ and } D = \begin{bmatrix} 7 & 8 \\ 9 & 10 \end{bmatrix}.$$

7) Identify whether Matrix E can be subtracted from Matrix F:

$$E = \begin{bmatrix} 1 & 2 & 3 \\ 4 & 5 & 6 \end{bmatrix} \quad \text{and} \quad F = \begin{bmatrix} 7 & 8 \\ 9 & 10 \end{bmatrix}.$$

8) Identify if the following two matrices are suitable for addition or subtraction:

$$P = \begin{bmatrix} 2 & 3 & 4 \\ 5 & 6 & 7 \end{bmatrix} \quad \text{and} \quad Q = \begin{bmatrix} 8 & 9 & 10 \\ 11 & 12 & 13 \end{bmatrix}.$$

9) Identify which pair of matrices can be added or subtracted:

$$R = \begin{bmatrix} 1 & 2 \\ 3 & 4 \\ 5 & 6 \end{bmatrix} \text{ and } S = \begin{bmatrix} 7 & 8 \\ 9 & 10 \end{bmatrix}, \qquad T = \begin{bmatrix} 11 & 12 \\ 13 & 14 \end{bmatrix} \text{ and } U = \begin{bmatrix} 15 & 16 \\ 17 & 18 \end{bmatrix}.$$

10) Identify whether the following two matrices can be added or subtracted:

$$V = \begin{bmatrix} 1 & 2 & 3 \\ 4 & 5 & 6 \\ 7 & 8 & 9 \end{bmatrix} \quad \text{and} \quad W = \begin{bmatrix} 10 & 11 & 12 \\ 13 & 14 & 15 \\ 16 & 17 & 18 \end{bmatrix}.$$

Solve:

11) Multiply the following matrices $A = \begin{bmatrix} 1 & 3 \\ 2 & 4 \end{bmatrix}$ and $B = \begin{bmatrix} 4 & 6 \\ 5 & 7 \end{bmatrix}$.

12) If $A = \begin{bmatrix} 1 & 2 \\ 3 & 4 \end{bmatrix}$, and $C = \begin{bmatrix} 7 & 8 \\ 9 & 10 \end{bmatrix}$, calculate $A \times C$.

13) Perform the following matrix multiplication $A \times B$, given that matrix $A = \begin{bmatrix} 2 & 4 \\ 6 & 8 \end{bmatrix}$, and matrix $B = \begin{bmatrix} 1 & 3 \\ 2 & 5 \end{bmatrix}$.

14) Multiply the matrices: $A = \begin{bmatrix} 3 & 2 \\ 4 & 1 \end{bmatrix}$ and $B = \begin{bmatrix} 5 & 6 \\ 7 & 8 \end{bmatrix}$.

15) A is a 2×3 matrix and B is a 3×2 matrix. Find the size of the matrix resulting from multiplying A by B.

Solve:

16) Solve the following system of linear equations using the matrix method: $\begin{cases} 2x - y = 3 \\ 3x + y = 7 \end{cases}$

17) Solve the following system of linear equations using the matrix method: $\begin{cases} x+2y=6 \\ 2x-y=3 \end{cases}$

18) Solve the following system of linear equations using the matrix method: $\begin{cases} 5x-4y=2 \\ 7x+y=13 \end{cases}$

19) Solve the following system of linear equations using the matrix method: $\begin{cases} 3x-y=7 \\ 2x+4y=8 \end{cases}$

20) Solve the following system of linear equations using the matrix method: $\begin{cases} 4x-3y=1 \\ 2x+y=5 \end{cases}$

Fill in the Blank:

21) Given a 2×2 matrix, $A = \begin{bmatrix} a & b \\ 8 & 4 \end{bmatrix}$, the determinant of A, $\det(A)$ is calculated as $\det(A) = a \times 4 -$ _____.

22) For the matrix $B = \begin{bmatrix} -6 & -2 \\ d & 5 \end{bmatrix}$, calculate $\det(B) =$ _____ $- (-2) \times d$.

23) Find the determinant of 3×3 matrix, $C = \begin{bmatrix} 4 & 5 & 2 \\ 6 & e & 0 \\ 3 & 2 & i \end{bmatrix}$, $\det(C) = 4(ei - 0) - 5(6i - 0) +$ _____.

24) Evaluate $\det(D)$ for $D = \begin{bmatrix} f & 3 \\ 2 & -5 \end{bmatrix}$, where $\det(D) =$ _____ $- 2 \times 3$.

25) Compute the determinant of matrix $E = \begin{bmatrix} a & 6 & 3 \\ 0 & b & 1 \\ 7 & 2 & c \end{bmatrix}$, $\det(E) = a(b \times c - 2) - 6(0 - 7) + 3(0 -$ _____ $)$.

Solve:

26) Find the inverse of the matrix: $A = \begin{bmatrix} 5 & 7 \\ 3 & 4 \end{bmatrix}$

27) Find the inverse of the matrix: $B = \begin{bmatrix} 2 & 1 \\ 1 & 1 \end{bmatrix}$

28) Find the inverse of the matrix: $C = \begin{bmatrix} 1 & 3 \\ 2 & 6 \end{bmatrix}$

29) Find the inverse of the matrix: $D = \begin{bmatrix} 4 & 3 \\ 2 & 1 \end{bmatrix}$

30) Find the inverse of the matrix: $E = \begin{bmatrix} 2 & -3 \\ -1 & 2 \end{bmatrix}$

Answer Keys

1) $Sales = \begin{bmatrix} 150 & 175 & 225 \\ 200 & 215 & 250 \\ 180 & 215 & 230 \end{bmatrix}$

2) $Sales = \begin{bmatrix} 120 & 180 & 100 \\ 150 & 200 & 170 \\ 140 & 190 & 150 \end{bmatrix}$

3) $Sales = \begin{bmatrix} 500 & 700 & 500 \\ 600 & 800 & 600 \\ 550 & 750 & 550 \\ 650 & 850 & 650 \end{bmatrix}$

4) $Sales = \begin{bmatrix} 120 & 150 & 100 \\ 140 & 170 & 120 \end{bmatrix}$

5) $Sales = \begin{bmatrix} 300 & 350 & 250 \\ 350 & 400 & 300 \\ 320 & 370 & 270 \end{bmatrix}$

6) (A,B) can be added/subtracted.

7) E cannot be subtracted from F.

8) P and Q can be added/subtracted.

9) (T,U) can be added/subtracted.

10) V and W can be added/subtracted.

11) $\begin{bmatrix} 19 & 27 \\ 28 & 40 \end{bmatrix}$

12) $\begin{bmatrix} 25 & 28 \\ 57 & 64 \end{bmatrix}$

13) $\begin{bmatrix} 10 & 26 \\ 22 & 58 \end{bmatrix}$

14) $\begin{bmatrix} 29 & 34 \\ 27 & 32 \end{bmatrix}$

15) 2×2.

16) $x = 2, y = 1$

17) $x = \frac{12}{5}, y = \frac{9}{5}$

18) $x = \frac{18}{11}, y = \frac{17}{11}$

19) $x = \frac{18}{7}, y = \frac{5}{7}$

20) $x = \frac{8}{5}, y = \frac{9}{5}$

21) $b \times 8$

22) -6×5

23) $2(6 \times 2 - 3 \times e)$

24) $f \times -5$

25) $7 \times b$

26) $\begin{bmatrix} -4 & 7 \\ 3 & -5 \end{bmatrix}$

27) $\begin{bmatrix} 1 & -1 \\ -1 & 2 \end{bmatrix}$

28) Matrix C has no inverse.

29) $\begin{bmatrix} -\frac{1}{2} & \frac{3}{2} \\ 1 & -2 \end{bmatrix}$

30) $\begin{bmatrix} 2 & 3 \\ 1 & 2 \end{bmatrix}$

Answers with Explanation

1) Each row in the matrix correspondingly represents Monday, Tuesday and Wednesday sales while the columns represent the sales of Burgers, Hot Dogs and Fries respectively.

2) The matrix is represented in such a way that each row corresponds to the respective branches (A, B and C) while the columns show the sales of Phones, Laptops and Tablets respectively.

3) The matrix is represented in such a way that each row corresponds to the respective days (Monday, Tuesday, Wednesday, Thursday) while the columns show the sales of Fruit, Dairy and Meat products respectively.

4) The matrix is represented with rows corresponding to the respective cities (City A and City B) while the columns show the sales of Fiction, Non-Fiction and Academic books respectively.

5) The rows in the matrix correspond to the respective outlets (Outlet A, Outlet B and Outlet C) while the columns show the sales of Shirts, Pants and Jackets respectively.

6) Matrix addition or subtraction can only be done on matrices of the same dimension. So (A, B) can be added or subtracted because both are 2×2. (C, D) cannot be added or subtracted because C is 3×2 and D is 2×2.

7) Matrix E cannot be subtracted from Matrix F because they have different dimensions. Here, E is 2×3 and F is 2×2.

8) That is correct. Matrix P and Matrix Q both have the same dimensions 2×3, so they can be added or subtracted.

9) Matrix addition or subtraction can only be done on matrices of the same dimension. So (T, U) can be added or subtracted because both are 2×2. (R, S) cannot be added or subtracted because R is 3×2 and S is 2×2.

10) V and W both have the same dimensions 3×3, so they can be added or subtracted.

11) $A \times B = \begin{bmatrix} (1 \times 4) + (3 \times 5) & (1 \times 6) + (3 \times 7) \\ (2 \times 4) + (4 \times 5) & (2 \times 6) + (4 \times 7) \end{bmatrix} = \begin{bmatrix} 19 & 27 \\ 28 & 40 \end{bmatrix}$.

12) $A \times C = \begin{bmatrix} (1 \times 7) + (2 \times 9) & (1 \times 8) + (2 \times 10) \\ (3 \times 7) + (4 \times 9) & (3 \times 8) + (4 \times 10) \end{bmatrix} = \begin{bmatrix} 25 & 28 \\ 57 & 64 \end{bmatrix}.$

13) $A \times B = \begin{bmatrix} (2 \times 1) + (4 \times 2) & (2 \times 3) + (4 \times 5) \\ (6 \times 1) + (8 \times 2) & (6 \times 3) + (8 \times 5) \end{bmatrix} = \begin{bmatrix} 10 & 26 \\ 22 & 58 \end{bmatrix}.$

14) $A \times B = \begin{bmatrix} (3 \times 5) + (2 \times 7) & (3 \times 6) + (2 \times 8) \\ (4 \times 5) + (1 \times 7) & (4 \times 6) + (1 \times 8) \end{bmatrix} = \begin{bmatrix} 29 & 34 \\ 27 & 32 \end{bmatrix}.$

15) In matrix multiplication, if matrix A is of size $m \times n$ and matrix B is of size $n \times p$, then the product $C = A \times B$ is a new matrix of size $m \times p$. So, in this case, the size of the result matrix is 2×2.

16) The system of equations is already in the standard form. The matrix form would be $AX = B$, where $A = \begin{bmatrix} 2 & -1 \\ 3 & 1 \end{bmatrix}$, $X = \begin{bmatrix} x \\ y \end{bmatrix}$, and $B = \begin{bmatrix} 3 \\ 7 \end{bmatrix}$. The determinant of A is $(2 \times 1) - (3 \times -1) = 5$ which is non-zero, so A^{-1} exists. Therefore, we can solve for X using $X = A^{-1}B$, which gives us $x = 2, y = 1$.

17) Using matrices, we express the above system as $AX = B$, where $A = \begin{bmatrix} 1 & 2 \\ 2 & -1 \end{bmatrix}$, $X = \begin{bmatrix} x \\ y \end{bmatrix}$ and $B = \begin{bmatrix} 6 \\ 3 \end{bmatrix}$. The determinant of A is $(1 \times (-1)) - (2 \times 2) = -5$, which is non-zero, hence invertible. So, we can find X by calculating $X = A^{-1}B$, which gives values $x = \frac{12}{5}, y = \frac{9}{5}$.

18) This system can be written as $AX = B$, where $A = \begin{bmatrix} 5 & -4 \\ 7 & 1 \end{bmatrix}$, $X = \begin{bmatrix} x \\ y \end{bmatrix}$ and $B = \begin{bmatrix} 2 \\ 13 \end{bmatrix}$. The determinant of A is $(5 \times 1) - (-4 \times 7) = 33$, which is non-zero. Therefore, we can solve for X using $X = A^{-1}B$, yielding $x = \frac{18}{11}$, and $y = \frac{17}{11}$.

19) The given system can be represented as $AX = B$, where $A = \begin{bmatrix} 3 & -1 \\ 2 & 4 \end{bmatrix}$, $X = \begin{bmatrix} x \\ y \end{bmatrix}$ and $B = \begin{bmatrix} 7 \\ 8 \end{bmatrix}$. The determinant of A is $(12 - (-2)) = 14$, which is non-zero. Thus, we can solve for X using $X = A^{-1}B$, giving us $x = \frac{18}{7}$ and $y = \frac{5}{7}$.

20) Setting up matrix notation, we write this as $AX = B$, where $A = \begin{bmatrix} 4 & -3 \\ 2 & 1 \end{bmatrix}$, $X = \begin{bmatrix} x \\ y \end{bmatrix}$ and $B = \begin{bmatrix} 1 \\ 5 \end{bmatrix}$. The determinant of A is $(4 \times 1) - (-3 \times 2) = 10$, which is non-zero. Thereby, we can solve for X using $X = A^{-1}B$, giving $x = \frac{8}{5}, y = \frac{9}{5}$.

21) Filling in the missing variable, $\det(A) = a \times 4 - b \times 8$. The determinant of a 2×2 matrix is given by $ad - bc$.

22) The determinant $\det(B) = -6 \times 5 - (-2) \times d$, following the formula $ad - bc$.

23) For the final term, we are left with $2(6 \times 2 - 3 \times e)$ completing the formula for the determinant of a 3×3 matrix.

24) The equation for the determinant becomes $\det(D) = f \times -5 - 2 \times 3$.

25) The completed equation becomes $\det(E) = a(b \times c - 2) - 6(0 - 7) + 3(0 - 7 \times b)$.

26) We calculate $|A| = 5 \times 4 - 7 \times 3 = -1$, so A is non-singular and has an inverse. Using the formula, the inverse matrix is $\frac{1}{-1} \begin{bmatrix} 4 & -7 \\ -3 & 5 \end{bmatrix}$, which simplifies to $A^{-1} = \begin{bmatrix} -4 & 7 \\ 3 & -5 \end{bmatrix}$.

27) To solve, we first calculate the determinant: $|B| = 2 \times 1 - 1 \times 1 = 1$ indicating an inverse exists. Using the formula, we calculate the inverse matrix as $\frac{1}{1} \begin{bmatrix} 1 & -1 \\ -1 & 2 \end{bmatrix} = \begin{bmatrix} 1 & -1 \\ -1 & 2 \end{bmatrix}$.

28) In this case, $|C| = 1 \times 6 - 2 \times 3 = 0$, indicating that C is a singular matrix and does not have an inverse.

29) $|D| = 4 \times 1 - 3 \times 2 = -2$, so D is a non-singular matrix and has an inverse. Using the formula, the inverse matrix is $\frac{1}{-2} \begin{bmatrix} 1 & -3 \\ -2 & 4 \end{bmatrix} = \begin{bmatrix} -\frac{1}{2} & \frac{3}{2} \\ 1 & -2 \end{bmatrix}$.

30) $|E| = 2 \times 2 - (-3) \times (-1) = 1$, so E is a non-singular matrix and has an inverse. Using the formula, the inverse matrix is $\frac{1}{1} \begin{bmatrix} 2 & 3 \\ 1 & 2 \end{bmatrix} = \begin{bmatrix} 2 & 3 \\ 1 & 2 \end{bmatrix}$.

6. Polynomial Operations

6.1　Writing Polynomials in Standard Form

A polynomial in algebra is an expression with variables and coefficients, typically having non-negative integer exponents. The standard form requires terms to be ordered by degree, from highest to lowest. A polynomial function $f(x)$ of degree n is of the form:

$$f(x) = a_n x^n + a_{n-1} x^{n-1} + \cdots + a_1 x + a_0,$$

where n is a non-negative integer and $a_0, a_1, \ldots, a_n$ are coefficients.

🔔 Key Point

Polynomial $f(x) = a_n x^n + \cdots + a_1 x + a_0$ with $n \geq 0$ and coefficients $a_0, \cdots, a_n$ is ordered by decreasing degree.

By writing the polynomial in standard form, you can easily identify the degree of the polynomial, which also helps in simplifying polynomials, factoring, performing polynomial division, and solving polynomial equations.

🔔 Key Point

Rewriting a polynomial in standard form clarifies its structure, degree, and simplifies arithmetic operations and solving.

Example: Write the polynomial $8 + 5x^2 - 3x^3$ in standard form.

Solution: The polynomial is not in standard form, as the term with the highest power of x is not the first term. In this case, the highest power of x is 3, so that the term, $-3x^3$, should be written first. The next term is the one with power 2, which is the term $5x^2$. Last, we write the constant term 8. Therefore, the polynomial $8 + 5x^2 - 3x^3$ written in standard form is $-3x^3 + 5x^2 + 8$.

Example: Write the polynomial $2x - 3x^2 + 4$ in standard form.

Solution: The highest degree in this case is 2, so the term with power 2, i.e., $-3x^2$, should be first. The next term is the one with power 1, i.e., $2x$. Finally, the constant 4 is written. Therefore, the polynomial $2x - 3x^2 + 4$ written in standard form is $-3x^2 + 2x + 4$.

6.2   Simplifying Polynomials

Simplifying polynomials, achieved by combining 'like terms' with identical variables and powers, reduces the number of terms, enhancing clarity and ease of operation. This process involves adding or subtracting coefficients according to the order of operations, thereby facilitating simpler understanding and more efficient arithmetic operations like addition, subtraction, and multiplication.

🔔 **Key Point**

Simplification of polynomials through the combination of like terms, which are terms with matching variables and exponents, lessens their complexity.

Example: Simplify the following polynomial: $3x^2y - 7x^3 + 2x^2y - x^3$.

Solution: First, let us group all like terms: our like terms are $3x^2y$ and $2x^2y$ as well as $-7x^3$ and $-x^3$. When we add these together, our simplified polynomial becomes:

$$(3x^2y + 2x^2y) + (-7x^3 - x^3) = 5x^2y - 8x^3.$$

Thus, the simplified form of the given polynomial is $5x^2y - 8x^3$.

Example: Simplify the polynomial $5xy^2 + 7x^2y - 3xy^2 + 2x^2y$.

Solution: Let us group our like terms: $5xy^2$ and $-3xy^2$, as well as $7x^2y$ and $2x^2y$. By adding these like terms together, we get the simplified polynomial:

$$(5xy^2 - 3xy^2) + (7x^2y + 2x^2y) = 2xy^2 + 9x^2y.$$

So, our given polynomial simplified is $2xy^2 + 9x^2y$.

6.3   Adding and Subtracting Polynomials

Adding and subtracting polynomials involves handling 'like terms,' but here we consider not just one but two or more polynomial expressions. In addition, it is essential to be cautious about the signs. We must take care to add and subtract correctly.

Key Point

> For polynomials, addition combines like terms, and subtraction also combines like terms after adjusting for sign changes.

Example: Add the following polynomials: $-4x^2 + 3x - 5 + 2x^3$ and $x^2 + 3x^3 - 4x + 5$.

   Solution: Firstly, we write the polynomials in standard form:

$$2x^3 - 4x^2 + 3x - 5 \quad \text{and} \quad 3x^3 + 1x^2 - 4x + 5.$$

Combining the like terms, we get:

$$2x^3 + 3x^3 = 5x^3, \quad -4x^2 + 1x^2 = -3x^2, \quad 3x - 4x = -x, \quad \text{and} \quad -5 + 5 = 0.$$

Thus, the addition of the given polynomials is $5x^3 - 3x^2 - x$.

Example: Subtract the following polynomials: $5x^3 - 3x^2 + 4x + 6$ from $3x^3 - 2x^2 + x - 3$.

   Solution: Align the polynomials as per the degree:

$$3x^3 - 2x^2 + x - 3 \quad \text{and} \quad -(5x^3 - 3x^2 + 4x + 6).$$

So to the second polynomial, yielding: $-5x^3 + 3x^2 - 4x - 6$. Combine like terms to get:

$$3x^3 - 5x^3 = -2x^3, \quad -2x^2 + 3x^2 = x^2, \quad x - 4x = -3x, \quad \text{and} \quad -3 - 6 = -9.$$

Thus, the result of the subtraction is $-2x^3 + x^2 - 3x - 9$.

6.4 Multiplying and Dividing Ponomials

When we multiply or divide monomials, we should remember to work with both aspects of the monomial, that is, the coefficient (numerical factor) and the variables (literal factors).

🔔 Key Point

Multiplying monomials involves multiplying coefficients and adding exponents with the same base, while dividing entails dividing coefficients and subtracting exponents with the same base.

Actually, we are applying the rule of exponents. The rules of exponents in case of multiplication and division states:

- For multiplication: $x^a \times x^b = x^{(a+b)}$.
- For division: $x^a \div x^b = x^{(a-b)}$.

Example: Multiply $6x^4y^2$ and $3x^2y^3$.

Solution: First, we multiply the coefficients: $6 \times 3 = 18$. Now we apply the rule of exponents to the variables x and y:

$$x^4 \times x^2 = x^{(4+2)} = x^6 \quad \text{and} \quad y^2 \times y^3 = y^{(2+3)} = y^5.$$

Combining them, we get: $6x^4y^2 \times 3x^2y^3 = 18x^6y^5$.

Example: Divide $15x^5y^3$ by $3x^2y$.

Solution: We will proceed similarly to multiplication, but this time we divide the coefficients: $15 \div 3 = 5$. And applying the rule of exponents during division for variables x and y, we get:

$$x^5 \div x^2 = x^{(5-2)} = x^3 \quad \text{and} \quad y^3 \div y^1 = y^{(3-1)} = y^2.$$

Hence, $\frac{15x^5y^3}{3x^2y} = 5x^3y^2$.

6.5   Multiplying a Polynomial and a Monomial

Multiplying a polynomial by a monomial uses a major principle in algebra, called the Distributive Property. The Distributive Property states that if you multiply a sum by a number, you can also think of it as multiplying each addend separately and then sum the products.

🔔 Key Point

The Distributive Property is expressed as:

$$a(b+c) = ab+ac \quad \text{and} \quad a(b-c) = ab-ac,$$

where a, b, and c are variables or numbers.

This principle holds true even when a, b, or c are polynomials. When a polynomial, be it a binomial, trinomial, or any other multi-term polynomial, is multiplied by a monomial, the multiplication distributes across all the terms of the polynomial. For instance, if we have $a(b+c+d)$, where a is a monomial, the multiplication distributes as $ab+ac+ad$.

Example: Multiply $3x^2$ by the polynomial $5x^3+4x-6$.

  Solution: Firstly, we distribute the monomial $3x^2$ across each term in the polynomial, giving us:

$$(3x^2 \times 5x^3) + (3x^2 \times 4x) - (3x^2 \times 6).$$

Next, we simplify: $15x^5 + 12x^3 - 18x^2$. You can see how we separately adjusted both the coefficients and the degrees of the terms during the multiplication operation.

Example: Multiply $-2x^3y$ by the polynomial $2x^2y - 3x + 5$.

  Solution: As before, we distribute the monomial $-2x^3y$ across each term in the polynomial:

$$(-2x^3y \times 2x^2y) - (2x^3y \times (-3x)) - (2x^3y \times 5).$$

Now, we simplify: $-4x^5y^2 + 6x^4y - 10x^3y$.

6.6   Multiplying Binomials

A binomial is a polynomial with two terms, examples being $x+2$ and $4y-9$, where each term is a monomial. To multiply two binomials, use the 'FOIL' method, an acronym for First, Outer, Inner, Last, indicating the order of term multiplication.

🔔 Key Point

The FOIL method for multiplying two binomials involves:

First: Multiply the first terms in each binomial.

Outer: Multiply the outer terms in the expression.

Inner: Multiply the inner terms.

Last: Multiply the last terms in each binomial.

Let us consider the multiplication of $(x+a)(x+b)$ as an example. Here, according to the FOIL method:

First: The first terms x and x multiply to give x^2.

Outer: The outer terms x and b multiply to give bx.

Inner: The inner terms a and x multiply to give ax.

Last: The last terms a and b multiply to give ab.

So,

$$(x+a)(x+b) = x^2 + bx + ax + ab = x^2 + (b+a)x + ab.$$

Example: Multiply $(x+2)(x-3)$.

Solution: We apply the FOIL method:

First: $x \times x = x^2$.

Outer: $x \times (-3) = -3x$.

Inner: $2 \times x = 2x$.

Last: $2 \times (-3) = -6$.

Consequently, $(x+2)(x-3) = x^2 - 3x + 2x - 6 = x^2 - x - 6$.

Example: Multiply $(2x-3)(x+4)$.

Solution: Applying the FOIL method again,

First: $2x \times x = 2x^2$.

Outer: $2x \times 4 = 8x$.

Inner: $-3 \times x = -3x$.

Last: $-3 \times 4 = -12$.

So, $(2x-3)(x+4) = 2x^2 + 8x - 3x - 12 = 2x^2 + 5x - 12$.

6.7   Factoring Trinomials

Factoring is a process of rewriting an expression (in this case, a trinomial) as a product of two or more other expressions. Factoring trinomials is a key skill that will prove valuable in solving many algebraic problems.

🔔 Key Point

To factor trinomials, you can use following methods:

- Using the 'FOIL' method, e.g., $(x+a)(x+b) = x^2 + (b+a)x + ab$.
- Using the 'Difference of Squares', e.g., $a^2 - b^2 = (a+b)(a-b)$.
- Using the 'Reverse FOIL' method, e.g., $x^2 + (b+a)x + ab = (x+a)(x+b)$.

In the "FOIL" technique, we factor a trinomial by finding two numbers that sum to be the coefficient of the x term and multiply to be the constant term. Keep in mind that the "Difference of Squares" method can only be applied when the trinomial is a difference of two squares. The "Reverse FOIL" method is often helpful when other methods are too complex or will not work.

Example: Factor the trinomial $x^2 - 5x + 6$.

Solution: Following the "FOIL" method, we need two numbers that add to -5 and multiply to 6. These numbers are -2 and -3. Hence, the factored form of $x^2 - 5x + 6$ is $(x-2)(x-3)$.

Example: Factor the trinomial $x^2 - 4$.

Solution: Here, we can apply the method of "Difference of Squares";

$$x^2 - 2^2 = (x+2)(x-2).$$

The factored form is $(x+2)(x-2)$.

Example: Factor the trinomial $x^2 - 4x + 4$.

Solution: Using the "Reverse FOIL" method, we can rewrite $x^2 - 4x + 4$ as $(x-2)(x-2)$, since

$-2 + (-2) = -4$ and $-2 \times (-2) = 4$. Thus, the factored form is $(x-2)(x-2)$ or $(x-2)^2$.

6.8   Choosing a Factoring Method for Polynomials

Factoring polynomials involves decomposing them into simpler parts that multiply to the original polynomial. It's crucial for simplifying expressions, solving equations, and grasping concepts like polynomial division and functions. The choice of factoring method depends on the polynomial's form and structure.

🔔 Key Point

Factoring methods for common polynomial types:

- *Monomial*: Identify common factors.
- *Binomial*: Check for difference of squares or sum/difference of cubes.
- *Trinomial*: Use trial and error or the FOIL method.
- *Four terms*: Apply factoring by grouping.
- *General polynomials*: Look for common factors, then explore special identities (e.g., difference of squares, sum/difference of cubes).

No single factoring method works best every time. The best one depends on what polynomial we are dealing with. Practice and experience will help you quickly identify what method to use for a given problem.

Example: Factor the polynomial $8x^3 - 12x^2$.

Solution: Looking at the polynomial, the common factor in both terms is $4x^2$. Hence, we have: $8x^3 - 12x^2 = 4x^2(2x - 3)$.

Example: Factor the polynomial $x^2 - 25$.

Solution: Here, the given expression is a difference of two squares. Hence, we have: $x^2 - 25 = (x+5)(x-5)$.

Example: Factor the polynomial $6x^2 - 3x - 9$.

Solution: In this case, we first look at the numbers. The numbers that multiply to $6 \times (-9) = -54$ and add up to -3 are -9 and 6. We then split the middle term and then factor by grouping, which gives: $6x^2 - 3x - 9 = 6x^2 - 9x + 6x - 9 = 3x(2x - 3) + 3(2x - 3) = 3(2x - 3)(x + 1)$.

6.9   Factoring by Greatest Common Factor

Factoring by Greatest Common Factor (GCF) simplifies a polynomial by identifying and extracting the largest monomial that evenly divides all terms of the polynomial.

🔔 Key Point

To find the Greatest Common Factor (GCF) of a polynomial:

- Determine the GCF of all terms.

- Express each term as a product of the GCF and a remaining factor.

- Extract the GCF from the polynomial using the Distributive Property.

This method is particularly useful when we deal with larger polynomials and need to simplify them before applying other factoring techniques. Also, remember that even when other methods of factoring could be used, factoring out the GCF is always a good first step.

Example: Factor the polynomial $18x^2y - 24xy^2 + 12x$.

Solution: Firstly, identify the greatest common factor (GCF) for all terms. Here, it is $6x$. Now, express each term as a product of the GCF and another term:

$$18x^2y = 6x \times 3xy, \quad -24xy^2 = 6x \times (-4y^2) \quad \text{and} \quad 12x = 6x \times 2.$$

Now, factor out the GCF from the polynomial using the distributive property:

$$18x^2y - 24xy^2 + 12x = 6x(3xy - 4y^2 + 2).$$

Example: Simplify the polynomial $x^3y^2 - x^3y^3 + y^1 - x^0y^0$.

Solution: To simplify this polynomial, we look for common factors in each term. The polynomial can be rearranged to group similar terms:

$$x^3y^2 - x^3y^3 + y - 1 = x^3y^2(1 - y) + (y - 1).$$

Here, we factor out x^3y^2 from the first two terms. Now, notice that $(1 - y)$ and $(y - 1)$ are similar but not identical. We can rewrite $(y-1)$ as $-1(1-y)$ to make them identical:

$$x^3y^2(1-y) - 1(1-y).$$

Now, both terms have a common factor of $(1-y)$. Factoring this out gives:

$$(1-y)(x^3y^2 - 1).$$

Therefore, the simplified form of the polynomial is $(1-y)(x^3y^2 - 1)$.

6.10 Factors and Greatest Common Factors

A factor of a number is a number that divides the original number without leaving a remainder. The GCF of two or more numbers is the largest factor that these numbers have in common.

🔔 Key Point

The GCF of a set of numbers is the largest number that divides all the numbers in the set without leaving a remainder.

 This concept is critical in simplifying fractions, factoring polynomials, and solving certain types of equations.

🔔 Key Point

There are several common methods to find the GCF of a set of numbers, including listing factors, prime factorization, and using the division method.

Example: Find the GCF of 72 and 120 using the method of listing factors.

Solution: First, we find the factors of both numbers.

Factors of 72: $\{1, 2, 3, 4, 6, 8, 9, 12, 18, 24, 36, 72\}$.

Factors of 120: $\{1, 2, 3, 4, 5, 6, 8, 10, 12, 15, 20, 24, 30, 40, 60, 120\}$.

The common factors are: $\{1, 2, 3, 4, 6, 8, 12, 24\}$. Of these, the GCF is 24. So, the GCF of 72 and 120 is 24.

Example: Use the prime factorization method to find the GCF of 48 and 60.

Solution: To use the prime factorization method, first find the prime factors of each number.

Prime factors of 48: $2^4 \times 3$.

Prime factors of 60: $2^2 \times 3 \times 5$.

Now, compare the prime factors of the two numbers. The GCF will be the product of the smallest power of each common prime factor. Hence, the GCF of 48 and 60 is $2^2 \times 3 = 12$.

Example: Find the GCF of 150 and 225 using the division method.

Solution: Here, we start with the larger number and divide it by the smaller number. $225 \div 150 = 1$ remainder 75. Then we replace the larger number with the smaller number and the divisor with the remainder, and repeat until the remainder is 0. $150 \div 75 = 2$ remainder 0. The last divisor, when the remainder becomes 0, is the GCF. So, the GCF of 150 and 225 is 75.

6.11   Operations with Polynomials

Operations with polynomials include addition, subtraction, multiplication, and division. In this section, we will learn how to apply the Distributive Property to simplify polynomial expressions.

🔔 **Key Point**

Polynomials can be added, subtracted, multiplied, or divided. Many of these operations involve the use of the Distributive Property.

🔔 **Key Point**

Subtraction of polynomials is similar to addition. However, every term of the subtracted polynomial changes its sign.

🔔 **Key Point**

To multiply polynomials, every term of the first polynomial is multiplied by every term from the second polynomial.

Example: $p(x) = 3x^2 + 2x - 1$ and $q(x) = x^2 - 3x + 4$. What is $p(x) + q(x)$?

Solution: Adding polynomials involves adding corresponding terms from the given polynomials.
$p(x) + q(x) = (3x^2 + x^2) + (2x - 3x) + (-1 + 4) = 4x^2 - x + 3$.

Example: $p(x) = 3x^2 + 2x - 1$ and $q(x) = x^2 - 3x + 4$. What is $p(x) - q(x)$?

Solution: Subtracting the polynomial $q(x)$ from $p(x)$ involves changing the sign of each term of $q(x)$ and then adding the terms.

$$p(x) - q(x) = (3x^2 - x^2) + (2x - (-3x)) + (-1 - 4) = 2x^2 + 5x - 5.$$

Example: Multiply the polynomials $p(x) = 2x + 3$ and $q(x) = x - 4$.

Solution: Multiplication of polynomials involves using the distributive property.

$$p(x) \times q(x) = [2x \times q(x)] + [3 \times q(x)]$$
$$= [(2x \times x) + 2x \times (-4)] + [3 \times x + 3 \times (-4)]$$
$$= 2x^2 - 8x + 3x - 12.$$

On simplifying and combining like terms, we get $p(x) \times q(x) = 2x^2 - 5x - 12$.

6.12   Even and Odd Functions

Functions can be categorized as even or odd based on their symmetry properties. An even function exhibits y-axis symmetry, satisfying $f(-x) = f(x)$ for all x in its domain. Conversely, an odd function has origin symmetry, meeting $f(-x) = -f(x)$ for all domain values.

🔔 Key Point

Functions can be categorized as even or odd based on symmetry properties:

- *Even functions* exhibit y-axis symmetry, characterized by $f(-x) = f(x)$.
- *Odd functions* demonstrate origin symmetry, indicated by $f(-x) = -f(x)$.

For a deeper understanding of function symmetries, observe the following plot and examples.

This plot demonstrates three types of functions: an odd function $y = x^3$ (solid), an even function $y = x^2$ (dashed), and a function that is neither even nor odd $y = x^3 + x^2$ (dotted), highlighting their distinct symmetry properties and shapes.

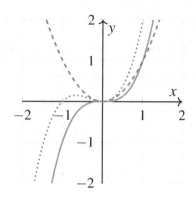

Example: Is the function $f(x) = x^2$ even, odd, or neither?

Solution: To validate if the function $f(x) = x^2$ is even, we find $f(-x)$ and check if it is equal to $f(x)$. We get, $f(-x) = (-x)^2 = x^2$. Since $f(-x) = f(x)$, the function $f(x) = x^2$ is an even function.

Example: Is the function $f(x) = x^3$ even, odd, or neither?

Solution: To confirm if the function $f(x) = x^3$ is odd, we find $f(-x)$ and check if it is equal to $-f(x)$. We get, $f(-x) = (-x)^3 = -x^3$. Since $f(-x) = -f(x)$, the function $f(x) = x^3$ is an odd function.

Example: Is the function $f(x) = x^3 + x^2$ even, odd, or neither?

Solution: Let us find $f(-x)$: $f(-x) = (-x)^3 + (-x)^2 = -x^3 + x^2$. We find that $f(-x)$ does not equal $f(x)$ nor $-f(x)$, so the function $f(x) = x^3 + x^2$ is neither even nor odd.

6.13   End Behavior of Polynomial Functions

In determining the end behavior of a polynomial, the leading term (the term with the highest degree) is the most important. If we let the polynomial function $P(x)$ be in the form $a_n x^n$, where n represents the degree of the polynomial and a_n is the coefficient of the leading term, then the leading term decides the end behavior of $P(x)$.

Key Point

The degree (n) and the leading coefficient (a_n) of a polynomial function $P(x) = a_n x^n + a_{n-1} x^{n-1} + \cdots + a_1 x + a_0$ govern the end behavior of the function.

- Let P be a polynomial function in the general form:

$$P(x) = a_n x^n + a_{n-1} x^{n-1} + \cdots + a_1 x + a_0.$$

- The domain of $P(x)$ is all real numbers, and the graph of $P(x)$ has no interruptions or breaks for any value of x.

- The end behavior of $P(x)$ is according to the following tables:

If	$a_n > 0$	$a_n < 0$
n in even	$P(x) \to +\infty$, an $x \to +\infty$	$P(x) \to -\infty$, as $x \to +\infty$
	$P(x) \to +\infty$, as $x \to -\infty$	$P(x) \to -\infty$, as $x \to -\infty$
n is odd	$P(x) \to +\infty$, as $x \to +\infty$	$P(x) \to -\infty$, as $x \to +\infty$
	$P(x) = -\infty$, as $x \to -\infty$	$P(x) \to +\infty$, as $x \to -\infty$

🔔 Key Point

The easiest way to visualize the end behavior of a polynomial is to sketch a graph. However, you should be able to predict the end behavior without sketching, based solely on the degree and sign of the leading coefficient.

Example: Determine the end behavior of the function $f(x) = 2x^4 - 3x^2 + x - 1$.

Solution: The leading term of $f(x)$ is $2x^4$. Since the degree is even (4) and the leading coefficient is positive (2), both tails of the function point up. Thus, the end behavior is:

$$f(x) \to +\infty, \text{ as } x \to +\infty,$$

$$f(x) \to +\infty, \text{ as } x \to -\infty.$$

Example: Analyze the end behavior of the function $g(x) = -3x^5 + 2x^3 - x + 4$.

Solution: The leading term of $g(x)$ is $-3x^5$. Thus, the end behavior is:

$$g(x) \to +\infty, \text{ as } x \to -\infty,$$

$$g(x) \to -\infty, \text{ as } x \to +\infty.$$

6.14   Remainder and Factor Theorems

The Remainder Theorem provides a fast and straightforward approach to finding the remainder when a polynomial function $P(x)$ is divided by a binomial of the form $x - a$. The Factor Theorem is an extension of the Remainder Theorem, which aids in expressing the polynomial as a product of a linear factor and a quotient.

🔔 Key Point

Remainder Theorem states that if a polynomial $P(x)$ is divided by $x - a$, then the remainder is $P(a)$.

🔔 Key Point

Factor Theorem states that a polynomial $P(x)$ has a factor $x - c$ if and only if $P(c) = 0$.

Example: Using the remainder theorem, find the remainder of dividing $P(x) = 2x^3 - 5x^2 + 3x - 8$ by $x + 3$.

Solution: Applying the remainder theorem, we find the value of the polynomial expression for -3. Therefore:

$$P(-3) = 2(-3)^3 - 5(-3)^2 + 3(-3) - 8 = -54 - 45 - 9 - 8 = -116.$$

So, the remainder of the division is -116.

Example: Verify whether $x + 2$ is a factor of $P(x) = x^3 - 2x^2 - 5x + 6$ using the Factor Theorem.

Solution: According to the Factor Theorem, $x + 2$ is a factor of $P(x)$ if $P(-2) = 0$. So, let's compute $P(-2)$:

$$P(-2) = (-2)^3 - 2(-2)^2 - 5(-2) + 6 = -8 - 8 + 10 + 6 = 0.$$

Since $P(-2) = 0$, we can verify that $x + 2$ is indeed a factor of $P(x)$ as per the Factor Theorem.

6.15 Polynomial Division (Long Division)

Polynomial division is a fundamental skill and is done using two main methods: Long Division and Synthetic Division. Polynomial Long Division resembles traditional long division but involves polynomials instead of numbers. Just like long division with integers, polynomial long division consists of several steps: division, multiplication, subtraction, and bringing down the next term.

🔔 Key Point

Long division of polynomials: Arrange both the dividend and the divisor in descending order of their degrees. Ensure that you include terms for any missing powers of x in the dividend with 0 coefficients.

Example: Divide $2x^3 - 3x^2 + 4x - 5$ by $x - 1$.

Solution: Arrange the dividend ($2x^3 - 3x^2 + 4x - 5$) and divisor ($x - 1$) in descending order of power. Divide the leading term of the dividend $2x^3$ by the leading term of the divisor x, the result is $2x^2$. Then, multiply the entire divisor by the result and subtract it from the dividend:

$$
\begin{array}{r|rrrr}
x-1 & 2x^3 & -3x^2 & +4x & -5 \\
- & 2x^3 & -2x^2 & & \\
\hline
& & -x^2 & +4x & -5 \\
& & -x^2 & +x & \\
\hline
& & & +3x & -5 \\
& & & +3x & -3 \\
\hline
& & & & -2 \\
\end{array}
$$

So, $2x^3 - 3x^2 + 4x - 5$ divided by $x - 1$ equals $2x^2 - x + 3$ with a remainder of -2.

6.16   Polynomial Division (Synthetic Division)

Synthetic Division method is particularly useful when dividing a polynomial by a linear divisor. Firstly, synthetic division requires us to identify the root of the divisor which is the solution to the equation if the divisor equaled zero.

🔔 Key Point

In a divisor of the form $x - a$, the root is a. For a divisor of the form $x + a$, the root is $-a$.

We then use this root to establish our synthetic division table.

🔔 Key Point

It is critical to ensure that the polynomial is written in standard form, and that a term is included for any missing degrees with a 0 coefficient.

Example: Apply synthetic division to divide $x^3 + 2x^2 - 5x + 2$ by $x - 3$.

Solution: Here, the root of the divisor $x - 3$ is 3. Firstly, arrange the coefficients of the dividend, $1, 2, -5, 2$, in a row and place the root 3 to the left. Then, bring down the first coefficient 1, and then multiply this by 3, writing the result under the next coefficient, 2 like this:

$$
\begin{array}{c|ccc}
3 & 1 & 2 & -5 & 2 \\
  &   & 3 & 15 & 30 \\
\hline
  & 1 & 5 & 10 & 32
\end{array}
$$

Now, sum the pairs of numbers in each column:

$$
\begin{array}{c|ccc}
3 & 1 & 2 & -5 & 2 \\
+ &   & 3 & 15 & 30 \\
\hline
  & 1 & 5 & 10 & 32
\end{array}
$$

We obtain $1, 5, 10, 32$. These give us the quotient and the remainder. The first 3 values are the coefficients of the quotient: $x^2 + 5x + 10$. The last value 32 is the remainder when $x^3 + 2x^2 - 5x + 2$ is divided by $x - 3$. Hence, the polynomial $x^3 + 2x^2 - 5x + 2$ divided by $x - 3$ is $x^2 + 5x + 10$ with a remainder of $+32$.

6.17   Finding Zeros of Polynomials

A *zero* or *root* of a polynomial is a specific value that makes the polynomial equal to zero. The maximum number of zeros a polynomial can have is equal to its degree. For example, a linear polynomial (degree 1) has at most 1 zero, while a quadratic polynomial (degree 2) can have up to 2 zeros.

- For a linear polynomial of the form $mx + b = 0$, the zero is found by solving $x = -\frac{b}{m}$.

- For a quadratic polynomial $ax^2 + bx + c = 0$, zeros are found using the quadratic formula: $x = \frac{-b \pm \sqrt{b^2 - 4ac}}{2a}$. The symbol $\pm$ indicates two possible solutions, stemming from the square root.

- For polynomials of degree higher than 2, we first attempt to factor the polynomial if possible. In cases where factoring is not straightforward, we use the Remainder Theorem or synthetic division, which we have covered in the previous section.

🔔 Key Point

The number of zeros of a polynomial is up to its degree, and various methods like direct solving, the quadratic formula, factoring, the Remainder Theorem, or synthetic division are used to find these zeros.

Example: Given the polynomial $P(x) = x^3 - 6x^2 + 11x - 6$. Determine if $x = 1$ is a zero of $P(x)$, as well as find all the zeros of $P(x)$.

Solution: To determine if $x = 1$ is a zero of $P(x) = x^3 - 6x^2 + 11x - 6$, it is sufficient to calculate $P(1)$:

$$P(1) = (1)^3 - 6(1)^2 + 11(1) - 6 = 1 - 6 + 11 - 6 = 0.$$

Since $P(1) = 0$, this means that $x = 1$ is a zero of $P(x)$. Now, we can express:

$$P(x) = (x - 1)(x^2 - 5x + 6).$$

Factoring $x^2 - 5x + 6$, we obtain:

$$x^2 - 5x + 6 = (x - 2)(x - 3).$$

Now, solve the following equation:

$$(x - 2)(x - 3) = 0.$$

Thus, the zeros of $P(x)$ are $x = 1$, $x = 2$, and $x = 3$.

6.18   Polynomial Identities

Polynomial identities simplify the expansion and factorization of polynomial expressions, streamlining algebraic operations by identifying recurring special structures.

Some of the most used polynomial identities are:

1) $(x + y)^2 = x^2 + 2xy + y^2$,

2) $(x - y)^2 = x^2 - 2xy + y^2$,

3) $(x + y)(x - y) = x^2 - y^2$.

These identities come in handy when we need to expand binomial expressions squared or used in multiplication. Further vital identities employed in algebra include:

4) $(x + a)(x + b) = x^2 + (a + b)x + ab$.

This expression is particularly useful when expanding binomial expressions.

5) $(x + y)^3 = x^3 + 3x^2y + 3xy^2 + y^3 = x^3 + y^3 + 3xy(x + y)$,

6) $(x - y)^3 = x^3 - 3x^2y + 3xy^2 - y^3 = x^3 - y^3 - 3xy(x - y)$.

These identities help us in expanding the cube of binomial expressions. Returning to our identities:

7) $(x+y+z)^2 = x^2 + y^2 + z^2 + 2xy + 2yz + 2zx$.

This identity is beneficial when dealing with squares of trinomial expressions. And finally, we have a few identities which revolve around cubes:

8) $x^3 + y^3 = (x+y)\left(x^2 - xy + y^2\right)$,

9) $x^3 - y^3 = (x-y)\left(x^2 + xy + y^2\right)$,

10) $x^3 + y^3 + z^3 - 3xyz = (x+y+z)\left(x^2 + y^2 + z^2 - xy - yz - zx\right)$,

🔔 Key Point

Polynomial identities describe relationships between algebraic terms with variables, such as:

- $(x+y)^2 = x^2 + 2xy + y^2$,
- $(x-y)^2 = x^2 - 2xy + y^2$,
- $(x+y)(x-y) = x^2 - y^2$.
- $(x+a)(x+b) = x^2 + (a+b)x + ab$,
- $(x+y)^3 = x^3 + 3x^2y + 3xy^2 + y^3 = x^3 + y^3 + 3xy(x+y)$,
- $(x-y)^3 = x^3 - 3x^2y + 3xy^2 - y^3 = x^3 - y^3 - 3xy(x-y)$,
- $x^3 + y^3 = (x+y)\left(x^2 - xy + y^2\right)$,
- $x^3 - y^3 = (x-y)\left(x^2 + xy + y^2\right)$.

Example: Expand the expression $(2x+3)^2$.

  Solution: To expand this expression, we use the algebraic identity

$$(x+y)^2 = x^2 + 2xy + y^2.$$

Here, $x = 2x$ and $y = 3$. So, $(2x+3)^2 = (2x)^2 + 2(2x)(3) + (3)^2 = 4x^2 + 12x + 9$.

Example: Expand the expression $(x-2)^3$.

  Solution: Here we can see that we have a binomial expression raised to the power of 3. Thus we utilize the identity

$$(x-y)^3 = x^3 - 3x^2y + 3xy^2 - y^3.$$

Here, $x = x$ and $y = 2$. So, $(x-2)^3 = x^3 - 3x^2(2) + 3x(2)^2 - (2)^3 = x^3 - 6x^2 + 12x - 8$.

Example: Factorize the expression $x^3 - 27$.

   Solution: Here we can see that this is a difference of cubes. Thus, we utilize the identity

$$x^3 - y^3 = (x - y)(x^2 + xy + y^2).$$

Here, $x = x$ and $y = 3$. So,

$$x^3 - 27 = x^3 - 3^3 = (x - 3)(x^2 + 3x + (3)^2) = (x - 3)(x^2 + 3x + 9).$$

6.19   Practices

True/False:

1) $3x^2 - 6x + 2$ is in standard form.

2) $x^2 + 4x^5 - 3x + 6$ is in standard form.

3) $-2x^3 + 5x^2 - x + 4$ is in standard form.

4) $7x^4 - 3x^2 + x - 5$ is in standard form.

5) $5 - 2x^2 + x^3 - 4x$ is in standard form.

Simplify Each Expression:

6) Simplify the polynomial $5x^3y + 7x^2y - 2x^3y + x^2y$.

7) Simplify the polynomial $3a^2b - a^2b + 2ab^2$.

8) Simplify the polynomial $2x^3y - x^2y^2 + 5x^2y^2 - x^3y$.

9) Simplify the polynomial $3m^n + 2n^m - m^n + n^m$.

10) Simplify the polynomial $5y^mn - 2y^mn + n^m - y^mn + n^m$.

Solve:

11) Find the difference of $4x^3 - 7x^2 + 3x - 9$ and $2x^3 + 4x^2 - 2x + 6$.

12) Solve the expression: $7x^3 - 5x^2 + 3x + 5 - (2x^3 + 3x^2 - x - 2)$.

13) Subtract $3x^3 - 2x^2 + x + 4$ from $5x^3 + 4x^2 - 3x + 2$.

14) Solve for $P(x)$ if $P(x) = 3x^3 + 7x^2 - 2x + 1 - (5x^3 - 3x^2 + x - 4)$.

15) Subtract $x^3 + 3x^2 - 4x + 5$ from $3x^3 - 2x^2 + x + 2$.

Simplify each expression:

16) Simplify: $-3x^2(4x^3 - 2x^2 + 5)$

17) Simplify: $7x(3x^2 - 5x + 4)$

18) Simplify: $8x^2(2x^3 - x^2 + x - 4)$

19) Simplify: $-2x^2(5x^3 + 4x^2 - 6)$

20) Simplify: $5x(2x^2 - 3x + 1)$

Solve:

21) Solve the equation $x^2 - 4x - 12 = 0$ for x.

22) Solve the equation $y^2 - 5y + 6 = 0$ for y.

23) Solve the equation $z^2 + 2z - 15 = 0$ for z.

24) Solve the equation $t^2 - 4 = 0$ for t.

25) Solve the equation $a^2 - 1 = 0$ for a.

Simplify Each Expression:

26) $20x^3 - 10x^2$

27) $4x^4y^3 - 2x^3y^4 + 6x^2y^2$

28) $28a^3b^2 - 35a^2b^3 + 7a^4b$

29) $12m^5n^3 + 3m^4n^4 - 15m^3n^2$

30) $16p^4q^3r^2 - 8p^3q^2r^3 + 4p^2q^4r$

Fill in the Blank:

31) The GCF of 18 and 24 is _____.

32) All factors of the number must be less than or equal to the _____.

33) Factors of a number are always _____ and _____.

34) A number is a _____ if it has exactly two different factors.

35) The GCF of a set of numbers _____ divide all the numbers in the set.

Fill in the Blank:

36) If a function f, matches the condition $f(-x) = $ _____, it is an even function.

37) A polynomial function $f(x) = x^4 - 2$ is _____. (Hint: Compute $f(-x)$ and compare to $f(x)$ and $-f(x)$).

38) A function with y-axis symmetry is _____.

39) If for a function f, $f(-x) = -f(x)$ for all values of x in its domain, then f is an _____ function.

40) An odd function has _____ symmetry.

Solve:

41) Apply the Remainder Theorem to find the remainder when the polynomial $P(x) = 2x^4 - 3x^3 + 4x^2 - 5x + 6$ is divided by $x - 2$.

42) Using the Remainder Theorem, find the remainder of $P(x) = x^3 - 2x^2 + x - 1$ divided by $x + 1$.

43) Find the remainder by dividing $P(x) = 3x^3 - 2x^2 + x + 1$ by $x - 3$ using the Remainder Theorem.

44) Determine the remainder of $P(x) = 5x^4 + 3x^2 - 2x + 1$ divided by $x + 2$ using the Remainder Theorem.

45) Use the Remainder Theorem to determine the remainder of $P(x) = 4x^3 - 5x^2 + x - 6$ divided by $x - 1$.

Solve:

46) Solve for $x^3 - x^2 + 2x - 1$ divided by $x - 1$.

47) Solve for $3x^4 - 2x^3 + x - 1$ divided by $x - 2$.

48) Solve for $x^3 - x^2 - 4x + 4$ divided by $x + 1$.

49) Solve for $x^3 + 7x^2 - 13x + 6$ divided by $x - 3$.

50) Solve for $x^4 - 5x^2 + x - 1$ divided by $x^2 - 3$.

True/False:

51) True or False: The polynomial $f(x) = x^3 + x$ has three real roots.

52) True or False: A polynomial of degree n will always have n zeros.

53) True or False: The polynomial $f(x) = x^2 - 2x + 1$ has one real root.

54) True or False: The polynomial $f(x) = x^3 + x^2 - x - 1$ has one real root and two complex roots.

55) True or False: If a polynomial has a degree of 2, it should have exactly two different real roots.

Solve:

56) Expand the expression $(3x+4)^2$.

57) Expand the expression $(x-4)^3$.

58) Factorize the expression $8x^3 - 27$.

59) Expand the expression $(2x+3)(2x-3)$.

60) Expand the expression $(x+3)(x-2)$.

Answer Keys

1) True

2) False

3) True

4) True

5) False

6) $3x^3y + 8x^2y$

7) $2a^2b + 2ab^2$

8) $x^3y + 4x^2y^2$

9) $2m^n + 3n^m$

10) $2y^mn + 2n^m$

11) $2x^3 - 11x^2 + 5x - 15$

12) $5x^3 - 8x^2 + 4x + 7$

13) $2x^3 + 6x^2 - 4x - 2$

14) $-2x^3 + 10x^2 - 3x + 5$

15) $2x^3 - 5x^2 + 5x - 3$

16) $-12x^5 + 6x^4 - 15x^2$

17) $21x^3 - 35x^2 + 28x$

18) $16x^5 - 8x^4 + 8x^3 - 32x^2$

19) $-10x^5 - 8x^4 + 12x^2$

20) $10x^3 - 15x^2 + 5x$

21) $x = -2, 6$

22) $y = 2, 3$

23) $z = 3, -5$

24) $t = -2, 2$

25) $a = -1, 1$

26) $10x^2(2x - 1)$

27) $2x^2y^2(2x^2y - xy^2 + 3)$

28) $7a^2b(4ab - 5b^2 + a^2)$

29) $3m^3n^2(4m^2n + mn^2 - 5)$

30) $4p^2q^2r(4p^2qr - 2pr^2 + q^2)$

31) 6

32) Number itself

33) Positive, integers

34) Prime number

35) Must

36) $f(x)$

37) Even

38) Even

39) Odd

40) Origin

41) 20

42) -5

43) 67

44) 97

45) $-6.$

46) $x^2 + 2 + \frac{1}{x-1}$

47) $3x^3 + 4x^2 + 8x + 17 + \frac{33}{x-2}$

48) $x^2 - 2x - 2 + \frac{6}{x+1}$

49) $x^2 + 10x + 17 + \frac{57}{x-3}$

50) $x^2 - 2 + \frac{x-7}{x^2-3}$

51) False

52) True

53) True

54) False

55) False

56) $9x^2 + 24x + 16$

57) $x^3 - 12x^2 + 48x - 64$

58) $(2x - 3)(4x^2 + 6x + 9)$

59) $4x^2 - 9$

60) $x^2 + x - 6$

Answers with Explanation

1) The polynomial is already in standard form as the terms are in the order of decreasing powers of x.

2) The polynomial in standard form is $4x^5 + x^2 - 3x + 6$ where terms are in the order of decreasing powers of x.

3) The polynomial is already in standard form as the terms are in the order of decreasing powers of x.

4) The polynomial is already in standard form as the terms are in the order of decreasing powers of x.

5) The polynomial in standard form is $x^3 - 2x^2 - 4x + 5$ where terms are in the order of decreasing powers of x.

6) Collecting like terms we have $(5x^3y - 2x^3y) + (7x^2y + x^2y) = 3x^3y + 8x^2y$.

7) Like terms are collected as: $(3a^2b - a^2b) + 2ab^2 = 2a^2b + 2ab^2$.

8) Combining like terms, we get $(2x^3y - x^3y) + (5x^2y^2 - x^2y^2) = x^3y + 4x^2y^2$.

9) Simplifying like terms, we get $(3m^n - m^n) + (2n^m + n^m) = 2m^n + 3n^m$.

10) Simplifying like terms, we get $(5y^mn - 2y^mn - y^mn) + 2n^m = 2y^mn + 2n^m$.

11) We apply the distributive property to the second polynomial and subtract like terms.

12) We use the distributive property to the second polynomial and subtract the like terms.

13) We apply the distributive property to the second polynomial and subtract like terms.

14) Subtract the polynomials by using the distributive property for the second polynomial and removing the like terms.

15) Apply the distributive property to the second polynomial and subtract like terms.

16) Apply the distributive property to multiply the monomial with the polynomial, resulting in $-12x^5 + 6x^4 - 15x^2$.

17) Applying the distributive property to multiply the monomial with the polynomial, we get $21x^3 - 35x^2 + 28x$.

18) Apply the distributive property to multiply the monomial with the polynomial, resulting in $16x^5 - 8x^4 + 8x^3 - 32x^2$.

19) Apply the distributive property to multiply the monomial with the polynomial, resulting in $-10x^5 - 8x^4 + 12x^2$.

20) Apply the distributive property to multiply the monomial with the polynomial, resulting in $10x^3 - 15x^2 + 5x$.

21) Factoring the equation gives $(x-6)(x+2) = 0$. Setting each factor equal to zero gives the solutions $x = 6$ and $x = -2$.

22) Factoring the equation gives $(y-2)(y-3) = 0$. Setting each factor equal to zero gives the solutions $y = 2$ and $y = 3$.

23) Factoring the equation gives $(z-3)(z+5) = 0$. Setting each factor equal to zero gives the solutions $z = 3$ and $z = -5$.

24) Factoring the equation using the difference of squares gives $(t-2)(t+2) = 0$. Setting each factor equal to zero gives the solutions $t = 2$ and $t = -2$.

25) Factoring the equation using the difference of squares gives $(a-1)(a+1) = 0$. Setting each factor equal to zero gives the solutions $a = 1$ and $a = -1$.

26) The GCF of the polynomial is $10x^2$. Factoring out the GCF, we get

$$10x^2(2x - 1).$$

27) The GCF of the polynomial is $2x^2y^2$. Factoring out the GCF, we get

$$2x^2y^2(2x^2y - xy^2 + 3).$$

28) The GCF of the polynomial is $7a^2b$. Factoring out the GCF, we get

$$7a^2b(4ab - 5b^2 + a^2).$$

29) The GCF of the polynomial is $3m^3n^2$. Factoring out the GCF, we get

$$3m^3n^2(4m^2n + mn^2 - 5).$$

30) The GCF of the polynomial is $4p^2q^2r$. Factoring out the GCF, we get

$$4p^2q^2r(4p^2qr - 2pr^2 + q^2)y.$$

31) The factors of 18 are 1, 2, 3, 6, 9, 18. The factors of 24 are 1, 2, 3, 4, 6, 8, 12, 24. The greatest common factor (GCF) is 6.

32) All factors of the number are less than or equal to the number itself.

33) Factors of a number are always positive and integers.

34) A number is a prime number if it has exactly two different factors.

35) The GCF of a set of numbers must divide all the numbers in the set leaving no remainder.

36) A function f is even if $f(-x) = f(x)$ for all values of x in its domain.

37) Plugging in $-x$ into the equation yields $(-x)^4 - 2 = x^4 - 2 = f(x)$. Thus, it is an even function.

38) Even functions have y-axis symmetry, which means $f(x) = f(-x)$.

39) A function f is odd if $f(-x) = -f(x)$ for all values of x in its domain.

40) An odd function has origin (or rotational) symmetry, which requires that $f(-x) = -f(x)$.

41) The Remainder Theorem states that to find the remainder we need to compute $P(2)$. By doing so, we get:

$$P(2) = 2(2)^4 - 3(2)^3 + 4(2)^2 - 5(2) + 6 = 32 - 24 + 16 - 10 + 6 = 20.$$

42) We need to calculate $P(-1)$ according to the Remainder Theorem, which gives us

$$(-1)^3 - 2(-1)^2 + (-1) - 1 = -1 - 2 - 1 - 1 = -5.$$

Hence, the remainder is -5.

43) Using the Remainder Theorem, we substitute $x = 3$ into $P(x)$ and find that

$$P(3) = 3(3)^3 - 2(3)^2 + (3) + 1 = 81 - 18 + 3 + 1 = 67.$$

Thus, the remainder is 67.

44) Using the Remainder Theorem, we need to find $P(-2)$ which yields

$$P(-2) = 5(-2)^4 + 3(-2)^2 - 2(-2) + 1 = 80 + 12 + 4 + 1 = 97.$$

Hence, the remainder is 97.

45) According to the Remainder theorem, we substitute $x = 1$ into the equation and compute

$$P(1) = 4(1)^3 - 5(1)^2 + 1 - 6 = 4 - 5 + 1 - 6 = -6.$$

Thus, the remainder is -6.

46) The polynomial $x^3 - x^2 + 2x - 1$ divided by $x - 1$ gives a quotient of $x^2 + 2$ with 1 remainder.

47) When $3x^4 - 2x^3 + x - 1$ is divided by $x - 2$ using synthetic division, the result is: $3x^3 + 4x^2 + 8x + 17$

remainder 33.

48) The polynomial $x^3 - x^2 - 4x + 4$ divided by $x + 1$ gives a quotient of $x^2 - 2x - 2$ with 6 remainder.

49) The polynomial $x^3 + 7x^2 - 13x + 6$ divided by $x - 3$ gives a quotient of $x^2 + 10x + 17$ with 57 remainder.

50) When $x^4 - 5x^2 + x - 1$ is divided by $x^2 - 3$ using synthetic division, the result is $x^2 - 2$ with remainder $x - 7$.

51) The given polynomial is of degree 3 and can be written as $f(x) = x(x^2 + 1)$. This polynomial has a real root at $x = 0$ and two complex roots coming from the quadratic part $(x^2 + 1)$.

52) A polynomial of degree n will always have n zeros, if we include both real and complex zeros.

53) The equations of the form $f(x) = (x - a)^2$ have only one real (repeated) root $x = a$.

54) The given polynomial has two real roots. $x = 1$ with multiplicity one and $x = -1$ with multiplicity two (repeated root).

55) Not necessarily. A polynomial of degree 2 can have two real roots, one real root (i.e., a repeated root), or two complex roots.

56) Using identity $(x + y)^2 = x^2 + 2xy + y^2$ with $x = 3x$ and $y = 4$:

$$(3x + 4)^2 = (3x)^2 + 2(3x)4 + (4)^2 = 9x^2 + 24x + 16.$$

57) Using identity $(x - y)^3 = x^3 - 3x^2y + 3xy^2 - y^3$ with $x = x$ and $y = 4$:

$$(x - 4)^3 = x^3 - 3x^2(4) + 3x(4)^2 - (4)^3 = x^3 - 12x^2 + 48x - 64.$$

58) This expression can be view as $x^3 - y^3$ with $x = 2x$ and $y = 3$.

So, we can use the identity $x^3 - y^3 = (x - y)(x^2 + xy + y^2)$:

$$8x^3 - 27 = (2x - 3)(4x^2 + (2x)3 + (3)^2) = (2x - 3)(4x^2 + 6x + 9).$$

59) We can use the identity $(x+y)(x-y) = x^2 - y^2$ with $x = 2x$ and $y = 3$:

$$(2x+3)(2x-3) = (2x)^2 - (3)^2 = 4x^2 - 9.$$

60) Using identity $(x+a)(x+b) = x^2 + (a+b)x + ab$ with $a = 3$ and $b = -2$:

$$(x+3)(x-2) = x^2 + (3-2)x + (3)(-2) = x^2 + x - 6.$$

7. Functions Operations

7.1 Function Notation

Functions in mathematics map each input to a unique output, operating like machines that produce specific outputs for varied inputs. Function notation, such as $f(x)$ or $g(x)$, concisely represents these operations, where 'f' denotes the function and 'x' the input.

Evaluating a function refers to the process of replacing the function's variable, or placeholder, with a given input value or expression. In the context of function notation, this involves substituting x in $f(x)$ with the chosen value to determine the resultant output.

🔔 Key Point

Functions in math link each input to a unique output, represented concisely by notations like $f(x)$, where 'f' is the function and 'x' the input.

Example: Suppose we have a function $f(x) = 3x + 2$. What is $f(4)$?

Solution: To evaluate this function for $x = 4$, we plug in 4 into the function:

$$f(4) = (3)(4) + 2 = 12 + 2 = 14.$$

Example: Consider another function $g(x) = 5x^2 - 1$. What is $g(3)$?

Solution: To find $g(3)$, replace the x in $g(x)$ with 3:

$$g(3) = (5)(3^2) - 1 = (5)(9) - 1 = 45 - 1 = 44.$$

7.2   Adding and Subtracting Functions

Operations such as addition and subtraction can be applied to functions, creating new functions and aiding in their simplification and analysis.

For any two functions, denoted as $f(x)$ and $g(x)$, we can create two new functions by adding or subtracting the original ones. The operations are as follows:

$$(f + g)(x) = f(x) + g(x),$$
$$(f - g)(x) = f(x) - g(x).$$

🔔 Key Point

Adding or subtracting functions $f(x)$ and $g(x)$ yields

$$(f \pm g)(x) = f(x) \pm g(x),$$

combining them like algebraic expressions.

Example: Suppose we have two functions defined as follows: $f(x) = 3x + 2$, and $g(x) = x^2 - 5$. Find the sum and difference of these functions.

Solution: When we add the functions $f(x)$ and $g(x)$, we get:

$$(f + g)(x) = f(x) + g(x) = (3x + 2) + (x^2 - 5),$$

which simplifies to: $(f + g)(x) = x^2 + 3x - 3$. Similarly, when we subtract the function $g(x)$ from $f(x)$, we get:

$$(f - g)(x) = f(x) - g(x) = (3x + 2) - (x^2 - 5),$$

which simplifies to: $(f - g)(x) = -x^2 + 3x + 7$.

Example: If $f(x) = 2x^2$ and $g(x) = -3x + 1$, find $f(x) + g(x)$ and $f(x) - g(x)$.

Solution: For addition, we have:

$$(f + g)(x) = f(x) + g(x) = 2x^2 + (-3x + 1),$$

which simplifies to: $(f + g)(x) = 2x^2 - 3x + 1$. For subtraction, we have:

$$(f - g)(x) = f(x) - g(x) = 2x^2 - (-3x + 1),$$

which simplifies to: $(f - g)(x) = 2x^2 + 3x - 1$.

7.3   Multiplying and Dividing Functions

Mathematical functions, like $f(x)$ and $g(x)$, can be multiplied or divided to produce new functions, enhancing their management and evaluation. The multiplication of two functions, often denoted as $(f \cdot g)(x)$, is simply the product of their individual results; that is, $(f \cdot g)(x) = f(x) \cdot g(x)$. Likewise, division of the functions, shown as $\left(\frac{f}{g}\right)(x)$, describes the quotient when using the output of one function as the divisor of the other, i.e., $\left(\frac{f}{g}\right)(x) = \frac{f(x)}{g(x)}$, considering $g(x) \neq 0$.

🔔 Key Point

> For functions $f(x)$ and $g(x)$, multiplication and division create the new functions $(f \cdot g)(x) = f(x) \cdot g(x)$ and $\left(\frac{f}{g}\right)(x) = \frac{f(x)}{g(x)}$, considering $g(x) \neq 0$.

Example: If $f(x) = 2x + 3$ and $g(x) = x - 1$, find $(f \cdot g)(x)$ and $\left(\frac{f}{g}\right)(x)$.

Solution: Here, we just need to apply the definitions of functions multiplication and division. For the multiplication of f and g, we get

$$(f \cdot g)(x) = f(x) \cdot g(x) = (2x + 3)(x - 1) = 2x^2 + 3x - 2x - 3 = 2x^2 + x - 3.$$

For the division of f by g, we get $\left(\frac{f}{g}\right)(x) = \frac{f(x)}{g(x)} = \frac{2x+3}{x-1}$, considering $x \neq 1$.

Example: If $f(x) = x^2$ and $g(x) = 3x$, find $(f.g)(x)$ and $\left(\frac{f}{g}\right)(x)$.

Solution: Applying our definitions of function operations, we find:

For multiplication: $(f \cdot g)(x) = f(x) \cdot g(x) = (x^2)(3x) = 3x^3$.

For division: $\left(\frac{f}{g}\right)(x) = \frac{f(x)}{g(x)} = \frac{x^2}{3x} = \frac{1}{3}x$, considering $x \neq 0$.

7.4 Composition of Functions

Function composition involves combining functions such that the output of one function becomes the input for the next. This is denoted as "function f composed with g at x" or "f of g at x". In this notation, $g(x)$ is evaluated first and its outcome is then used in f. It is important to note that $f(g(x))$ is generally not the same as $g(f(x))$, illustrating the non-commutative property of function composition.

🔔 Key Point

The notation for the composition of two functions, f and g, is $(f \circ g)(x)$ or $f(g(x))$.

Example: If $f(x) = 3x + 2$ and $g(x) = x^2$, find $f(g(x))$ and $g(f(x))$.

Solution: Substituting $g(x)$ into $f(x)$, we get:

$$f(g(x)) = f(x^2) = 3x^2 + 2.$$

Now, on the other hand, substituting $f(x)$ into $g(x)$, we get:

$$g(f(x)) = g(3x + 2) = (3x + 2)^2 = 9x^2 + 12x + 4.$$

Example: If $f(x) = x^2$ and $g(x) = 2x + 1$, find $f(g(x))$ and $g(f(x))$.

Solution: Substituting $g(x)$ into $f(x)$, we get:

$$f(g(x)) = f(2x + 1) = (2x + 1)^2 = 4x^2 + 4x + 1.$$

Now, substituting $f(x)$ into $g(x)$, we get:

$$g(f(x)) = g(x^2) = 2x^2 + 1.$$

7.5   Writing Functions

A function, likened to a machine, maps inputs (domain) to outputs (range) based on a specific rule, which defines their relationship. Functions can be represented through equations, graphs, tables, or expressions, each offering a unique perspective on their behavior. In function tables, columns for inputs, outputs, and sometimes the method of derivation illustrate this relationship.

🔔 Key Point

A function represents a special relationship between two variables, characterized by inputs (domain), outputs (range), and the rule (function rule) that specifies how inputs transform into outputs.

Example: Assume we have a function $f(x) = 3x + 2$. In table format, express the outputs for the inputs -1, 0, and 1.

Solution: Given the function $f(x) = 3x + 2$, we substitute each input (x-value) into the function to find the corresponding output ($f(x)$-value).

For $x = -1$, $f(-1) = 3(-1) + 2 = -3 + 2 = -1$.

For $x = 0$, $f(0) = 3(0) + 2 = 0 + 2 = 2$.

For $x = 1$, $f(1) = 3(1) + 2 = 3 + 2 = 5$.

So, in a table, this can be represented as:

Input x	Output $f(x)$
-1	-1
0	2
1	5

The inputs go into the function and, following the function rule, become the corresponding outputs.

7.6   Parent Functions

The parent function represents the simplest form of a function, serving as a foundational template for more complex functions derived via transformations. It has a 'core' set of points, unique to its type, that are altered through transformations. Key parent functions include constant, linear, absolute-value, polynomial, rational, radical, exponential, and logarithmic types.

🔔 Key Point

A parent function is the simplest form of a type of function, from which more complex functions can be derived through transformations

Transformations of a function $f(x)$ with a constant $k > 0$:

Transformation	Form
Up/Down	$f(x)+k$ or $f(x)-k$
Left/Right	$f(x+k)$ or $f(x-k)$
Narrower/Wider	$f(kx)$
Stretch/Shrink	$kf(x)$
Reflection	$-f(x)$ or $f(-x)$

Note: Despite these transformations, the core properties of the parent function (except in the case of reflection) like concavity and general shape are preserved.

🔔 Key Point

Function $f(x)$ transformations with constant $k > 0$ include vertical ($f(x) \pm k$), horizontal ($f(x \pm k)$), scaling ($kf(x)$, $f(kx)$), and reflection ($-f(x)$, $f(-x)$), preserving core properties except in reflections.

Example: What is the parent function for $f(x) = 2x^2 - 4x + 3$?

Solution: The parent function for $f(x) = 2x^2 - 4x + 3$ is $f(x) = x^2$, because $f(x) = 2x^2 - 4x + 3$ can be written as $f(x) = 2(x-1)^2 + 1$.

Here, the parent function has been transformed by stretching vertically by a factor of 2, shifting 1 unit to the right, and then upwards by 1 unit.

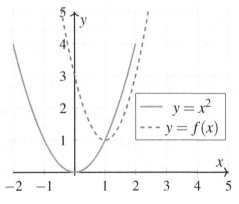

Example: Transform the parent function $f(x) = x^2$ by shifting 2 units to the right and 3 units down.

Solution: The transformed function is $f(x) = (x-2)^2 - 3$.

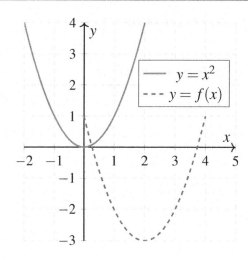

7.7   Function Inverses

An inverse function, symbolically represented as $f^{-1}(x)$, is a function that undoes the operation of the original function $f(x)$. If $f(x) = y$, then $f^{-1}(y) = x$. That is, if original function f transforms x into y, its inverse f^{-1} will transform y back into x.

🔔 Key Point

Function f and its inverse f^{-1} undo each other: $f(f^{-1}(y)) = y$ and $f^{-1}(f(x)) = x$.

Now, there might be a question about how to find this inverse function, $f^{-1}(x)$. It is quite straightforward. First, replace $f(x)$ with y. This makes the equation easier to work with. Then, swap x and y. Finally, solve for y.

Example: Find the inverse of the function $f(x) = 2x + 3$.

Solution: First, let us replace $f(x)$ with y. We get $y = 2x + 3$. Now, we swap x and y. This gives us $x = 2y + 3$. Finally, we solve for y. Subtract 3 from both sides, i.e., $x - 3 = 2y$. Then divide each side by 2: $y = \frac{x-3}{2}$. Therefore, the inverse function is $f^{-1}(x) = \frac{x-3}{2}$.

7.8   Inverse Variation

Inverse variation is a specific type of proportionality where one quantity decreases when the other increases, or vice versa. Significantly, the product of the quantities involved in an inverse variation always stays constant. This constant is often represented as k.

A model of inverse variation can be represented by the equation $xy = k$ or equivalently $y = \frac{k}{x}$. Here, k is a constant value and neither x nor y are equal to zero.

> ## 🔔 Key Point
>
> Inverse variation is characterized by the product of two variables remaining constant. This constant
> value is symbolized by k.

Let us take two points adhering to the inverse variation, represented as (x_1, y_1) and (x_2, y_2). These points can be expressed by two identical equations: $x_1 y_1 = k$ and $x_2 y_2 = k$. Both equations reflect the fundamental definition of inverse variation: the product of x and y is always the same.

Example: Let us imagine a situation where a balloon is being filled with a constant amount of air at a steady rate. If we consider the air volume of the balloon to be x and the rate at which the balloon is being filled to be y, how would you represent this situation with an inverse variation equation?

Solution: In this case, as the volume of the balloon increases (x increases), the rate at which the balloon is being filled decreases (y decreases). Since this is an inverse variation, $xy = k$. That is, the volume of air in the balloon multiplied by the rate at which the balloon is being filled is a constant. Or, equivalently, $y = \frac{k}{x}$.

Example: Given $x_1 = 2$, $y_1 = 5$, and $x_2 = 4$, find the value of y_2. The given values of x_1 and y_1 follow the inverse variation rule.

Solution: $k = x_1 y_1 = (2)(5) = 10$. Now, using x_2 value and k, we find y_2 by inverse variation rule. Given $x_2 y_2 = k$. Substituting the value of k, we have $4y_2 = 10$. Solving for y_2, we get $y_2 = \frac{10}{4}$.

7.9 Graphing Functions

To graph a function is to plot its possible outputs or y-values on the y-axis against the possible inputs or x-values on the x-axis. The most common types of functions are linear and quadratic functions.

> ## 🔔 Key Point
>
> A linear function can be expressed in the form $f(x) = ax + b$; its graph is a straight line in the
> coordinate plane.

🔔 **Key Point**

A quadratic function can be expressed in the form $f(x) = ax^2 + bx + c$; its graph is a parabola in the coordinate plane.

Synthetic substitution involves substituting random x values into an equation to plot points. For quadratic functions, identify the vertex for a symmetrical U shape, then find 2-3 points on each side of the vertex to graph.

Example: Let us try to graph a linear function $f(x) = 3x + 2$.

Solution: To draw the graph of this function, we can substitute random x values and determine their corresponding y values for the given equation, such as:

- If $x = 0$, $f(0) = 3(0) + 2 = 2$. Hence, the point (0, 2) lies on the graph.
- If $x = 1$, $f(1) = 3(1) + 2 = 5$. Hence, the point (1, 5) lies on the graph.

Placing these points on the graph and drawing a straight line through them will give us the graph of the function $f(x) = 3x + 2$.

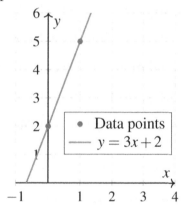

Example: Now let us try to graph a quadratic function $f(x) = x^2 - 2x + 1$.

Solution: The first step is to identify the vertex of the parabola. Since our equation is in the form $f(x) = a(x - h)^2 + k$, we can find the vertex at the point (h, k). In our case, h is 1 and k is 0, so the vertex is at (1, 0). Now, let us choose random values on both sides of 1 to graph. We suggest choosing $x = 0$ and $x = 2$. Substitute these into the equation to find the y value.

- For $x = 0$, we have $f(0) = (0)^2 - 2(0) + 1 = 1$. So, the coordinates are (0, 1).
- For $x = 2$, we have $f(2) = (2)^2 - 2(2) + 1 = 1$. So, the coordinates are (2, 1).

When we graph this, we will draw a parabolic curve through the points (0, 1), (1, 0), and (2, 1).

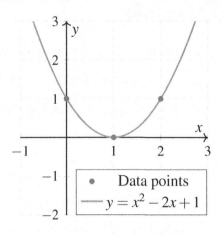

7.10   Domain and Range of Function

The set of all possible inputs a function can have is called the *domain*, while the corresponding set of all possible outputs is known as the *range*.

Key Point

> The domain of a function $f(x)$ is the set of all possible input values (typically x values), and the range of $f(x)$ is the set of all corresponding output values (usually y values).

Determining the domain of a function depends on the function's nature. A few methods to identify the domain are as follows:

1) For a Polynomial Function, the domain includes all real numbers. Polynomial functions do not have any restrictions on the x values.

2) For a Square Root Function, $y = \sqrt{f(x)}$, the domain includes all x values where $f(x) \geq 0$, since negative values under the square root lead to non-real numbers.

3) For an Exponential Function, the domain includes all real numbers, similar to polynomial functions.

4) For a Logarithmic Function, $y = \log(f(x))$, the domain includes all x values where $f(x) > 0$, because the logarithm is only defined for positive numbers.

5) For a Rational Function, $y = \frac{f(x)}{g(x)}$, the domain includes all x values where $g(x) \neq 0$, since division by zero, is undefined.

6) For a Piecewise Function, the domain is the union of all the smaller domains within the function.

7) By looking at a function's graph, we can also determine the domain, which is essentially the image of the graph on the x-axis, and the range, the image of the graph on the y-axis.

Key Point

The domain of a function varies: Polynomials and Exponentials include all real numbers; Square Roots $\sqrt{f(x)}$ require $f(x) \geq 0$; Logarithms $\log(f(x))$ need $f(x) > 0$; Rationals $\frac{f(x)}{g(x)}$ exclude $g(x) = 0$; Piecewise functions combine individual domains; and graph analysis can also determine domains.

Example: Determine the domain and range for the function given by $y = \sqrt{x-2}$.

Solution: We know that under a square root, inequality should be $x - 2 \geq 0$. Solving this inequality, we obtain $x \geq 2$. Therefore, the domain is $x \geq 2$, or in interval notation, $x \in [2, \infty)$.

For the range, since the square root function gives only non-negative values, the range is $y \geq 0$, or expressed in interval notation, $y \in [0, \infty)$.

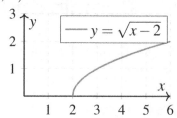

Example: Determine the domain and range for the function given by $y = \log(x+3)$.

Solution: Considering the properties of a logarithm function, the domain is derived from $x + 3 > 0$, giving $x > -3$.

In interval notation, the domain is $x \in (-3, \infty)$. A logarithmic function can take all real numbers as output, so the range is $y \in (-\infty, \infty)$.

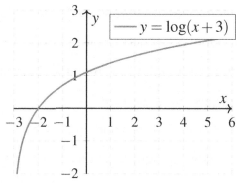

7.11 Piecewise Function

A piecewise function, as its name implies, consists of multiple sub-functions, each defining a segment of the domain, allowing different formulas for different intervals to model complex behaviors. An operation of the piecewise function could be generally represented as the following:

$$f(x) = \begin{cases} f_1(x) & \text{if } x \in \text{Domain of } f_1(x) \\ f_2(x) & \text{if } x \in \text{Domain of } f_2(x) \\ \vdots & \vdots \\ f_n(x) & \text{if } x \in \text{Domain of } f_n(x) \end{cases}$$

Here $n \geq 2$, and the domain of the function is the union of all the individual domains for each function, $f_1(x), f_2(x), \ldots, f_n(x)$.

🔔 Key Point

Piecewise functions are divided into segments within their domains, each governed by a distinct formula.

A very common piecewise function that we use often is the "Absolute Value Function". Absolute value is the distance of a number from zero, and it is never negative. Because of this, an absolute value function is represented as a piecewise function:

$$f(x) = |x| = \begin{cases} x & \text{if } x \geq 0 \\ -x & \text{if } x < 0 \end{cases}$$

Example: Plot the function $f(x) = \begin{cases} x+2 & \text{if } x \leq 1 \\ -x+3 & \text{if } x > 1 \end{cases}$

Solution: Here we have two lines given by $y = x+2$ and $y = -x+3$. The first line applies to all values of x that are less than or equal to 1. So, plot this line for $x \leq 1$ shading in the portion of the line where $x \leq 1$. Similarly, the second line is executed for all values of x that are more than 1, $x > 1$. So, plot this line for $x > 1$ shading in the portion of the line where $x > 1$.

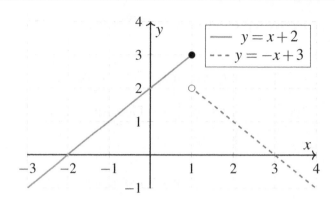

7.12   Positive, Negative, Increasing, and Decreasing Functions

For a function $f(x)$ in interval I, f is positive when $f(x) > 0$ for every x in I, indicating its graph lies above the x-axis. Conversely, f is negative when $f(x) < 0$ for every x in I, with its graph below the x-axis.

🔔 Key Point

In interval I, positive functions have graphs above the x-axis, while negative functions have graphs below it.

A function f's behavior between any two points x_1 and x_2 in its domain determines if it is increasing or decreasing:

- f is *increasing* if for any $x_1 < x_2$ in the interval, $f(x_1) \le f(x_2)$, meaning function values do not decrease as x increases.

- f is *decreasing* if for any $x_1 < x_2$, $f(x_1) \ge f(x_2)$, implying function values do not increase with increasing x.

🔔 Key Point

A function is *increasing* if its output rises or remains constant as x increases, and *decreasing* if its output falls or remains constant.

Example: For the function $f(x) = x^2$, is $f(x)$ positive, negative, increasing or decreasing in the interval $I = [-1, 1]$?

Solution: In the interval $[-1, 1]$, for any value of x that you pick, $f(x) = x^2$ will always be positive or zero as the squaring operation ensures that.

So, $f(x)$ is positive in the interval $[-1,1]$. However, neither is $f(x)$ increasing nor decreasing in the entire interval because, from $x = -1$ to $x = 0$, $f(x)$ decreases, whereas from $x = 0$ to $x = 1$, $f(x)$ increases.

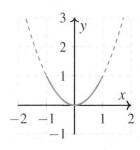

Example: Let $f(x) = -x^3$. Determine whether $f(x)$ is positive, negative, increasing, or decreasing in the interval $I = [-2, 2]$.

Solution: In the interval $[-2, 2]$, for any value of x from 0 to 2, $f(x) = -x^3$ will be negative because of the negative sign in front of the cubic term.

However, for x from -2 to 0, $f(x)$ will be positive. So, $f(x)$ is neither purely positive nor negative in this interval. Focusing on whether $f(x)$ is increasing or decreasing, we see a fall from $x = -2$ to $x = 2$, so $f(x)$ is decreasing in the entire interval.

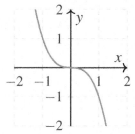

7.13   Practices

Solve:

1) Evaluate the function $f(x) = 2x^2 - 3$ for $x = -1$.

2) Find $g(0)$ for the function $g(x) = 3x + 1$.

3) Evaluate $h(2)$ for the function $h(x) = 2x^3 - 5x^2 + 3x - 1$.

4) Find $f(3)$ for the function $f(x) = x^2 - 4x + 4$.

5) Evaluate $g(-2)$ for the function $g(x) = 3x^2 - x + 2$.

Fill in the Blank:

6) Given the functions $f(x) = x^2 + 3x + 2$ and $g(x) = 2x - 3$, fill in the blank:

$$(f - g)(x) = \underline{\hspace{2cm}}.$$

7) Given the functions $f(x) = 4x^2 + 5x + 6$ and $g(x) = 3x^2 + 4x + 5$, fill in the blank:

$$(f + g)(x) = \underline{\hspace{2cm}}.$$

8) If $f(x) = 5x + 4$ and $g(x) = x^2 - 6x + 9$, fill in the blank:

$$(f - g)(x) = \underline{\hspace{2cm}}.$$

9) Consider $f(x) = 2x^3 + x^2 - x - 1$ and $g(x) = -x^3 + 3x + 2$, fill in the blank:

$$(f + g)(x) = \underline{\hspace{2cm}}.$$

10) If $f(x) = x^4 - 3x + 1$ and $g(x) = 2x^4 + 4x - 1$, fill in the blank:

$$(f - g)(x) = \underline{\hspace{2cm}}.$$

Solve:

11) If $f(x) = 4 - 3x$ and $g(x) = 7 - 2x$, find $f(g(x))$.

12) If $a(t) = t + 6$ and $b(t) = t^2$, find $a(b(t))$.

13) If $h(x) = x - 1$ and $p(x) = x^2 + 4x - 5$, find $h(p(x))$.

14) If $r(x) = 3x$ and $s(x) = x^2$, find $r(s(x))$.

Equation Solving:

15) For the function $r(x) = 6x - 3$, find the input x when $r(x) = 9$.

16) Solve $f(x) = 4x + 2 = 14$ to find the value of x.

17) Considering the function $g(x) = -2x + 5$, find the input x when $g(x) = 1$.

18) Let $h(x) = 5x - 2$. Solve for x when $h(x) = 13$.

19) Solve for x given that $f(x) = 3x + 4 = 10$.

Fill in the Blank:

20) Identify the parent function of $f(x) = 3(x+2)^2 - 1$. The parent function is $f(x) =$ _____.

21) Transform the function $f(x) = x^3$ by shifting 3 units to the left and 2 units up. The transformed function is $f(x) =$ _____.

22) Reflect the function $f(x) = x^4$ over the x-axis. The transformed function is $f(x) =$ _____.

23) Transform the function $f(x) = \frac{1}{x}$ by shifting 4 units to the right. The transformed function is $f(x) =$ _____.

24) The parent function of $f(x) = -\sqrt{x+1} + 2$ is $f(x) =$ _____.

Solve:

25) Find the inverse of the function $f(x) = 3x - 7$.

26) Find the inverse of the function $f(x) = \frac{2}{x} + 6$.

27) Find the inverse of the function $f(x) = 4x^2 + 2$.

28) Find the inverse of the function $f(x) = \sqrt{x} + 5$.

29) Find the inverse of the function $f(x) = 5x^3 + 1$.

Graph Plotting:

30) Plot the graph of the linear function $f(x) = -2x + 5$.

31) Plot the graph of the quadratic function $f(x) = -x^2 + 4x - 3$.

32) Plot the graph of the linear function $f(x) = \frac{x}{2} - 3$.

33) Plot the graph of the quadratic function $f(x) = 2x^2 - 8x + 7$.

34) Plot the graph of the linear function $f(x) = 3 - x$.

Fill in the Blank:

35) The domain of a polynomial function includes all _____ numbers.

36) The domain of a square root function $g(x) = \sqrt{f(x)}$ is where $f(x)$ is _____ to 0.

37) For a logarithmic function $g(x) = \log f(x)$, the domain includes all x values where $f(x) >$ _____.

38) The domain for a Rational function $h(x) = \frac{f(x)}{g(x)}$, includes values of x where $g(x)$ is not equal to _____.

39) By looking at a function's graph, you determine the domain, which is essentially the image on the _____-axis and the range, the image on the _____-axis.

Solve:

40) For the function $f(x) = 4x + 1$, is $f(x)$ positive, negative, increasing or decreasing in the interval $[1, 2]$?

41) Let $f(x) = -3x + 2$. Establish whether $f(x)$ is positive, negative, increasing, or decreasing in the interval $[-1, 0]$.

Answer Keys

1) -1

2) 1

3) 1

4) 1

5) 16

6) $x^2 + x + 5$

7) $7x^2 + 9x + 11$

8) $-x^2 + 11x - 5$

9) $x^3 + x^2 + 2x + 1$

10) $-x^4 - 7x + 2$

11) $f(g(x)) = -17 + 6x$

12) $a(b(t)) = t^2 + 6$

13) $h(p(x)) = x^2 + 4x - 6$

14) $r(s(x)) = 3x^2$

15) 2

16) 3

17) 2

18) 3

19) 2

20) $f(x) = x^2$

21) $f(x) = (x+3)^3 + 2$

22) $f(x) = -x^4$

23) $f(x) = \frac{1}{x-4}$

24) $f(x) = \sqrt{x}$

25) $f^{-1}(x) = \frac{x+7}{3}$

26) $f^{-1}(x) = \frac{2}{x-6}$

27) $f^{-1}(x) = \frac{\sqrt{x-2}}{2}, f^{-1}(x) = -\frac{\sqrt{x-2}}{2}$

28) $f^{-1}(x) = (x-5)^2$

29) $f^{-1}(x) = \sqrt[3]{\frac{x-1}{5}}$

30) See answer details.

31) See answer details.

32) See answer details.

33) See answer details.

34) See answer details.

35) real

36) greater than or equal

37) 0

38) 0

39) x, y

40) positive and increasing

41) positive and decreasing

Answers with Explanation

1) Substitute $x = -1$ into $f(x)$, we get $f(-1) = 2(-1)^2 - 3 = 2 - 3 = -1$.

2) Substitute $x = 0$ into $g(x)$, we have $g(0) = 3(0) + 1 = 1$.

3) Substitute $x = 2$ into $h(x)$, we have $h(2) = 2(2)^3 - 5(2)^2 + 3(2) - 1 = 1$.

4) Substitute $x = 3$ into $f(x)$, we get $f(3) = (3)^2 - 4(3) + 4 = 1$.

5) Substitute $x = -2$ into $g(x)$, we have $g(-2) = 3(-2)^2 - (-2) + 2 = 16$.

6) By definition $(f - g)(x) = f(x) - g(x)$, so $(f - g)(x) = (x^2 + 3x + 2) - (2x - 3)$. By simplifying, we have

$$x^2 + 3x - 2x + 2 + 3 = x^2 + x + 5.$$

7) By definition $(f + g)(x) = f(x) + g(x)$, so

$$(f + g)(x) = (4x^2 + 5x + 6) + (3x^2 + 4x + 5).$$

By simplifying, we get $7x^2 + 9x + 11$.

8) By definition $(f - g)(x) = f(x) - g(x)$, so

$$(f - g)(x) = (5x + 4) - (x^2 - 6x + 9).$$

We simplify to get $-x^2 + 11x - 5$.

9) By definition $(f + g)(x) = f(x) + g(x)$, so

$$(f + g)(x) = (2x^3 + x^2 - x - 1) + (-x^3 + 3x + 2).$$

We simplify this to $x^3 + x^2 + 2x + 1$.

10) By definition $(f - g)(x) = f(x) - g(x)$, thus

$$(f - g)(x) = (x^4 - 3x + 1) - (2x^4 + 4x - 1).$$

This simplifies to $-x^4 - 7x + 2$.

11) Substitute $g(x)$ into $f(x)$: $f(g(x)) = f(7 - 2x) = 4 - 3(7 - 2x) = -17 + 6x$.

12) Substitute $b(t)$ into $a(t)$: $a(b(t)) = a(t^2) = t^2 + 6$.

13) Substitute $p(x)$ into $h(x)$:

$$h(p(x)) = h(x^2 + 4x - 5) = (x^2 + 4x - 5) - 1 = x^2 + 4x - 6.$$

14) Substitute $s(x)$ into $r(x)$: $r(s(x)) = r(x^2) = 3x^2$.

15) To find x in $6x - 3 = 9$, add 3 to both sides to get $6x = 12$ and then divide by 6, yielding $x = 2$.

16) From $4x + 2 = 14$, subtract 2 from both sides to get $4x = 12$. Dividing by 4 yields $x = 3$.

17) Set $-2x + 5 = 1$. Subtract 5 from both sides to obtain $-2x = -4$. Dividing by -2 gives $x = 2$.

18) From $5x - 2 = 13$, add 2 to both sides to get $5x = 15$. Dividing by 5 results in $x = 3$.

19) For $3x + 4 = 10$, subtract 4 from both sides to find $3x = 6$. Dividing by 3 yields $x = 2$.

20) Despite the transformations, the parent function remains x^2 as it defines the basic form of the function.

21) The function was shifted 3 units to the left which is represented by $(x + 3)$, and 2 units up represented by the $+2$.

22) Reflection over the x-axis is represented by the negative sign before the function.

23) The function was shifted 4 units to the right which is represented by $(x - 4)$.

24) Despite the transformations, the parent function remains $\sqrt{x}$ as it defines the basic form of the function.

25) Replace $f(x)$ with y, so the equation becomes $y = 3x - 7$. Then, switch x and y to get $x = 3y - 7$. Finally, solve for y to find the inverse function: $y = \frac{x+7}{3}$. Therefore, the inverse function is $f^{-1}(x) = \frac{x+7}{3}$.

26) We replace $f(x)$ with y to get $y = \frac{2}{x} + 6$. Swap x and y: $x = \frac{2}{y} + 6$. Finally, solve for y: $y = \frac{2}{x-6}$. Thus, the inverse function is $f^{-1}(x) = \frac{2}{x-6}$.

27) We start by letting $f(x) = y$, so $y = 4x^2 + 2$. Swap x and y to get $x = 4y^2 + 2$. Solving for y in this case gives two solutions: $y = \frac{\sqrt{x-2}}{2}$ and $y = -\frac{\sqrt{x-2}}{2}$. Therefore, the inverse function is $f^{-1}(x) = \frac{\sqrt{x-2}}{2}$ and $f^{-1}(x) = -\frac{\sqrt{x-2}}{2}$.

28) Starting with $y = \sqrt{x} + 5$, we swap x and y to get $x = \sqrt{y} + 5$. Solving for y gives $y = (x-5)^2$, so the inverse function is $f^{-1}(x) = (x-5)^2$.

29) Replace $f(x)$ with y, so $y = 5x^3 + 1$. Swap x and y to get $x = 5y^3 + 1$. Solve for y to obtain the inverse function $y = \sqrt[3]{\frac{x-1}{5}}$. That's why $f^{-1}(x) = \sqrt[3]{\frac{x-1}{5}}$.

30) Substitute a few values of x into the function to obtain the corresponding y values. For $x = 0$, the corresponding y value is 5. For $x = 2$, the corresponding y value is 1.

So the points $(0,5)$ and $(2,1)$ lie on the graph. We then joined these points to obtain the line.

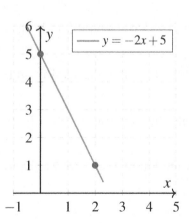

31) The vertex for the parabola is $x = 2$, which gives $y = 1$. We then pick some points to the left and right of $x = 2$ and substitute them into the equation to find their corresponding y values.

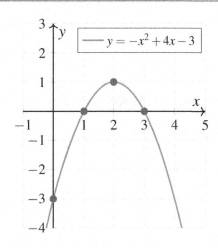

Setting $x = 1$ we get $y = 0$ and setting $x = 3$, we also have $y = 0$. We then plot the vertex and the other obtained points and draw the parabola.

32) We substitute a few values of x into the function to get the corresponding y values. Setting $x = 0$ we get $y = -3$. Setting $x = 2$, we get $y = -2$.

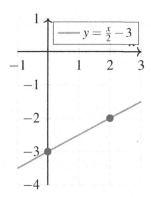

So the points $(0, -3)$ and $(2, -2)$ lie on the graph. We then join these points to obtain the line.

33) The vertex is at $x = 2$, giving $y = -1$.

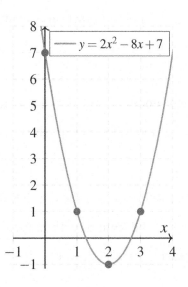

Then we choose some points to the left and right of $x = 2$ and substitute them into our function to find their corresponding y values. Setting $x = 1$ gives $y = 1$ and setting $x = 3$ gives $y = 1$. Now, we can plot our graph.

34) We fill in some x values in the function to get the corresponding y values. For $x = -1$, we get $y = 4$, and for $x = 1$, we get $y = 2$.

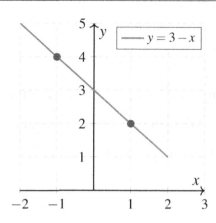

The points $(-1, 4)$ and $(1, 2)$ lie on the line. So, we join these points to construct the line.

35) Polynomial functions do not have any restrictions on the x values, hence, the domain includes all real numbers.

36) Under a square root, only non-negative numbers are defined in the real number system, hence the domain of $\sqrt{f(x)}$ is where $f(x) \geq 0$.

37) The logarithm is only defined for positive numbers; hence the domain includes all x values where $f(x) > 0$.

38) For a rational function, we cannot have the denominator as zero. Therefore, the domain includes all x values where $g(x) \neq 0$.

39) The domain of the function is obtained by projecting the graph to the x-axis, and the range is obtained by projecting to the y-axis.

40) For the function $f(x) = 4x + 1$, within the interval $[1, 2]$, the function $f(x)$ always gives a positive value which implies the function is positive.

Observing the sign of the coefficient of x, it is positive, hence as we progress in the right direction, the function value increases. Thus $f(x)$ is increasing in the interval $[1, 2]$.

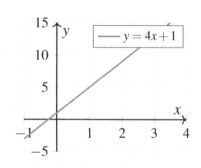

41) In the interval $[-1, 0]$, $f(x) = -3x + 2$ gives a value that is always greater than zero, so $f(x)$ is positive.

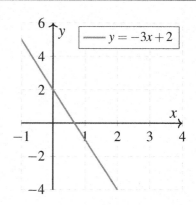

However, as we move rightwards along the x-axis, the function values decrease due to the negative coefficient of x. Hence, $f(x)$ is decreasing.

8. Exponential Functions

8.1 Exponential Function

An exponential function is defined as $f(x) = a^x$, where a is a positive real number, not equal to 1. This function exhibits exponential growth for $a > 1$ and decay for $0 < a < 1$, with its domain being $\mathbb{R}$ and range $(0, +\infty)$. The graph of $f(x)$ always intersects the y-axis at $(0, 1)$, reflecting the y-intercept.

🔔 Key Point

- Exponential functions $f(x) = a^x$ demonstrate growth for $a > 1$ (Exponential Growth) and decay for $0 < a < 1$ (Exponential Decay).

- These functions share a consistent Domain: $\mathbb{R}$, Range: $(0, +\infty)$, and y-intercept: 1.

Example: Let us graph $f(x) = 2^x$, and $g(x) = -5f(x) + 1$. We then need to identify if any of these portray exponential decay and to provide their domain, range, and y-intercept.

Solution: The base of the function $f(x) = 2^x$ is $2 > 1$, and hence, $f(x)$ is exponential growth with Domain: $\mathbb{R}$, Range: $(0, +\infty)$, and y-intercept of 1.

For the function $g(x) = -5f(x) + 1$, considering its graph, the y-intercept is -4. The domain is still $\mathbb{R}$, but the range is now $(-\infty, 1)$, indicating a state of exponential decay.

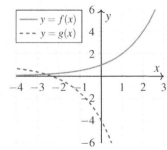

8.2   Linear, Quadratic, and Exponential Models

A "*linear function*", which follows the standard representation $y = mx + b$, is characterized by having its highest exponent as 1. Its graph is hence represented by a straight line.

A "*quadratic function*" is represented by $y = ax^2 + bx + c$ and is a special type of polynomial function with the highest exponent as 2. Its graph is hence represented by a parabolic curve.

A "*Exponential function*" represents a function in which variables form part of the exponent, typically following the standard form $y = e^x$.

The following diagram visually compares these three model types:

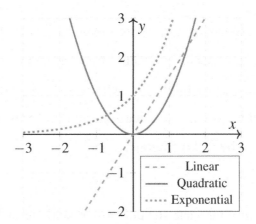

Key Point

A linear function always results in a straight-line graph, a quadratic function results in a parabolic graph, and an exponential function results in a curve.

Example: Determine whether the following table of values represents a linear function, an exponential function, or a quadratic function.

x	−5	−3	−1	1	3
y	−5	−2	1	4	7

Solution: Let us extract the first difference between y-values and determine if it is consistent.

- For -5 and -3, $-2 - (-5)$ equals 3

- For -3 and -1, $1 - (-2)$ equals 3

- For -1 and 1, $4 - 1$ equals 3

- For 1 and 3, $7 - 4$ equals 3

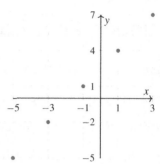

Since the first difference is the same for all pairs of y-values, which is 3, we then conclude that the function is linear. For a better understanding, refer to the figure.

8.3   Linear vs Exponential Growth

The distinction between linear and exponential growth lies in the pattern of change in y as x uniformly increases. *Linear growth* is characterized by a consistent increment in y for each unit increase in x, leading to an arithmetic progression and graphically depicted as a straight line. On the other hand, *exponential growth* is marked by y increasing at a rate proportional to its current value for each uniform step in x, resulting in a geometric progression and visually represented by a curved graph.

🔔 Key Point

Linear growth shows a constant y increase for uniform x increments (straight-line graph), while exponential growth multiplies y by a constant factor for each x increment (curved graph).

Example: If 75 students graduate from high school every year. Assuming this pattern continues, is this linear, exponential, or neither? List the data as follows: $(1,75)$, $(2,150)$, $(3,225)$, $(4,300)$ and so on.

Solution: Considering that each year (x value) increases by 1 unit and the number of students graduated (y value) increases with a constant difference of 75, it can be concluded that this is a linear growth.

Example: Using the data in this table:

x	0	1	2	3	4	5
y	3	6	12	24	48	96

Determine whether this relationship is linear, exponential, or neither.

Solution: From the table, the growth of x is by 1 unit, and the values of y increase by a constant ratio (multiplication by 2). Thus, the relationship is exponential.

Example: According to the following diagram, determine whether this relationship is linear, exponential, or neither.

Solution: In this graph represented in the above figure, the x values increase by 3 units, however, the difference between the y values is not constant. Moreover, the ratios between subsequent y values are not constant either. Therefore, this pattern can be categorized as neither linear nor exponential.

8.4   Practices

Fill in the Blank:

1) An exponential function can be written as $f(x) =$ _____^{x}. Fill in the blank.

2) If the base a is larger than 1, the exponential function represents _____ growth.

3) If a function has the form $f(x) = a^x$, the y-intercept is always _____.

4) The domain of $f(x) = a^x$ is _____.

5) If $0 < a < 1$, the function exhibits _____.

Analyze the Graph:

6) Consider the graph of the function $y = f(x)$ shown below, and classify the graph as Linear, Quadratic, or Exponential.

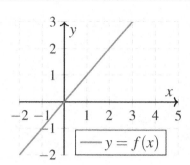

7) Consider the graph of the function $y = g(x)$ as below, and classify the graph as Linear, Quadratic, or Exponential.

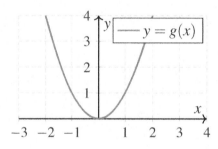

8) Consider the graph of the function $y = h(x)$ as below, and classify the graph as Linear, Quadratic, or Exponential.

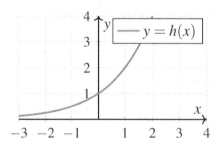

Analyze the Graph:

9) Refer to the figure below and decide if the growth pattern is linear, exponential, or neither.

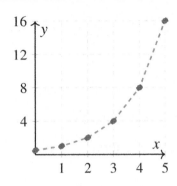

10) Analyze the following graph and determine whether the growth is linear, exponential, or neither.

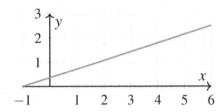

11) Determine the type of growth represented in the following graph.

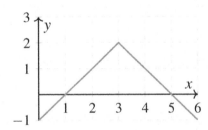

12) Is the growth represented in the following graph linear, exponential, or neither?

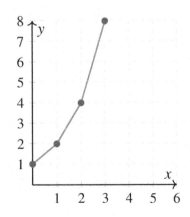

Solve:

13) You have $5,000 in a savings account that gains 5% interest each year. Determine the type of growth (linear or exponential) that best describes the situation.

14) A car depreciates in value by $2,500 each year. What type of growth is this considered?

15) You start a new job and your salary is $40,000. Your employer promises a 2% raise each year. Determine the type of growth (linear or exponential) that best describes the situation.

16) If a species of flower grows by adding 3 flowers to its population every week, what type of growth is this?

17) A bacterium population doubles every 6 hours. After 24 hours, is the growth of the bacterial population linear or exponential?

Answer Keys

1) a

2) Exponential

3) 1

4) $\mathbb{R}$

5) Exponential Decay

6) Linear

7) Quadratic

8) Exponential

9) Exponential

10) Linear

11) Neither

12) Exponential

13) Exponential

14) Linear

15) Exponential

16) Linear

17) Exponential

Answers with Explanation

1) In the general form, the exponential function is written as $f(x) = a^x$, where $a \in \mathbb{R}^+ \setminus \{1\}$.

2) If $a > 1$, then the function shows exponential growth.

3) For $f(x) = a^x$, if we substitute $x = 0$, we will have $y = 1$. Hence, the y-intercept is 1.

4) For $f(x) = a^x$, the function is defined for all real values of x. Hence, the domain is $\mathbb{R}$.

5) A function with $0 < a < 1$ shows exponential decay.

6) The graph is a straight line, which is characteristic of a linear function.

7) The graph is a parabola, which is characteristic of a quadratic function.

8) The graph is a curve, which has characteristic of an exponential function.

9) The graph shows increasing y values as x goes up, with a multiplier signifying exponential growth.

10) The graph depicts a straight line, showing a fixed increase in y values as x goes up, which is a characteristic of linear growth.

11) The graph does not show a constant difference (linear growth) nor a consistent multiplier (exponential growth), so it is neither.

12) The graph depicts successive y values that are multiplied by a constant as x increases, symbolizing exponential growth.

13) The initial balance is multiplied by a constant (interest rate) each year. This is an example of exponential growth.

14) The car's value decreases at a constant rate each year, making this an example of linear growth.

15) The salary, starting from an initial amount, is multiplied by a constant (increase rate) yearly. This is a case of exponential growth.

16) Since the population of flowers grows by the same amount each week, this is a characteristic of linear growth.

17) Given that the population of the bacteria doubles (a multiplier) every 6 hours, this represents exponential growth.

9. Logarithms

9.1   Evaluating Logarithms

Logarithms offer an alternative representation of exponentiation. The logarithmic equation $\log_b y = x$ corresponds to the exponential form $y = b^x$.

🔔 Key Point

Key logarithmic rules are applicable under conditions where $a > 0$, $a \neq 1$, $M > 0$, $N > 0$, and k is a real number. These rules are:

- Rule 1: Product Rule - $\log_a(M \cdot N) = \log_a M + \log_a N$
- Rule 2: Quotient Rule - $\log_a\left(\frac{M}{N}\right) = \log_a M - \log_a N$
- Rule 3: Power Rule - $\log_a M^k = k\log_a M$
- Rule 4: Base Identity - $\log_a a = 1$
- Rule 5: Logarithm of One - $\log_a 1 = 0$
- Rule 6: Inverse Property - $a^{\log_a M} = M$

Example: Evaluate: $\log_2 32$

Solution: Rewrite 32 as 2^5:

$$\log_2 32 = \log_2(2)^5.$$

Using Rule 3:

$$\log_2(2)^5 = 5\log_2 2.$$

Then applying Rule 4, $\log_2 2 = 1$, thus $5\log_2 2 = 5(1) = 5$. Therefore, $\log_2 32 = 5$.

Example: Evaluate: $3\log_5 125$

    Solution: Rewrite 125 as 5^3:

$$3\log_5 125 = 3\log_5(5)^3.$$

Applying Rule 3:

$$3\log_5(5)^3 = 9\log_5 5.$$

Then using Rule 4, $\log_5 5 = 1$, so $9\log_5 5 = 9$. Therefore, $3\log_5 125 = 9$.

Example: Evaluate: $\log_3(3)^5$

    Solution: Use Rule 3:

$$\log_3(3)^5 = 5\log_3 3.$$

Then, using Rule 4, $\log_3 3 = 1$, so $5\log_3 3 = 5$. Therefore, $\log_3(3)^5 = 5$.

9.2   Properties of Logarithms

The main properties of logarithms are the product rule, the power rule, and the quotient rule. These properties will help us manipulate logarithmic expressions into forms that are easier to simplify or understand.

🔔 Key Point

Properties of Logarithms:

$$a^{\log_a b} = b \qquad\qquad\qquad\qquad \log_a \tfrac{1}{x} = -\log_a x$$

$$\log_a 1 = 0 \qquad\qquad\qquad\qquad \log_a x^p = p\log_a x$$

$$\log_a a = 1 \qquad\qquad\qquad\qquad \log_{a^k} x = \tfrac{1}{k}\log_a x, \text{ for } k \neq 0$$

$$\log_a(x\cdot y) = \log_a x + \log_a y \qquad\qquad \log_a x = \log_{a^c} x^c$$

$$\log_a \tfrac{x}{y} = \log_a x - \log_a y \qquad\qquad \log_a x = \tfrac{1}{\log_x a}$$

Example: Expand this logarithm, $\log_a(3 \times 5) =?$

 Solution: Use logarithm rule : $\log_a(x \cdot y) = \log_a x + \log_a y$. Then:

$$\log_a(3 \times 5) = \log_a 3 + \log_a 5.$$

Example: Condense this expression to a single logarithm: $\log_a 2 - \log_a 7$.

 Solution: Use logarithm rule :$\log_a x - \log_a y = \log_a \frac{x}{y}$. Then:

$$\log_a 2 - \log_a 7 = \log_a\left(\tfrac{2}{7}\right).$$

Example: Expand this logarithm, $\log\left(\frac{1}{7}\right) =?$

 Solution: Use log rule: $\log_a \frac{1}{x} = -\log_a x$. Then:

$$\log\left(\frac{1}{7}\right) = -\log 7.$$

9.3   Natural Logarithms

The natural logarithm, denoted as $\ln x$ or $\log_e x$, is the logarithm to the base e, where $e \approx 2.71$, a fundamental mathematical constant.

Key Point

> A natural logarithm uses the base e (approximately 2.71) and is expressed as $\ln x$ or $\log_e x$, representing the logarithm of x to the base e.

The function $y = \ln x$ or equivalently $y = \log_e x$ can be graphically represented as follows:

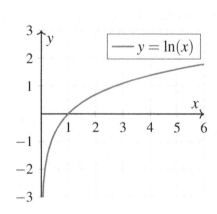

Example: Expand the natural logarithm: $\ln(4x^2)$.

    Solution: We could use log rules to expand this expression:

$$\log_a(xy) = \log_a x + \log_a y.$$

Therefore: $\ln(4x^2) = \ln(4) + \ln(x^2)$. Then, we use another log rule:

$$\log_a M^k = k \log_a(M).$$

So: $\ln(4) + \ln(x^2) = \ln(4) + 2\ln(x)$.

Example: Condense the following expression to a single logarithm: $\ln x - \log_e(2y)$.

    Solution: We can use the log property: $\log_a x - \log_a y = \log_a\left(\frac{x}{y}\right)$. Hence:

$$\ln x - \log_e(2y) = \ln\left(\frac{x}{2y}\right).$$

Example: Solve this equation for x: $e^x = 6$.

    Solution: Taking the natural logarithm of both sides of the equation, we have:

$$\ln(e^x) = \ln(6).$$

Using the log property $\log_a x^b = b \log_a x$, we get: $x \ln(e) = \ln(6)$. But $\ln(e) = 1$. So, the solution is $x = \ln(6)$.

Example: Solve this equation for x: $\ln(4x - 2) = 1$.

    Solution: Using the property that $\log_a a^n = n$, we can rewrite 1 as a logarithm: $1 = \ln(e^1) = \ln(e)$. Then our equation becomes: $\ln(4x - 2) = \ln(e)$. Since the logs are equal, their arguments must also be equal: $4x - 2 = e$. Solving this equation, we find: $x = \frac{e+2}{4}$.

9.4   Solving Logarithmic Equations

The primary goal in solving logarithmic equations is to isolate the variable and convert the equation to exponential form. By default, logarithms without a specified base are assumed to have a base of 10. Combining multiple logarithms into a single logarithm can simplify the equation. It is crucial to verify potential solutions by substituting them back into the original equation, as some may be extraneous.

🔔 **Key Point**

> Solve logarithmic equations by isolating the variable, converting them to exponential form, combining logarithms, and verifying the validity of solutions.

Example: Find the value of x in this equation: $\log_2\left(36 - x^2\right) = 4$.

Solution: To solve this, we first convert the logarithm equation to an exponential one using the rule: $y = \log_b(x)$ if and only if $x = b^y$. In this case, $36 - x^2 = 2^4$, we get: $36 - x^2 = 16$, then $x^2 = 36 - 16 = 20$. Now, to find x, take the square root of both sides: $x = \pm\sqrt{20} = \pm 2\sqrt{5}$. After finding the values, it is crucial to check if they satisfy the original equation. Substituting for positive $2\sqrt{5}$: $\log_2\left(36 - (2\sqrt{5})^2\right) = 4$. This simplifies to $\log_2 16 = 4$, which holds true. Repeating for $-2\sqrt{5}$,

$$\log_2\left(36 - (-2\sqrt{5})^2\right) = 4.$$

We get $\log_2 16 = 4$, which is also true. Hence, the solutions $x = \pm 2\sqrt{5}$ are valid.

Example: Find the value of x in this equation: $\log(5x + 2) = \log(3x - 1)$.

Solution: When logarithms with the same base are equal, the arguments must also be equal. Starting from the equation, we have $5x + 2 = 3x - 1$, simplifying further: $2x = -3$. Finally, we get: $x = -\frac{3}{2}$. Checking this solution, we substitute back into the original equation: $\log(5(-1.5) + 2) = \log(3(-1.5) - 1)$, we get: $\log(-5.5) = \log(-5.5)$. We can clearly see that both sides of the equation result in logarithms of negative numbers, which are undefined. Therefore, $x = -\frac{3}{2}$ is an extraneous solution and there is no solution for this equation.

9.5   Practices

 Solve:

1) $\log_3(9) = $ _____

2) $\log_{10}(100) = $ _____

3) $\log_a a^n =$ _____

4) $2^{\log_2 8} =$ _____

5) $\log_2(4) + \log_2(8) =$ _____

Simplify Each Expression:

6) Simplify: $\log_a 8 + \log_a 2$

7) Simplify: $\log_b 25 - \log_b 5$

8) Simplify: $\log_3 27^2$

9) Simplify: $\log_4 16 + \log_4 \frac{1}{2}$

10) Simplify: $\log_6 36 - \log_6 6$

Fill in the Blank:

11) The function $\ln x$ is undefined when the x is _____.

12) The base of a natural logarithm is always _____.

13) According to log properties, the logarithm of a product is equal to _____.

14) $\ln(e)$ equals _____.

15) Rewrite the following logarithm as a single log, $\ln x^8 + \ln y^2$ equals _____.

Solve:

16) Solve: $\log_4(3x + 2) = 2$.

17) Solve: $\log_2(7x - 1) = 3$.

18) Solve: $\log_5(x^2 - 3) = 2$.

19) Solve: $\log_{10}(x + 5) = 1$.

20) Solve: $\log_3(5(x - 2)) = 2$.

Answer Keys

1) 2

2) 2

3) n

4) 8

5) 5

6) $\log_a 16$

7) $\log_b 5$

8) 6

9) $\frac{3}{2}$

10) 1

11) less than or equal to 0

12) e

13) the sum of the logarithms

14) 1

15) $\ln(x^8 y^2)$.

16) $x = \frac{14}{3}$

17) $x = \frac{9}{7}$

18) $x = \pm 2\sqrt{7}$

19) $x = 5$

20) $x = \frac{19}{5}$

Answers with Explanation

1) Rewrite 9 as 3^2. So, $\log_3(9) = \log_3(3)^2 = 2\log_3(3) = 2$ by Rules 3 and 4.

2) Rewrite 100 as 10^2. So, $\log_{10}(100) = \log_{10}(10)^2 = 2\log_{10}(10) = 2$ by Rules 3 and 4.

3) Based on Rule 3: $\log_a M^k = k\log_a M$, so $\log_a a^n = n\log_a a = n$ by Rule 4.

4) Based on Rule 6: $a^{\log_a k} = k$, so $2^{\log_2 8} = 8$.

5) Based on Rules 3 and 4, $\log_2(4) + \log_2(8) = \log_2(2)^2 + \log_2(2)^3 = 2 + 3 = 5$.

6) By the product rule of logarithms, $\log_a 8 + \log_a 2 = \log_a(8 \times 2) = \log_a 16$.

7) By the quotient rule, $\log_b 25 - \log_b 5 = \log_b\left(\frac{25}{5}\right) = \log_b 5$.

8) By the power rule, $\log_3 27^2 = 2\log_3 27 = 2 \times 3 = 6$.

9) Utilizing the product and inverse logarithm rules,

$$\log_4 16 + \log_4 \frac{1}{2} = \log_4\left(16 \times \frac{1}{2}\right) = \log_4 8 = \frac{3}{2}$$

10) Using the quotient rule, $\log_6 36 - \log_6 6 = \log_6\left(\frac{36}{6}\right) = \log_6 6 = 1$.

11) The function $\ln x$ is undefined when the x is less than or equal to 0..

12) The base of a natural logarithm is always e.

13) The logarithm of a product is equal to the sum of the logarithms.

14) $\ln(e)$ equals 1.

15) According to log properties $\ln x^8 + \ln y^2$ equals $\ln(x^8 y^2)$.

16) Apply exponential form, $3x + 2 = 4^2 = 16$. Solve for x, $x = \frac{14}{3}$. Checked back into the equation, it gives a valid result.

17) By applying exponential form, $7x - 1 = 2^3 = 8$. Solve for x, $x = \frac{9}{7}$. Checked back into the equation, it gives a valid result.

18) Apply exponential form, $x^2 - 3 = 5^2 = 25$. Solve for x, $x = \pm\sqrt{28} = \pm 2\sqrt{7}$. Checked back into the equation, it gives valid results.

19) By applying exponential form, $x + 5 = 10^1 = 10$. Solve for x, $x = 5$. Checked back into the equation, it gives a valid result.

20) By applying exponential form, $5(x - 2) = 3^2 = 9$. Solve for x, $x = \frac{19}{5}$. Checked back into the equation, it gives a valid result.

10. Radical Expressions

10.1 Simplifying Radical Expressions

Simplification of radical expressions aims to achieve their most elementary form, enhancing ease in solving equations. Complete simplification is attained when radicals are absent from the denominator and the radicand contains no perfect square factors other than 1.

🔔 Key Point

Simplify radicals by:

- Exponent manipulation: $\sqrt[n]{x^a} = x^{\frac{a}{n}}$.
- Multiplication: $\sqrt[n]{xy} = x^{\frac{1}{n}} y^{\frac{1}{n}}$.
- Division: $\sqrt[n]{\frac{x}{y}} = \frac{x^{\frac{1}{n}}}{y^{\frac{1}{n}}}$.
- Product of radicals: $\sqrt[n]{x} \times \sqrt[n]{y} = \sqrt[n]{xy}$.

Example: Simplify the square root of $\sqrt{144x^2}$.

Solution: First, remember to find the square root of each factor in the expression. Here, the factorization of $144x^2$ is $144 = 12 \times 12$ and $x^2 = x \times x$. Then, apply the radical rule: $\sqrt[n]{a^n} = a$ to each factor. Hence $\sqrt{12^2} = 12$ and $\sqrt{x^2} = |x|$. Finally, apply the property of radicals that the multiplication inside a radical symbol can be separated, and we get: $\sqrt{144x^2} = \sqrt{12^2} \times \sqrt{x^2} = 12|x|$. Hence, the simplified form is $12|x|$.

Example: Write the radical form $\sqrt[3]{x^4}$ in exponential form.

Solution: To write a radical in exponential form, use the formula $\sqrt[n]{x^a} = x^{\left(\frac{a}{n}\right)}$. Thus, $\sqrt[3]{x^4} = x^{\left(\frac{4}{3}\right)}$, which is the exponential form of the given radical.

Example: Simplify $\sqrt{8x^3}$.

Solution: We start by factoring $8x^3$ into $2^3 \times x \times x \times x$. Now we must identify perfect squares, that is, $2^2 \times 2 \times x^2 \times x = 2^2 \times x^2 \times 2x$. Then we proceed to write the radical expression as a product of square roots: $\sqrt{8x^3} = \sqrt{2^2 x^2} \times \sqrt{2x}$ By applying the radical rule $\sqrt[n]{a^n} = a$, we get: $\sqrt{2^2 x^2} \times \sqrt{2x} = 2|x|\sqrt{2x}$. We conclude that the simplified form of $\sqrt{8x^3}$ is $2|x|\sqrt{2x}$.

Example: Simplify $\sqrt{27a^5 b^4}$.

Solution: Break down $27a^5 b^4$ into its prime factors: $27a^5 b^4 = 3^3 \times a^5 \times b^4$. Identify perfect squares to obtain $27a^5 b^4 = 3^2 \times 3 \times a^4 \times a \times b^4$. Then rewrite the radical expression, $\sqrt{27a^5 b^4} = \sqrt{3^2 \times a^4 \times b^4} \times \sqrt{3a}$. Using the rule $\sqrt[n]{a^n} = a$, we have: $\sqrt{3^2 \times a^4 \times b^4} \times \sqrt{3a} = 3 \times a^2 \times b^2 \times \sqrt{3a} = 3a^2 b^2 \sqrt{3a}$. Therefore, the simplified form of $\sqrt{27a^5 b^4}$ is $3a^2 b^2 \sqrt{3a}$.

10.2   Simplifying Radical Expressions Involving Fractions

To simplify radicals with fractions, separate the simplification of the numerator and denominator, factorize them into primes, and reduce common factors. Key steps include:

1. Simplifying the numerator's radical.
2. Simplifying the denominator's radical.
3. Rewriting and reducing the fraction.

🔔 Key Point

The principal square root of a number is not negative; square roots of negative numbers are undefined.

Example: Simplify the expression $\sqrt{\frac{32}{50}}$.

Solution: Start by simplifying both the numerator and the denominator under the square root: $\sqrt{\frac{32}{50}} = \sqrt{\frac{2^5}{2 \times 5^2}}$. This can then be simplified by taking the square root of the numerator and the denominator separately: $\sqrt{\frac{2^5}{2\times 5^2}} = \frac{\sqrt{2^5}}{\sqrt{2\times 5^2}}$. Further simplification gives: $\frac{\sqrt{2^5}}{\sqrt{2\times 5^2}} = \frac{4\sqrt{2}}{5\sqrt{2}}$. So, $\sqrt{\frac{32}{50}} = \frac{4}{5}$.

Example: Simplify the expression $\sqrt{\frac{45}{125}}$.

Solution: Starting with the given expression, $\sqrt{\frac{45}{125}} = \sqrt{\frac{3^2\times 5}{5^3}}$. We simplify by taking the square root of the numerator and the denominator separately: $\sqrt{\frac{3^2\times 5}{5^3}} = \frac{\sqrt{3^2\times 5}}{\sqrt{5^3}}$. Simplifying further yields: $\frac{\sqrt{3^2\times 5}}{\sqrt{5^3}} = \frac{3\sqrt{5}}{5\sqrt{5}}$. This can be simplified by removing the common factor of $\sqrt{5}$ in the numerator and the denominator: $\frac{3\sqrt{5}}{5\sqrt{5}} = \frac{3}{5}$. So, $\sqrt{\frac{45}{125}} = \frac{3}{5}$.

10.3   Multiplying Radical Expressions

Multiplication of radical expressions is akin to simplifying radicals in fractions but with an emphasis on multiplication.

🔔 Key Point

The process of multiplying radical expressions typically involves:

1. Multiplying the coefficients outside the radicals.

2. Multiplying the contents inside the radicals.

3. Simplifying the resulting expression, as needed.

Example: Evaluate $\sqrt{16} \times \sqrt{9}$.

Solution: We start by factoring the numbers: $16 = 4^2$ and $9 = 3^2$. Therefore, we have $\sqrt{16} \times \sqrt{9} = \sqrt{4^2} \times \sqrt{3^2}$. By the radical rule $\sqrt[n]{a^n} = a$, we get $\sqrt{4^2} \times \sqrt{3^2} = 4 \times 3 = 12$.

Example: Evaluate $2\sqrt{5} \times 3\sqrt{2}$.

Solution: First, we multiply the numbers outside the radicals: $2 \times 3 = 6$. Therefore, we get $2\sqrt{5} \times 3\sqrt{2} = 6\sqrt{5}\sqrt{2}$. Next, applying the radical rule $\sqrt{a}\sqrt{b} = \sqrt{ab}$, we simplify the above expression to get $6\sqrt{5}\sqrt{2} = 6\sqrt{5\times 2} = 6\sqrt{10}$.

Example: Evaluate $5\sqrt{12a^3b^3} \times \sqrt{3ab^2}$.

Solution: First, we multiply the expressions inside the radicals:

$$12a^3b^3 \times 3ab^2 = 36a^4b^5.$$

We factorize the resulting expression to get

$$36a^4b^5 = 3^2 \times 2^2 \times a^4 \times b^5.$$

Now, we have

$$5\sqrt{12a^3b^3}\sqrt{3ab^2} = 5\sqrt{3^2 \times 2^2 \times a^4 \times b^5} = 5(3)(2)a^2b^2\sqrt{b} = 30a^2b^2\sqrt{b}.$$

Therefore, the result is $30a^2b^2\sqrt{b}$.

10.4   Adding and Subtracting Radical Expressions

When performing addition and subtraction with radical expressions, it is imperative to restrict the operation to terms that share identical radical components.

🔔 Key Point

When working with radical expressions, only terms with similar radicals can be combined, while "unlik" radical terms cannot be added or subtracted.

Example: Simplify $4\sqrt{5} + 3\sqrt{5}$.

   Solution: First, we acknowledge that both expressions are like terms because they have the same radical part $\sqrt{5}$. Now, we add the multipliers outside the radical parts together. $4 + 3 = 7$. Hence, our result is: $4\sqrt{5} + 3\sqrt{5} = 7\sqrt{5}$.

Example: Simplify $3\sqrt{2} + 2\sqrt{5} + 5\sqrt{2}$.

   Solution: In this instance, $\sqrt{2}$ is our recurring radical part, so we add their multipliers together, $3\sqrt{2} + 5\sqrt{2} = 8\sqrt{2}$. However, the $2\sqrt{5}$ term remains as it is because this term does not have the same radical part as the others. Hence, the result is $3\sqrt{2} + 2\sqrt{5} + 5\sqrt{2} = 8\sqrt{2} + 2\sqrt{5}$.

10.5   Domain and Range of Radical Functions

When addressing the domain and range of radical functions, it is essential to adhere to the fundamental rule: Negative numbers cannot be placed under the square root; therefore, the expression within the square root must always be non-negative.

Determining the Domain of Radical Functions: For a function given as $y = \sqrt{f(x)}$, finding the domain entails identifying all values of x for which the expression $f(x)$ is non-negative. To establish the domain of a specific function, we set $f(x)$ greater than or equal to zero and solve for x, resulting in a domain represented as $x : f(x) \geq 0$.

Determining the Range of Radical Functions: The inherent nature of the square root function guarantees that its output is consistently non-negative. Consequently, for a linear function $f(x)$, the range of a function in the form $y = c\sqrt{f(x)} + k$ can be expressed as follows: $y \geq k$ if $c \geq 0$, and $y \leq k$ if $c \leq 0$.

Key Point

Domain and range of radical functions:

Domain: For $y = \sqrt{f(x)}$, it includes x values where $f(x) \geq 0$.

Range: In $y = c\sqrt{f(x)} + k$, the range is $y \geq k$ if $c \geq 0$ and $y \leq k$ if $c \leq 0$.

Example: Find the domain and range of the radical function $y = \sqrt{x - 2}$.

Solution: To find the domain, ensure non-negative values under the square root.

Solve $x - 2 \geq 0$ to get $x \geq 2$. Thus, the domain is $x \geq 2$. Now, we need to find the range. Clearly, the radical function provides non-negative outputs, so considering $k = 0$ in our rule and $c = 1$ is positive, the range of function is $y \geq 0$.

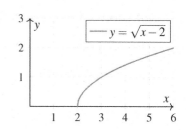

Example: Find the domain and range of the radical function $y = -3\sqrt{2x - 3} + 1$.

Solution: To find the domain, ensure non-negative values under the square root.

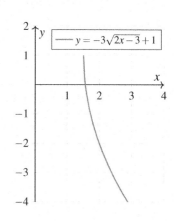

We solve $2x - 3 \geq 0$ to get $x \geq \frac{3}{2}$. The domain is $x \geq \frac{3}{2}$. For the range, note when $k = 1$ in our range rule, and since $c = -3$ is negative, the range would be $y \leq 1$.

10.6 Radical Equations

Radical Equations are equations that contain a variable within a radical. To solve these equations, we follow a specific process:

1. Isolate the radical on one side of the equation.

2. Square both sides of the equation to eliminate the radical.

3. Solve the equation that results.

4. Check your solutions in the original equation to avoid extraneous solutions.

Remember that when you square both sides of an equation, you introduce the possibility of extraneous solutions, which are solutions that satisfy the squared equation but not the original equation. Therefore, always check your answer in the original equation.

🔔 Key Point

Solve radical equations by isolating the radical, squaring both sides, solving, and checking for extraneous solutions.

Example: Solve the equation $\sqrt{x} - 8 = 12$.

Solution: First, we start by isolating the radical. We add 8 to both sides to get $\sqrt{x} = 20$. Next, we square both sides to get rid of the square root on the left side, resulting in $x = 400$. Finally, to verify if it is not an extraneous solution, we plug $x = 400$ into the original equation.

Since $\sqrt{400} - 8 = 12$, we see that $x = 400$ is indeed the solution. As we can see from the figure, the solution $x = 400$ coincides with the intersection of the curves $\sqrt{x}$ and $y = 20$.

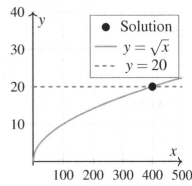

Example: Solve the equation $\sqrt{x+2} = 6$.

Solution: First, we square both sides of the equation, which gives $x + 2 = 36$.

Subtract 2 from each side to find $x = 34$. To verify, let us substitute the solution back into the equation. We confirm that $\sqrt{34+2} = 6$, so $x = 34$ is indeed the solution. From the figure, as we see, the solution $x = 34$ corresponds to the point where the curves $y = \sqrt{x+2}$ and $y = 6$ intersect.

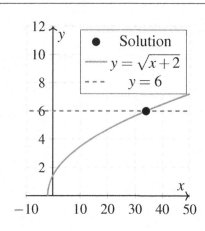

Example: Solve the equation $2\sqrt{x-5}+1 = 4$.

Solution: Begin by isolating the radical. Subtract 1 from each side to obtain $2\sqrt{x-5} = 3$. Next, divide by 2 on both sides to find $\sqrt{x-5} = \frac{3}{2}$. Square both sides to remove the square root. This yields $x - 5 = \frac{9}{4}$ or $x = \frac{29}{4}$.

Finally, fill in $x = \frac{29}{4}$ into the original equation to double-check our answer. We find that it indeed does make the original equation true. We can see from the figure that the point $x = \frac{29}{4}$ is indeed the intersection of the curves, thereby confirming it as the solution.

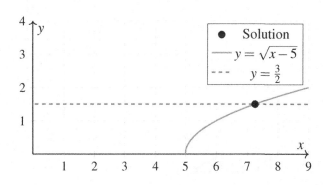

10.7   Solving Radical Inequalities

A radical inequality is an inequality that contains a root (or radical) expression.

The steps for solving radical inequalities are as follows:

1. Write the radical expression on one side of the inequality and any other expression on the other side.

2. Raise both sides of the inequality to the power equal to the index of the radical.

3. Simplify the inequality and solve it as you would any other equation.

🔔 **Key Point**

When dealing with a radical expression with an even index, ensure that the result is non-negative.

Example: Solve the inequality: $2\sqrt[3]{1-x} - 3 \geq 0$

    Solution: First, we rewrite the inequality as: $2\sqrt[3]{1-x} \geq 3$, and then $\sqrt[3]{1-x} \geq \frac{3}{2}$. Next, we raise both sides of the inequality to the power of 3: $\left(\sqrt[3]{1-x}\right)^3 \geq \left(\frac{3}{2}\right)^3$ and hence, $1-x \geq \frac{27}{8}$. Finally, we simplify and solve for x: $x \leq 1 - \frac{27}{8} = -\frac{19}{8}$. Hence, the solution to this inequality is $x \in (-\infty, -\frac{19}{8}]$.

Example: Solve the inequality: $1 - \sqrt{x+3} < 0$

    Solution: First, we rewrite the inequality as $1 < \sqrt{x+3}$ or $\sqrt{x+3} > 1$. Next, we raise both sides of the inequality to the power of 2 and get, $x+3 > 1$. Finally, we simplify and solve for x: $x > 1 - 3 = -2$. However, as we are dealing with a square root, the expression under the root, $x+3$, must also be greater or equal to zero. This gives an additional condition, which is, $x \geq -3$. Taking both conditions into account, our solution is $-2 < x < +\infty$. This fact is also evident in the following figure.

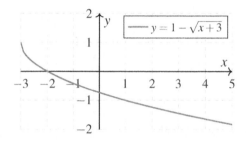

10.8 Practices

Simplify Each Expression:

1) Simplify $\sqrt{16y^8}$.

2) Simplify $\sqrt{25x^6y^4}$.

3) Simplify $\sqrt[4]{16a^8}$.

4) Simplify $\sqrt[3]{64x^9}$.

5) Simplify $\sqrt[3]{27x^9}$.

True/False:

6) True or False: The principal square root of a number cannot be negative.

7) True or False: The square root of a negative number is undefined.

8) True or False: $\sqrt{\frac{1}{4}} = \frac{1}{2}$.

9) True or False: $\sqrt{\frac{1}{9}} = \frac{1}{3}$.

10) True or False: $\sqrt{\frac{4}{16}} = \frac{1}{2}$.

Solve:

11) What number is equivalent to $\sqrt{9} \times \sqrt{16}$?

12) What is the simplified form of $\sqrt{4} \times \sqrt{25}$?

13) Find $\sqrt{49} \times \sqrt{81}$.

14) Find $3\sqrt{4} \times 2\sqrt{5}$.

15) Find the simplified form of $5\sqrt{36} \times 3\sqrt{4}$.

Fill in the Blank:

16) If a and b are like terms, then $a\sqrt{7} + b\sqrt{7} =$ _____ $\sqrt{7}$.

17) $a\sqrt{5} + b\sqrt{7}$, _____ simplified to a single term. (can be/cannot be)

18) Simplify $7\sqrt{2} - 2\sqrt{2}$ to the form _____ $\sqrt{2}$.

19) $3\sqrt{2} + 2\sqrt{2} =$ _____.

20) Simplify $3\sqrt{8} + 2\sqrt{8} - \sqrt{8}$ to the form _____ $\sqrt{8}$.

Solve:

21) Find the domain and range of the function $f(x) = \sqrt{x-1}$.

22) Determine the domain and range of the function $f(x) = 3\sqrt{x+2} - 1$.

23) Find the domain and range of the function $f(x) = \frac{1}{2}\sqrt{2x+1} + 3$.

24) Determine the domain and range of the function $f(x) = -\sqrt{x-4} + 5$.

25) Find the domain and range of the function $f(x) = \sqrt{2x-3} + 2$.

Plot and analyze:

26) $\sqrt{x+3} = 5$

27) $4\sqrt{x} - 2 = 8$

28) $3\sqrt{x-4} + 2 = 5$

29) $\sqrt{2x-3} = 4$

30) $2\sqrt{x+3} - 7 = 5$

Solve:

31) Solve the inequality: $\sqrt[3]{2x+1} - 2 \geq 0$

32) Solve the inequality: $3 - \sqrt{x-1} > 0$

33) Solve the inequality: $\sqrt[3]{x^2 - 10x + 25} \leq 5$

34) Solve the inequality: $1 - \sqrt[3]{2x^3 + 3} < 0$

35) Solve the inequality: $2\sqrt[3]{x^2 - 2} + 1 \geq 0$

Answer Keys

1) $4y^4$

2) $5|x|^3 y^2$

3) $2a^2$

4) $4x^3$

5) $3x^3$

6) True

7) True

8) True

9) True

10) True

11) 12

12) 10

13) 63

14) $12\sqrt{5}$

15) 180

16) $(a+b)\sqrt{7}$

17) cannot be

18) $5\sqrt{2}$

19) $5\sqrt{2}$

20) $4\sqrt{8}$

21) Domain: $x \geq 1$, Range: $y \geq 0$

22) Domain: $x \geq -2$, Range: $y \geq -1$

23) Domain: $x \geq -0.5$, Range: $y \geq 3$

24) Domain: $x \geq 4$, Range: $y \leq 5$

25) Domain: $x \geq \frac{3}{2}$, Range: $y \geq 2$

26) one solution

27) one solution

28) one solution

29) one solution

30) one solution

31) $x \in \left[\frac{7}{2}, +\infty\right)$

32) $x \in [1, 10)$

33) $x \in \left[5 - 5\sqrt{5}, 5 + 5\sqrt{5}\right]$

34) $x \in (-1, +\infty)$

35) $x \in \left(-\infty, -\sqrt{\frac{15}{8}}\right] \cup \left[\sqrt{\frac{15}{8}}, +\infty\right)$

Answers with Explanation

1) Factorizing $16y^8$ we get $16 = 4 \times 4$ and $y^8 = y^4 \times y^4$. Using the rule $\sqrt[n]{a^n} = a$, $\sqrt{4^2} = 4$ and $\sqrt{y^4} = y^2$. Therefore, $\sqrt{16y^8} = 4y^4$.

2) Simplifying each factor individually, we get $\sqrt{25} = 5$, $\sqrt{x^6} = |x|^3$ and $\sqrt{y^4} = y^2$. Therefore, $\sqrt{25x^6y^4} = 5|x|^3y^2$.

3) Using the rule $\sqrt[n]{x^a} = x^{\frac{a}{n}}$, we have $\sqrt[4]{16a^8} = 16^{\frac{1}{4}} \times a^{\frac{8}{4}} = 2a^2$.

4) Using the rule $\sqrt[n]{x^a} = x^{\frac{a}{n}}$, we have $\sqrt[3]{64x^9} = 64^{\frac{1}{3}} \times a^{\frac{9}{3}} = 4x^3$.

5) Using the rule $\sqrt[n]{x^a} = x^{\frac{a}{n}}$, we have $\sqrt[3]{27x^9} = 27^{\frac{1}{3}} \times x^{\frac{9}{3}} = 3x^3$.

6) By definition, the principal square root of a number is non-negative.

7) Square roots of negative numbers are undefined in real numbers.

8) Taking square root of $\frac{1}{4}$ gives $\frac{1}{2}$.

9) Taking square root of $\frac{1}{9}$ gives $\frac{1}{3}$.

10) Taking square root of $\frac{4}{16}$ gives $\frac{2}{4} = \frac{1}{2}$.

11) The problem simplifies to $\sqrt{9} \times \sqrt{16} = 3 \times 4 = 12$.

12) The problem simplifies to $\sqrt{4} \times \sqrt{25} = 2 \times 5 = 10$.

13) The problem simplifies to $\sqrt{49} \times \sqrt{81} = 7 \times 9 = 63$.

14) The problem simplifies to $3\sqrt{4} \times 2\sqrt{5} = 3 \times 2 \times 2\sqrt{5} = 12\sqrt{5}$.

15) The problem simplifies to $5\sqrt{36} \times 3\sqrt{4} = 5 \times 6 \times 3 \times 2 = 180$.

16) Like radicals can be added together by adding the coefficients: $a\sqrt{7} + b\sqrt{7} = (a+b)\sqrt{7}$.

17) Since the radicals are not the same, the terms cannot be combined.

18) Like radicals can be subtracted by subtracting the coefficients: $7\sqrt{2} - 2\sqrt{2} = 5\sqrt{2}$.

19) Since the radicals are the same, the terms can be combined. So as the final result we have $5\sqrt{2}$.

20) Like radicals can be added and subtracted by manipulating the coefficients: $3\sqrt{8} + 2\sqrt{8} - \sqrt{8} = 4\sqrt{8}$.

21) Non-negative values under the square root yields $x - 1 \geq 0$ or $x \geq 1$ as the domain. On the other hand, for every non-negative value $y \geq 0$, by choosing $x = y^2 + 1$, which belongs to domain, we have $\sqrt{x - 1} = y$. So, the range is $y \geq 0$.

22) For non-negative inputs to the square root, we find $x \geq -2$ as the domain. The function's lowest value is -1, hence the range is $y \geq -1$.

23) Solving $2x + 1 \geq 0$ yields the domain $x \geq -0.5$, and as the function value is always above 3, the range is $y \geq 3$.

24) Solving $x - 4 \geq 0$ yields the domain $x \geq 4$, and as the function has a maximum value of 5, the range is $y \leq 5$.

25) Solving $2x - 3 \geq 0$ yields $x \geq \frac{3}{2}$. As the square root function always yields non-negative values and is shifted up by 2, the range is $y \geq 2$.

26) This is a radical function $y = \sqrt{x + 3}$ shifted 3 units to the left.

The intersection point with $y = 5$ gives the solution of $x = 22$ to the radical equation.

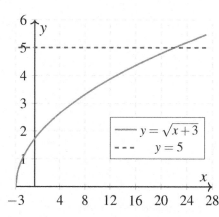

27) The graph is shifted 2 units down from the original root function and widened by a factor of 4.

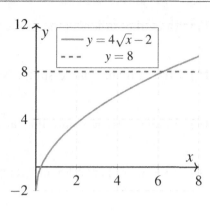

The solution $x = 6.25$ corresponds to the intersection of the curves with the horizontal line $y = 8$.

28) The graph is a radical function shifted 4 units to the right and 2 units up, and ever regressed by a factor of 3.

The solution $x = 5$ corresponds to the intersection of the radical function and the horizontal line $y = 5$.

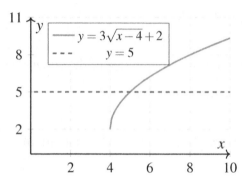

29) The solution to the equation $x = \frac{19}{2}$ corresponds to the point of intersection between the curve of the function $y = \sqrt{2x - 3}$ and the horizontal line $y = 4$.

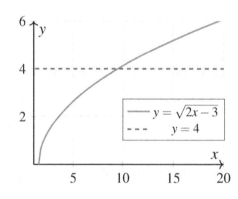

30) This is a radical function $y = 2\sqrt{x + 3} - 7$ shifted 3 units to the left and 7 units down from the origin while widened by a factor of 2.

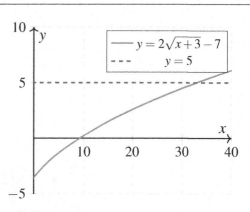

The intersection point with $y = 5$ gives the solution to the radical equation at $x = 33$.

31) The inequality is rewritten as $\sqrt[3]{2x+1} \geq 2$. Both sides are then cubed to get $2x+1 \geq 8$, which is simplified to get $x \geq \frac{7}{2}$ which is the solution $\left[\frac{7}{2}, +\infty\right)$.

32) After rewriting the inequality as $3 > \sqrt{x-1}$, both sides are squared to get $9 > x-1$. After simplification, it becomes $x < 10$, and considering the root we also have $x \geq 1$. The overlapping area is $x \in [1, 10)$

33) The inequality can be rewritten as $(x-5)^{\frac{2}{3}} \leq 5$ after factoring as a perfect square. Raising both sides to the cube yields $(x-5)^2 \leq 125$. Solving this inequality gives $x \in \left[5 - 5\sqrt{5}, 5 + 5\sqrt{5}\right]$.

34) We rewrite the inequality as $1 < \sqrt[3]{2x^3 + 3}$, raising both sides to the cube yields $1 < 2x^3 + 3$. The resulting inequality, $x^3 > -1$, gives the solution $x \in (-1, +\infty)$.

35) Rewrite $2\sqrt[3]{x^2 - 2} \geq -1$, then cube both sides to get $x^2 - 2 \geq -\frac{1}{8}$. This simplifies to $x^2 \geq \frac{15}{8}$. The solutions are $x \in \left(-\infty, -\sqrt{\frac{15}{8}}\right] \cup \left[\sqrt{\frac{15}{8}}, +\infty\right)$.

11. Rational and Irrational Expressions

11.1 Rational and Irrational Numbers

A rational number, symbolized by $\mathbb{Q}$, is any number expressible as $\frac{p}{q}$ with integers p and non-zero q. This includes natural numbers, arithmetic numbers, and integers. Finite decimals also qualify as rationals, being representable as fractions with denominators as positive powers of 10.

🔔 Key Point

> Rational numbers, fractions $\frac{p}{q}$ with integer p and nonzero q, include natural and arithmetic numbers, and finite decimals. Also, There are infinite fractions between two rational numbers.

An irrational number is a real number that cannot be expressed as a fraction, having endless, non-periodic decimal digits, with examples like π, e, and $\sqrt{2}$.

$$\overset{\sqrt{2} \quad e \quad \pi}{\underset{\substack{-5 \quad -4 \quad -3 \quad -2 \quad -1 \quad 0 \;\; \frac{15}{99} \;\; 1 \quad 2 \quad 3 \;\; \frac{10}{3} \; 4 \quad 5}}{-\infty \xleftarrow{\hspace{10cm}} \infty}}$$

Example: Determine if $0.\overline{15}$ is a rational number or an irrational number.

Solution: All repeating decimals can be shown as the fraction of two integers, and therefore they will be rational numbers. We know $0.\overline{15}$ can be expressed as $\frac{15}{99}$. So, $0.\overline{15}$ is a rational number.

Example: Determine if $\sqrt{7}$ is a rational number or an irrational number.

    Solution: Irrational numbers cannot be written as a fraction whose numerator and denominator are integers. Since $\sqrt{7}$ is equal to $2.645751\ldots$ it is a decimal number whose decimal digits are endless, and it cannot be written as a fraction whose numerator and denominator are integers. So, $\sqrt{7}$ is an irrational number.

Example: Determine if -4.8 is a rational number or an irrational number.

    Solution: -4.8 is a rational number because it can be written as a fraction: $-\frac{48}{10}$.

11.2   Simplifying Rational Expressions

A *rational expression* is a fraction with polynomial numerator and denominator, like $\frac{1}{x}$ or $\frac{x^2}{x-1}$. Simplification involves factoring and canceling common factors, ensuring no division by zero.

Key Point

> Simplify rational expressions by dividing numerator and denominator by their Greatest Common Factor (GCF).

Example: Simplify $\frac{9x^2y}{3y^2}$.

    Solution: First, we cancel the common factor 3: $\frac{9x^2y}{3y^2} = \frac{3x^2y}{y^2}$. Next, cancel the common factor y: $\frac{3x^2y}{y^2} = \frac{3x^2}{y}$. So, $\frac{9x^2y}{3y^2} = \frac{3x^2}{y}$.

Example: Simplify $\frac{x^2+5x-6}{x+6}$.

    Solution: First, factor $x^2 + 5x - 6 = (x-1)(x+6)$. Then replace in the fraction:

$$\frac{x^2 + 5x - 6}{x+6} = \frac{(x-1)(x+6)}{x+6}.$$

Next, cancel the common factor: $(x+6)$. Finally, we have: $\frac{(x-1)(x+6)}{x+6} = x - 1$.

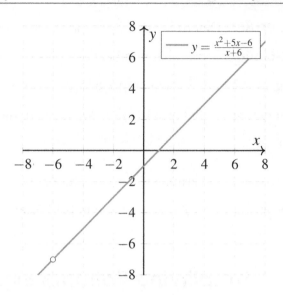

In the graph, we see that the fraction $\frac{x^2+5x-6}{x+6}$ simplifies to a straight line when $x+6 \neq 0$ or $x \neq -6$.

Example: Simplify $\frac{18a^3(b+1)c^2}{6a^2c(b^2-1)}$.

Solution: First, cancel the common factors in the numerator and the denominator: a^2, c, and 6:

$$\frac{18a^3(b+1)c^2}{6a^2c(b^2-1)} = \frac{3a(b+1)c}{(b^2-1)}.$$

Next, factorize $b^2 - 1 = (b+1)(b-1)$ and cancel the common factor $(b+1)$, we get:

$$\frac{3a(b+1)c}{(b^2-1)} = \frac{3a(b+1)c}{(b+1)(b-1)} = \frac{3ac}{b-1}.$$

Hence, $\frac{18a^3(b+1)c^2}{6a^2c(b^2-1)} = \frac{3ac}{b-1}$.

11.3   Graphing Rational Expressions

To graph a rational function, we need to identify any asymptotes and intercepts it may have. To graph a rational function, follow these steps:

1. **Vertical Asymptotes**:

   - Simplify the rational function to reveal potential vertical asymptotes.

   - Vertical asymptotes exist at values of x where the simplified denominator equals zero but not the numerator.

2. **Horizontal Asymptotes**:

- Determine if there is a horizontal asymptote based on the degrees of the numerator and denominator:

    a. If the degree of the numerator is less than the denominator, the horizontal asymptote is $y = 0$.

    b. If the degrees are equal, the asymptote is at $y = L$, where L is the ratio of the leading coefficients of the numerator and the denominator.

3. **Oblique (Slant) Asymptotes**:

    - If the degree of the numerator is one more than the degree of the denominator, there may be an oblique asymptote, derived from the long division of the numerator by the denominator.

After identifying these features (asymptotes and intercepts), plot the function, taking into account the behavior near these asymptotes and the graph's overall shape.

 **Key Point**

> To graph a rational function, identify and plot vertical asymptotes where the denominator equals zero, horizontal or oblique asymptotes based on polynomial degrees, and intercepts, then sketch the curve considering these features.

Example: Graph the rational function $f(x) = \frac{x^2 - x + 2}{x - 1}$.

Solution: The first step is simplification. But there is no common factor. Second, we find the y-intercept: set $x = 0$ and solve for y: $y = \frac{x^2 - x + 2}{x - 1} = \frac{0^2 - 0 + 2}{0 - 1} = -2$. This gives us a y-intercept at the point $(0, -2)$.

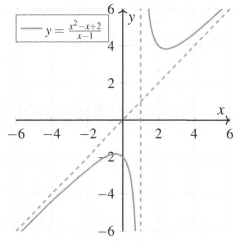

Next, we determine the asymptotes. The vertical asymptote is $x = 1$. The slant asymptote is $y = x$ (Divide the numerator by the denominator). There is no horizontal asymptote in this graph. Lastly, we test some x values and determine the corresponding y values to plot some additional points.

11.4   Multiplying Rational Expressions

Multiplying rational expressions is akin to the multiplication of ordinary fractions. It involves a straightforward process, applying the fundamental principles of fraction multiplication.

🔔 Key Point

To multiply rational expressions, multiply the numerators to form the new numerator and the denominators to form the new denominator. The resulting expression is the product of the two rational expressions.

This method requires simplifying the resulting expression, if possible, by factoring and reducing common factors in the numerator and denominator. It is essential to remember that this process adheres to the same rules as multiplying numerical fractions.

Example: Solve: $\frac{x+6}{x-1} \times \frac{x-1}{5}$.

Solution: We begin by multiplying the numerators together, following the rule defined for multiplying fractions: $\frac{a}{b} \times \frac{c}{d} = \frac{a \times c}{b \times d}$. Applying this to our rational expression: $\frac{x+6}{x-1} \times \frac{x-1}{5} = \frac{(x+6)(x-1)}{5(x-1)}$. Notice that the $x-1$ factor appears in both the numerator and denominator, which can be simplified. Thus, $\frac{(x+6)(x-1)}{5(x-1)} = \frac{(x+6)}{5}$.

Example: Solve: $\frac{x-2}{x+3} \times \frac{2x+6}{x-2}$.

Solution: We start again by multiplying the numerators and denominators together, following the rule of $\frac{a}{b} \times \frac{c}{d} = \frac{a \times c}{b \times d}$. Thus, $\frac{x-2}{x+3} \times \frac{2x+6}{x-2} = \frac{(x-2)(2x+6)}{(x+3)(x-2)}$. Notice that the factor $x-2$ appears in both the numerator and denominator. Therefore, we simplify by canceling it out. Thus, $\frac{(x-2)(2x+6)}{(x+3)(x-2)} = \frac{(2x+6)}{(x+3)}$. Taking a closer look at $2x+6$, we can identify it as a factorable expression. Factoring we get, $2x+6 = 2(x+3)$. Hence, the simplified expression becomes 2.

11.5   Dividing Rational Expressions

In dividing rational expressions, apply the 'Keep, Change, Flip' method: keep the first expression, change division to multiplication, and flip the second expression's numerator and denominator. Then multiply the numerators and denominators, simplifying the result.

🔔 Key Point

Divide rational expressions by keeping the first, changing division to multiplication, flipping the second, and then multiplying across numerators and denominators.

Example: Divide the rational expressions and simplify the result where applicable: $\frac{x+2}{3x} \div \frac{x^2+5x+6}{3x^2+3x}$.

Solution: We apply the division rule for fractions: $\frac{a}{b} \div \frac{c}{d} = \frac{a}{b} \times \frac{d}{c} = \frac{a \times d}{b \times c}$. Thus, we have: $\frac{x+2}{3x} \div \frac{x^2+5x+6}{3x^2+3x} = \frac{x+2}{3x} \times \frac{3x^2+3x}{x^2+5x+6}$, which simplifies to: $\frac{(x+2)(3x^2+3x)}{3x(x^2+5x+6)}$. Next, we factorize the expressions $3x^2 + 3x$ and $x^2 + 5x + 6$. After factorizing, we get: $3x^2 + 3x = 3x(x+1)$ and $x^2 + 5x + 6 = (x+2)(x+3)$. After substituting these in, and simplifying, we get $\frac{x+1}{x+3}$.

Example: Divide the rational expressions and simplify the result where applicable: $\frac{5x}{x+3} \div \frac{x}{2x+6}$.

Solution: Follow the fraction division rule: $\frac{a}{b} \div \frac{c}{d} = \frac{a}{b} \times \frac{d}{c} = \frac{a \times d}{b \times c}$. This simplifies our problem to: $\frac{5x}{x+3} \div \frac{x}{2x+6} = \frac{5x}{x+3} \times \frac{2x+6}{x} = \frac{10x(x+3)}{x(x+3)}$. After canceling the common factor, the resulting solution is 10.

11.6   Adding and Subtracting Rational Expressions

The procedure for adding and subtracting rational expressions closely mirrors the one used for adding and subtracting fractions. To add or subtract rational expressions, adhere to these steps:

1. **Identify the Least Common Denominator (LCD):**

   - Determine the LCD for all expressions. If denominators differ, find the LCD to establish a common base.

2. **Rewrite Each Expression Using the LCD:**

   - Convert each rational expression to an equivalent form with the LCD, akin to creating equivalent fractions.

3. **Perform the Addition or Subtraction:**

   - With a unified denominator, add or subtract the numerators of the expressions.

4. **Simplify the Resulting Expression:**

   - Simplify the final expression through factoring and reducing, if possible.

This methodology ensures accurate combination of expressions, preserving mathematical correctness.

🔔 **Key Point**

To add or subtract rational expressions, find the Least Common Denominator (LCD), rewrite each expression with it, then add or subtract the numerators and simplify the result.

Example: Solve $\frac{4}{2x+3} + \frac{x-2}{2x+3}$.

Solution: The denominators are equal. Thus, use the fractions addition rule $\frac{a}{c} \pm \frac{b}{c} = \frac{a \pm b}{c}$. So,

$\frac{4}{2x+3} + \frac{x-2}{2x+3} = \frac{4+(x-2)}{2x+3} = \frac{x+2}{2x+3}$.

Example: Solve $\frac{x+4}{x-5} + \frac{x-4}{x+6}$.

Solution: Find the least common denominator of $x-5$ and $x+6$, which is $(x-5)(x+6)$. So,

$\frac{x+4}{x-5} + \frac{x-4}{x+6} = \frac{(x+4)(x+6)}{(x-5)(x+6)} + \frac{(x-4)(x-5)}{(x+6)(x-5)} = \frac{2x^2+x+44}{x^2+x-30}$.

Example: Simplify the expression: $\frac{1}{x-3} + \frac{1}{x+1}$.

Solution: Find the least common denominator of $x-3$ and $x+1$, which is $(x-3)(x+1)$. So,

$\frac{1}{x-3} + \frac{1}{x+1} = \frac{(x+1)+(x-3)}{(x+1)(x-3)} = \frac{2x-2}{x^2-2x-3}$.

11.7 Rational Equations

The common denominator method requires finding a common denominator for all fractions, and replacing the numerators and denominators with equivalent terms. This allows us to cancel out the denominator, resulting in a linear or quadratic equation.

🔔 **Key Point**

> The common denominator method involves finding a common denominator for all fractions and equating the numerators, leading to a linear or quadratic equation.

🔔 **Key Point**

> Cross-multiplication equates the product of the numerator of one fraction with the denominator of another, and is effective for equations of the form $\frac{a}{b} = \frac{c}{d}$.

Example: Solve $\frac{x-2}{x+1} = \frac{x+4}{x-2}$.

Solution: This equation is an ideal candidate for cross-multiplication; By cross-multiplying, we get $(x-2)(x-2) = (x+4)(x+1)$. Expanding, we get

$$x^2 - 4x + 4 = x^2 + 5x + 4.$$

Subtracting $x^2 + 5x$ from both sides gives us $9x = 0$, yielding $x = 0$.

Example: Solve $\frac{2x}{x-3} = \frac{2x+2}{2x-6}$.

    Solution: We can use the common denominator method here. On multiplying the numerator and denominator of the left side fraction by 2, it becomes $\frac{4x}{2x-6}$. Since the denominators on either side of the equation are equal, their numerators must be equal too. So, $4x = 2x + 2$. Solving yields $x = 1$.

11.8   Simplifying Complex Fractions

A complex fraction has fractions in its numerator, denominator, or both. Simplification involves converting mixed numbers, separating into divisions, and applying fraction division, with further simplification as needed.

Key Point

> Simplifying a complex fraction, where either numerator or denominator is a fraction, involves converting to improper fractions, separating into division, and applying fraction division rules.

Example: Simplify the complex fraction $\dfrac{\frac{3}{5}}{\frac{2}{25} - \frac{5}{16}}$.

    Solution: First, simplify the denominator:

$$\frac{2}{25} - \frac{5}{16} = -\frac{93}{400}.$$

Then turn the complex fraction into a division problem:

$$\frac{\frac{3}{5}}{\frac{2}{25} - \frac{5}{16}} = \frac{\frac{3}{5}}{-\frac{93}{400}} = \frac{3}{5} \div \left(-\frac{93}{400}\right).$$

Using the Keep, Change, Flip rule (Keep the first fraction, Change the division sign to multiplication, Flip the second fraction), we get:

$$\frac{3}{5} \div \left(-\frac{93}{400}\right) = \frac{3}{5} \times \left(-\frac{400}{93}\right) = -\frac{240}{93} = -\frac{80}{31} = -2\frac{18}{31}.$$

Example: Simplify the complex fraction $\dfrac{\frac{2}{5} \div \frac{1}{3}}{\frac{5}{9} + \frac{1}{3}}$.

Solution: Start by simplifying the numerator: $\frac{2}{5} \div \frac{1}{3} = \frac{6}{5}$. Next, simplify the denominator: $\frac{5}{9} + \frac{1}{3} = \frac{8}{9}$. Convert the complex fraction into a division problem:

$$\frac{\frac{2}{5} \div \frac{1}{3}}{\frac{5}{9} + \frac{1}{3}} = \frac{\frac{6}{5}}{\frac{8}{9}} = \frac{6}{5} \div \frac{8}{9}.$$

Applying the Keep, Change, Flip rule:

$$\frac{6}{5} \div \frac{8}{9} = \frac{6}{5} \times \frac{9}{8} = \frac{54}{40} = \frac{27}{20} = 1\frac{7}{20}.$$

11.9   Maximum and Minimum Points

Function $f(x)$ has local maxima/minima where $f(a)$ is the highest/lowest in an interval, and absolute maxima/minima if it is the highest/lowest in the domain. Local extrema occur if $f(a) > f(x)$ or $f(a) < f(x)$ for all $x \neq a$ in an interval, while absolute extrema occur if $f(a)$ is the largest or smallest value for all x in the domain.

🔔 **Key Point**

Functions may have multiple local extrema but only one absolute maximum or minimum.

Graphing the function is the most effective way to identify these points.

Example: Find the maximum points of the function: $f(x) = x^3 - 3x + 1$.

Solution: The function has a local maximum at $x = -1$: $f(-1) = 3$ and a local minimum at $x = 1$: $f(1) = -1$.

The function does not have an absolute maximum nor minimum as the function's range tends to infinity.

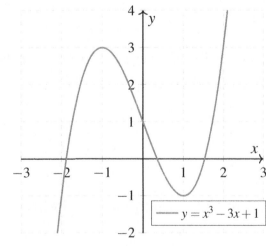

11.10 Solving Rational Inequalities

Solve a rational inequality by first writing it with the rational expression on the left and zero on the right. Identify points where numerator and denominator are zero (critical points), divide the input values into intervals using these points, and test an arbitrary point in each interval to check the inequality. Graphing can also be used for solving.

Key Point

Solve rational inequalities by setting them to zero, finding critical points where numerator or denominator equals zero, testing intervals around these points, and using graphing as needed.

Example: Illustrate how to solve rational inequality $\frac{x^2+3}{x+3} < 2$.

Solution: It starts with writing the inequality into the general form. It results in $\frac{x^2-2x-3}{x+3} < 0$, identifying the zeros by equating the numerator and denominator to zero, yielding $x = -3$, $x = 3$ and $x = -1$. The last step is to check each interval of the $(-\infty, -3)$, $(-3, -1)$, $(-1, 3)$, and $(3, \infty)$ to determine whether it satisfies the inequality. Considering an arbitrary value from each interval between the critical points, such as -4, -2, 0, and 4, when plugged into the inequality, reveals that only the values from the intervals $(-\infty, -3)$ and $(-1, 3)$ can make the inequality hold, thus providing the solution set. Hence, the solution is $x \in (-\infty, -3) \cup (-1, 3)$.

11.11 Irrational Functions

Irrational functions, represented as $f(x) = \sqrt[n]{(g(x))^m}$ or $f(x) = (g(x))^{\frac{m}{n}}$, involve variables under an n-th root or with a rational exponent. Their domain depends on the index n: for odd n, it matches $g(x)$'s domain; for even n, it includes x-values where $g(x) \geq 0$.

Key Point

The domain of an irrational function depends on the radical's index and the properties of the function within the radical.

Example: Find the domain of the irrational function $y = \dfrac{\sqrt{x}}{1 - \sqrt{x+2}}$.

Solution: For this function, the denominator must not equal zero, so from the equation $1 - \sqrt{x+2} = 0$, we find that $x \neq -1$. Moreover, since our expression contains $\sqrt{x}$ and $\sqrt{x+2}$, the domain of the function also requires $x \geq 0$ and $x \geq -2$ simultaneously. Hence, using these conditions, the domain of the given function is $[0, \infty)$.

11.12 Direct, Inverse, Joint, and Combined Variation

Variation types include direct, inverse, joint, and combined. Direct variation ($y = cx$) has variables changing in proportion, inverse variation ($y = \frac{c}{x}$) inversely relates two variables, joint variation ($y = cxz$) links one variable to the product of others, and combined variation ($y = c\left(\frac{x}{z}\right)$) mixes direct and inverse relationships.

🔔 Key Point

Types of variations: direct ($y = cx$), inverse ($y = \frac{c}{x}$), joint ($y = cxz$), and combined ($y = c\left(\frac{x}{z}\right)$).

Example: If $x = 6$ and $c = 5$, find y for a direct variation.

Solution: For a direct variation, we use the equation $y = cx$. By substituting the values of x and c into the equation, we get: $y = (5)(6)$. So, $y = 30$.

Example: When $x = 5$ and $y = 3$, find the constant of variation for an inverse relationship and the equation that relates y and x inversely.

Solution: For an inverse relationship, $y = \frac{c}{x}$, therefore $c = xy$. Substitute $x = 5$ and $y = 3$ into the equation, and solve for c: $c = (5)(3) = 15$. Hence, the equation that relates y and x inversely is $y = \frac{15}{x}$.

11.13 Practices

🔢 True/False:

1) A rational number can be expressed as a fraction with integers in the numerator and denominator and the denominator cannot be zero. True or False?

2) If you multiply two rational numbers, the result is always a rational number.

3) If a function has a local minimum point, it must also have a local maximum point.

4) A local maximum point is always a absolute maximum point.

Simplify Each Expression:

5) Simplify the rational expression: $\frac{4x^2-16}{2x-4}$

6) Simplify the rational expression: $\frac{3y^3-3y^2}{y^2}$

7) Simplify the rational expression: $\frac{x^3+6x^2+9x}{x(x+3)}$

8) Simplify the rational expression: $\frac{a^3-1}{a-1}$

9) Simplify the rational expression: $\frac{2x^3+4x^2}{2x^2}$

Analyze the graph:

10) What is the y-intercept of the graph of the function $f(x) = \frac{x^2+x+2}{x-1}$?

11) What are the asymptotes for the graph of the function $f(x) = \frac{x^2-2x+1}{x-2}$?

12) What are the asymptotes of the function $f(x) = \frac{x^2+2x+1}{x-1}$?

13) What are the asymptotes of the function $f(x) = \frac{x^2+x-1}{x-2}$?

14) What is the y-intercept of the function $f(x) = \frac{x^2+2x+1}{x-2}$?

Simplify Each Expression:

15) Simplify: $\frac{x-1}{x+2} \times \frac{x+2}{2x-3}$

16) Simplify: $\frac{x+3}{x^2-9} \times \frac{x^2-9}{2x+6}$

17) Simplify: $\frac{x^2+7x+10}{x+2} \times \frac{x+2}{2x^2+7x-15}$

18) Simplify: $\frac{3x-6}{x-2} \times \frac{x+2}{3x+6}$

19) Simplify: $\frac{2x+8}{3x-6} \times \frac{x+2}{2x+4}$

Solve:

20) $\frac{x+5}{x-6} - \frac{3x-2}{x-6} = 0$

21) $\frac{2x+9}{x^2-4} + \frac{3x-1}{x^2-4} = 0$

22) $\frac{2}{x-5} + \frac{3}{x+1} = \frac{5}{x-4}$

23) $\frac{4}{x+5} - \frac{5}{3x-8} = \frac{1}{x-2}$

24) $\frac{2x-1}{x^2+3x+2} + \frac{x+4}{x^2+3x+2} = 0$

 Plot the graph:

25) Plot $y = x^2 - 4x + 4$.

26) Plot $y = \frac{2}{3}x + 1$.

 Solve:

27) Simplify the complex fraction $\dfrac{\frac{4}{9}}{\frac{3}{2} + \frac{1}{3}}$.

28) Simplify $\dfrac{\frac{5}{7} - \frac{2}{3}}{\frac{7}{8} + \frac{3}{2}}$.

29) Simplify the complex fraction $\dfrac{\frac{2}{3} \times \frac{2}{7}}{\frac{5}{2} - \frac{1}{3}}$.

30) Simplify the complex fraction $\dfrac{\frac{7}{9} + \frac{1}{3}}{\frac{5}{3} - \frac{2}{7}}$.

31) Simplify $\dfrac{\frac{3}{2} \div \frac{2}{5}}{\frac{1}{2} + \frac{3}{5}}$.

 Find the Maximum and Minimum Points:

32) $f(x) = x^3 - 3x - 7$.

33) $f(x) = -x^2 - 4x - 3$.

34) $f(x) = x^2 - 4x + 6$.

35) $f(x) = x^2 - 4x + 4$.

36) $f(x) = x^3 - 12x + 20$.

Fill in the Blank:

37) There are _____ rational numbers between any two distinct rational numbers.

38) The symbol used to denote the set of rational numbers is _____.

39) The number 3.14159 is a _____ number.

40) In the irrational function $f(x) = \sqrt[n]{g(x)}$, the _____ and _____ determine the domain of the function.

41) If n is an even number and $g(x) \geq 0$, the domain of $f(x) = \sqrt[n]{g(x)}$ is _____.

42) If the index n in the irrational function $f(x) = \sqrt[n]{g(x)}$ is odd, the domain of $f(x)$ is the same as the domain of _____.

43) The mathematical form of an irrational function can be written as $f(x) = $ _____ or $f(x) = $ _____, where $g(x)$ is a rational function.

44) In the function $y = \frac{\sqrt{x}}{2 - \sqrt{x+1}}$, the domain of this function requires $x \geq$ _____ and $x \neq$ _____.

Answer Keys

1) True

2) True

3) False

4) False.

5) $2x + 4$

6) $3y - 3$

7) $x + 3$

8) $a^2 + a + 1$

9) $x + 2$

10) -2

11) $x = 2, y = x$

12) $x = 1, y = x + 3$

13) $x = 2, y = x + 3$

14) $-\frac{1}{2}$

15) $\frac{x-1}{2x-3}$

16) $\frac{1}{2}$

17) $\frac{x+2}{2x-3}$

18) 1

19) $\frac{x+4}{3x-6}$

20) $x = \frac{7}{2}$

21) $x = -\frac{8}{5}$

22) $x = \frac{77}{13}$

23) $x = \frac{39 \pm \sqrt{905}}{4}$

24) No answer

25)

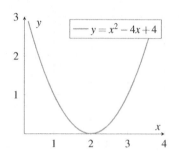

26)

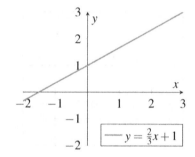

27) $\frac{8}{33}$

28) $\frac{8}{399}$

29) $\frac{8}{91}$

30) $\frac{70}{87}$

31) $\frac{75}{22}$

32) Local maximum: $(-1, -5)$, local minimum: $(1, -9)$

33) Local maximum: $(-2, 1)$.

34) Absolute minimum: $(2, 2)$

35) Absolute minimum: $(2, 0)$

36) Local maximum: $(-2, 36)$, local minimum: $(2, 4)$.

37) Infinite

38) $\mathbb{Q}$

39) Rational.

40) Index n, $g(x)$

41) All x values

42) $g(x)$

43) $\sqrt[n]{g(x)^m}$, $(g(x))^{\frac{m}{n}}$

44) 0, 3

Answers with Explanation

1) This is true because the definition of a rational number is any number that can be written as a fraction where both the denominator and numerator are integers and the denominator cannot be zero.

2) This is true because by multiplying two rational numbers $\frac{a}{b}$ and $\frac{c}{d}$, we get the rational number $\frac{ac}{bd}$.

3) This is false because we can consider the function $f(x) = x^2$, which has a local minimum (at $x = 0$) but no local maximum.

4) A local maximum point is where the function attains a maximum value within a restricted part of its domain, but it does not necessarily mean that this value is the highest value of the function over its entire domain.

5) To simplify this expression, we factor out the common factor of 4 in the numerator, and the common factor of 2 in the denominator. Thus the expression becomes $\frac{4(x^2-4)}{2(x-2)}$. The numerator factors into $4(x^2 - 4) = 4(x-2)(x+2)$. This gives us the final answer of $2x + 4$.

6) In this rational expression, we can cancel out y^2 from the numerator and the denominator which reduces to $3y - 3$.

7) The numerator can be factored as $x(x^2 + 6x + 9)$, which simplifies to $x(x+3)^2$. When this is divided by $x(x+3)$, it cancels out to leave behind $x + 3$.

8) The numerator $a^3 - 1$ factors into $(a-1)(a^2 + a + 1)$. The term $a - 1$ cancels from the numerator and the denominator, leaving behind $a^2 + a + 1$.

9) We can cancel the common factor of $2x^2$ in numerator and denominator, which simplifies to $x + 2$.

10) The y-intercept is the point where the function crosses the y-axis.

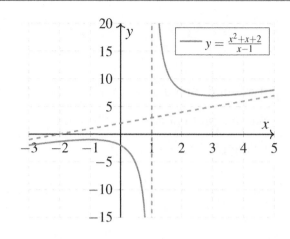

This occurs at $x = 0$. Hence, when $x = 0$, $f(x) = -2$. Thus, the y-intercept is -2.

11) The function approaches a vertical asymptote at $x = 2$.

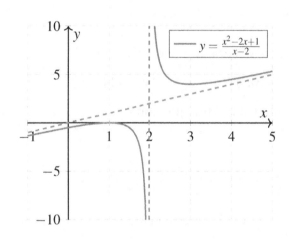

Regarding the oblique asymptote, if we perform polynomial long division or synthetic division, we find that: $f(x) = x + \frac{1}{x-2}$. So, it is clear that $y = x$ is the oblique (diagonal) asymptote for the function.

12) The denominator is zero at $x = 1$.

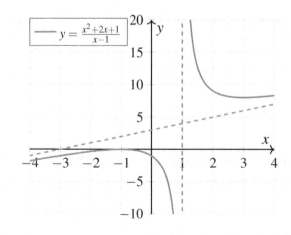

Since the numerator is not zero at $x = 1$, the function has a vertical asymptote at $x = 1$. For the oblique (diagonal) asymptote, we can perform polynomial long division. Doing so, we find that: $f(x) = x + 3 + \frac{4}{x-1}$. This indicates that $y = x + 3$ is the oblique asymptote.

13) The graph approaches $x = 2$ vertically, so the vertical asymptote is $x = 2$.

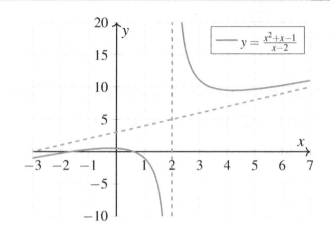

Using polynomial long division for $\frac{x^2+x-1}{x-2}$ we find that the quotient is $x+3$. Thus, the oblique asymptote is $y = x+3$.

14) The y-intercept is the point at which the function crosses the y-axis.

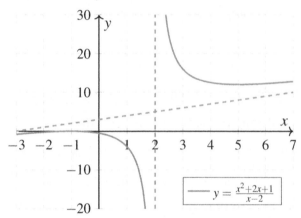

This occurs at $x = 0$. So, when $x = 0$, $f(0) = -\frac{1}{2}$. Thus, the y-intercept of the function is $-\frac{1}{2}$.

15) The $x+2$ term in the numerator and the denominator cancel out, leaving us with $\frac{x-1}{2x-3}$.

16) $x^2 - 9$ and $x+3$ cancel out from the numerator and the denominator, resulting in $\frac{1}{2}$.

17) We have $x^2 + 7x + 10 = (x+2)(x+5)$ and $2x^2 + 7x - 15 = (2x-3)(x+5)$. By eliminating common factors in the numerator and denominator we get $\frac{x+2}{2x-3}$.

18) We can first reduce $3x - 6$ to $3(x-2)$, and $3x + 6$ to $3(x+2)$. After that, all terms cancel out, leaving 1.

19) Simplified first to $2(x+4)$, the factor $x+2$ cancels out, leaving us with $\frac{x+4}{3x-6}$.

20) Merge the fractions using fractions subtraction rule. We have $\frac{x+5-(3x-2)}{x-6} = 0$ which simplifies to $-2x+7 = 0$. Solving this equation for x gives $x = \frac{7}{2}$.

21) The fractions have common denominators. Using fractions addition rule to simplify, we have: $\frac{2x+9+3x-1}{x^2-4} = \frac{5x+8}{x^2-4} = 0$. Setting the numerator equal to zero gives $5x + 8 = 0$. Solving for x, we find that $x = -\frac{8}{5}$.

22) The LCD is $(x-5)(x+1)(x-4)$. Transform the original equation to:

$$\frac{2(x+1)(x-4)}{(x-5)(x+1)(x-4)} + \frac{3(x-5)(x-4)}{(x-5)(x+1)(x-4)} = \frac{5(x-5)(x+1)}{(x-5)(x+1)(x-4)}.$$

Further simplifying gives: $x = \frac{77}{13}$.

23) The LCD is $(x+5)(3x-8)(x-2)$. Transform the original equation to:

$$\frac{4(3x-8)(x-2)}{(x+5)(3x-8)(x-2)} - \frac{5(x+5)(x-2)}{(x+5)(3x-8)(x-2)} = \frac{(x+5)(3x-8)}{(x+5)(3x-8)(x-2)}.$$

Simplifying gives: $4x^2 - 78x + 154 = 0$. Hence we obtain two solutions: $x = \frac{39 \pm \sqrt{905}}{4}$.

24) The fractions have common denominators. Use the fractions addition rule to simplify. We have $\frac{2x-1+x+4}{x^2+3x+2} = \frac{3x+3}{x^2+3x+2} = 0$. Simplifying gives $x = -1$. But -1 is the root of denominator. Therefore, it will not be acceptable.

25) The graph is a parabola opening upwards with the vertex at the point $(2,0)$.

26) The graph is a straight line with a positive slope of $\frac{2}{3}$ and the y-intercept as 1.

27) First simplify the denominator, next convert the complex fraction into a division problem and then apply the Keep, Change, Flip rule.

28) Simplify the numerator and denominator separately, convert into a division problem, then use the Keep, Change, Flip rule.

29) Simplify the numerator and denominator separately, convert into a division problem then use the Keep, Change, Flip rule.

30) Simplify the numerator and the denominator separately, convert into a division, then apply the Keep, Change, Flip rule.

31) Simplify the numerator and denominator separately, convert into a division problem, then use the Keep, Change, Flip rule.

32) $f(x)$ has a local maximum at $x = -1$ and a local minimum at $x = 1$.

At $x = -1$: $f(-1) = (-1)^3 - 3(-1) - 7 = -5$. So, the local

maximum is at $(-1, -5)$.

At $x = 1$: $f(1) = 1^3 - 3(1) - 7 = -9$. Thus, the local mini-

mum is at $(1, -9)$.

$f(x)$ has no absolute maximum or minimum since its range

extends to infinity.

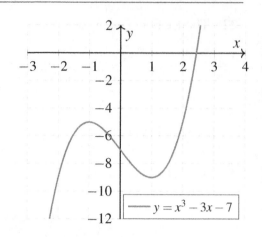

33) The function $f(x) = -x^2 - 4x - 3$ is a quadratic function. The vertex of this function occurs at $x = -\frac{-4}{2 \times -1} = -2$.

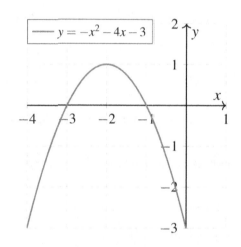

Since the coefficient of x^2 is negative, the graph opens

downwards, making the vertex a maximum point. Thus,

the function has a maximum at $(-2, 1)$ and no mini-

mum, as the function's range extends to negative infin-

ity.

34) The function $f(x) = x^2 - 4x + 6$ is a quadratic function.

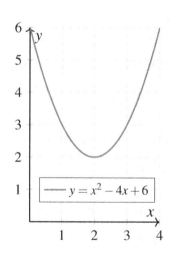

The vertex of the function is at $(2, 2)$. Since the coefficient of x^2 is

positive, the graph opens upwards, making the vertex a minimum

point. Therefore, the function has a minimum at $(2, 2)$ and no

maximum, as the function's range extends to infinity.

35) The function $f(x) = x^2 - 4x + 4$ is a quadratic function.

The vertex occurs at $x = -\frac{-4}{2 \times 1} = 2$. Since the coefficient of x^2 is positive, the graph opens upwards, making the vertex a minimum point. Thus, the function has a minimum at $(2,0)$ and no maximum as the function's range extends to infinity.

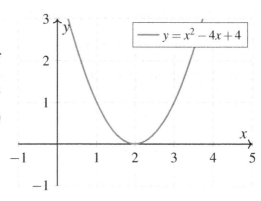

36) At $x = 2$: $f(2) = 2^3 - 12 \times 2 + 20 = 8 - 24 + 20 = 4$. This is a local minimum.

At $x = -2$: $f(-2) = (-2)^3 - 12 \times (-2) + 20 = -8 + 24 + 20 = 36$. This indicates a local maximum.

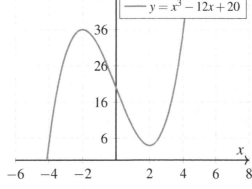

The function $f(x)$ does not have an absolute maximum or minimum since its range extends to infinity.

37) This is because you can always find another rational midway between any two given rationals, hence, there can be infinite rational numbers between any two rational numbers.

38) The symbol $\mathbb{Q}$ is used to denote the set of all rational numbers - both positive and negative.

39) 3.14159 is rational since it has a finite number of integers after the decimal point. Hence, it is a decimal representation terminates.

40) The domain of an irrational function is dependent on the index of the radical as well as the expression under the radical.

41) If n is an even number, the domain of $f(x)$ is equal to all values of x where $g(x) \geq 0$.

42) If n is an odd number, then the domain of $f(x)$ is the same as the domain of $g(x)$.

43) An irrational function $f(x)$ may be expressed as $\sqrt[n]{(g(x))^m}$ or $f(x) = (g(x))^{\frac{m}{n}}$, where $g(x)$ is a rational function.

44) The denominator should not equal zero. From the equation $2 - \sqrt{x+1} = 0$, we find that $x \neq 3$. Since the numerator and denominator contain the square root of x and $x + 1$, respectively, we require that $x \geq 0$ and $x \geq -1$, which results in $x \geq 0$.

12. Trigonometric Functions

12.1 Angles of Rotation

In trigonometry, an angle θ is formed by the rotation of a ray around its vertex. The ray's initial position is the angle's initial side, and its position post-rotation is the terminal side.

🔔 Key Point

An angle is said to be in standard position when the initial side is along the positive x-axis and its vertex (endpoint) is at the origin.

If two angles in standard position share the same terminal side, they are said to be coterminal.

🔔 Key Point

The reference angle, denoted by θ_{ref}, is the smallest angle formed by the terminal side of the given angle with the x-axis.

The standard position of an angle:

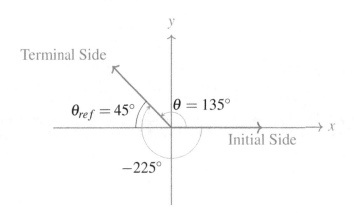

Example: Find a coterminal angle of $330°$ within the interval $-360° < \theta < 360°$.

   Solution: Coterminal angles can be found by adding or subtracting multiples of $360°$

$$\theta = 330° + 360° = 690°.$$

However, this is outside the given interval hence, we find a negative alternative

$$\theta = 330° - 360° = -30°.$$

Therefore, the coterminal angle within the desired range is $-30°$.

Example: Find a coterminal angle to $45°$ in the interval $-360° < \theta < 360°$.

   Solution: Similarly, coterminal angles can be found by adding or subtracting multiples of $360°$

$$\theta = 45° + 360° = 405°.$$

However, this is outside the given interval, hence we check with subtraction

$$\theta = 45° - 360° = -315°.$$

Hence, the required coterminal angle is $-315°$.

12.2 Angles and Angle Measure

Degrees and radians serve as the fundamental units for measuring angles. We should acquire the skills needed to switch between these two measurement systems.

🔔 Key Point

To convert an angle from degrees to radians, use the following formula:

$$\text{Radian} = \text{Degree} \times \frac{\pi}{180}.$$

To convert an angle from radians to degrees, use this formula:

$$\text{Degree} = \text{Radian} \times \frac{180}{\pi}.$$

Example: Convert 45 degrees to radians.

Solution: To achieve this, we employ the conversion factor for transforming degrees into radians:

$$\text{Radian} = \text{Degree} \times \frac{\pi}{180}.$$

Upon substituting the given value of 45 degrees into the formula, we find:

$$\text{Radian} = 45 \times \frac{\pi}{180} = \frac{\pi}{4}.$$

Example: Convert $\frac{\pi}{3}$ radians to degrees.

Solution: In this case, we apply the formula that converts radians to degrees:

$$\text{Degree} = \text{Radian} \times \frac{180}{\pi}.$$

By plugging in the given radian measure of $\frac{\pi}{3}$, we obtain:

$$\text{Degree} = \frac{\pi}{3} \times \frac{180}{\pi} = 60.$$

12.3   Right-Triangle Trigonometry

Right-triangle trigonometry focuses on the relationships between angles and sides of right triangles. In these triangles, one angle measures $90°$, and the remaining angles sum to $90°$. The longest side, opposite the $90°$ angle, is the hypotenuse. The other two sides, adjacent or opposite to a chosen angle θ, are the legs.

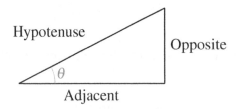

Figure 12.1: Right triangle with labeled sides relative to θ.

Key Point

In a right triangle with one angle θ:

- The side opposite θ is known as the "opposite side."
- The side adjacent to θ is known as the "adjacent side."
- The longest side is called the "hypotenuse."

Key Point

The Pythagorean Theorem states that in a right triangle, the sum of the squares of the legs (a and b) equals the square of the hypotenuse (c), expressed as $c^2 = a^2 + b^2$.

Example: In a right triangle, the lengths of the opposite side and adjacent side to angle θ are 3 units and 4 units. Find the length of the hypotenuse.

Solution: The hypotenuse of a right triangle can be calculated using the Pythagorean theorem, which states $c^2 = a^2 + b^2$, where a and b are the lengths of the legs, and c is the length of the hypotenuse. Given the legs are 3 units and 4 units long, the equation becomes:

$$c^2 = 3^2 + 4^2 \Rightarrow c^2 = 9 + 16 \Rightarrow c^2 = 25 \Rightarrow c = 5 \text{ units.}$$

Thus, the hypotenuse of the triangle is 5 units long.

12.4 Trigonometric Ratios

The sine, cosine, and tangent functions are fundamental trigonometric ratios linking angles to sides of right triangles, essential for solving various problems. These functions are algebraically derived from the unit circle.

🔔 Key Point

In a right triangle, the trigonometric ratios are:

$$\sin(\theta) = \frac{\text{opposite}}{\text{hypotenuse}}, \quad \cos(\theta) = \frac{\text{adjacent}}{\text{hypotenuse}}, \quad \text{and} \quad \tan(\theta) = \frac{\text{opposite}}{\text{adjacent}}.$$

Example: In a right triangle with a right angle at vertex B, the hypotenuse measures $10\,\text{cm}$, the base $8\,\text{cm}$, and the height $6\,\text{cm}$. If $\angle ACB = \theta$, find $\sin(\theta)$ and $\cos(\theta)$.

Solution: We employ the formulas $\sin(\theta) = \frac{\text{opposite}}{\text{hypotenuse}}$ and $\cos(\theta) = \frac{\text{adjacent}}{\text{hypotenuse}}$. Inserting the given side lengths, we find:

$$\sin(\theta) = \frac{6}{10},$$

$$\cos(\theta) = \frac{8}{10}.$$

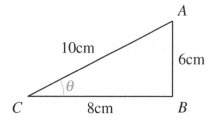

12.5 Function Values and Ratios of Special and General Angles

The angles $30°$, $45°$, $60°$, and $90°$ are key in trigonometry for their simple, exact trigonometric ratios and frequent occurrences in geometric shapes, essential for foundational trigonometric concepts and applications.

🔔 Key Point

The table below shows exact values for $\sin(\theta)$, $\cos(\theta)$, and $\tan(\theta)$ at special angles, aiding in quick calculation and generalization to any angle.

θ	$0°$	$30°$	$45°$	$60°$	$90°$
$\sin(\theta)$	0	$\frac{1}{2}$	$\frac{\sqrt{2}}{2}$	$\frac{\sqrt{3}}{2}$	1
$\cos(\theta)$	1	$\frac{\sqrt{3}}{2}$	$\frac{\sqrt{2}}{2}$	$\frac{1}{2}$	0
$\tan(\theta)$	0	$\frac{\sqrt{3}}{3}$	1	$\sqrt{3}$	undefined

Understanding the relationships between sine and cosine functions can simplify trigonometric calculations and expressions.

🔔 Key Point

Practical properties:

$$\sin(\theta) = \cos\left(90° - \theta\right), \quad \cos(\theta) = \sin(90° - \theta),$$
$$\cos(-\theta) = \cos(\theta), \quad \text{and} \quad \sin(-\theta) = -\sin(\theta).$$

Example: Find the exact value for $\sin\left(150°\right)$.

Solution: Using the property $\sin(x) = \cos\left(90° - x\right)$, we get

$$\sin\left(150°\right) = \cos\left(90° - 150°\right) = \cos\left(-60°\right) = \cos\left(60°\right) = \frac{1}{2}.$$

Example: Find the exact value for $\cos(120°)$.

Solution: Using the property $\cos(x) = \sin\left(90° - x\right)$, we get

$$\cos 120° = \sin\left(90° - 120°\right) = \sin\left(-30°\right) = -\sin\left(30°\right) = -\frac{1}{2}.$$

Example: Find the exact value for $\sin\left(135°\right)$.

Solution: Using the property $\sin(x) = \cos\left(90° - x\right)$, we get

$$\sin\left(135°\right) = \cos\left(90° - 135°\right) = \cos\left(-45°\right) = \cos\left(45°\right) = \frac{\sqrt{2}}{2}.$$

12.6 Missing Sides and Angles of a Right Triangle

Using sine, cosine, or tangent, we can calculate an unknown side of a right triangle if we know one side length and one non-right angle.

Key Point

In right triangles, unknown sides can be calculated using

$$\sin(\theta) = \tfrac{\text{opposite}}{\text{hypotenuse}}, \quad \cos(\theta) = \tfrac{\text{adjacent}}{\text{hypotenuse}}, \quad \text{and} \quad \tan(\theta) = \tfrac{\text{opposite}}{\text{adjacent}},$$

given one side length and a non-right angle.

Example: We want to find the length of the side AC in the following right triangle:

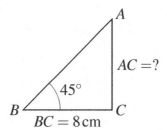

Solution: We can use the sine function, which is defined as the ratio of the opposite side to the hypotenuse: $\sin 45° = \tfrac{AC}{8}$. By rearranging the equation, we get:

$$AC = 8(\sin 45°) = 8\left(\tfrac{\sqrt{2}}{2}\right) = 4\sqrt{2}.$$

12.7 The Reciprocal Trigonometric Functions

The first reciprocal function we consider is the secant function, denoted by $\sec(\theta)$. If the cosine of an angle θ is given by $\cos(\theta)$, then the secant of θ is defined as its reciprocal. Similarly, the cosecant function, denoted by $\csc(\theta)$, is the reciprocal of the sine function. Lastly, the cotangent function, abbreviated as $\cot(\theta)$, is the reciprocal of the tangent function.

The reciprocal trigonometric functions are defined for angle θ as follows:

if $\cos(\theta) \neq 0$, $\sec(\theta) = \frac{1}{\cos(\theta)}$,

if $\sin(\theta) \neq 0$, $\csc(\theta) = \frac{1}{\sin(\theta)}$,

if $\tan(\theta) \neq 0$, $\cot(\theta) = \frac{1}{\tan(\theta)}$.

Example: Find the value of $\sec(\theta)$ if $\cos(\theta) = \frac{2}{7}$ using the reciprocal identity.

   Solution: According to the reciprocal identity of secant, if $\cos(\theta) = \frac{2}{7}$, then

$$\sec(\theta) = \frac{1}{\cos(\theta)} = \frac{7}{2}.$$

Example: Evaluate $\cot(\theta)$ if $\tan(\theta) = 3$.

   Solution: Using the reciprocal identity for cotangent, $\cot(\theta) = \frac{1}{\tan(\theta)}$. So, if $\tan(\theta) = 3$, then

$$\cot(\theta) = \frac{1}{3}.$$

Example: Calculate $\csc(\theta)$ if $\sin(\theta) = \frac{4}{5}$.

   Solution: According to the reciprocal identity for cosecant, if $\sin(\theta) = \frac{4}{5}$, then

$$\csc(\theta) = \frac{1}{\sin(\theta)} = \frac{5}{4}.$$

12.8   Co-functions

Co-function identities illustrate the relationship between sine, cosine, tangent, cotangent, secant, and cosecant of complementary angles.

Key Point

The five key co-function identities for complementary angles are:

1. $\sin(90° - x) = \cos(x)$,

2. $\cos(90° - x) = \sin(x)$,

3. $\cot(90° - x) = \tan(x)$,

4. $\sec(90° - x) = \csc(x)$,

5. $\csc(90° - x) = \sec(x)$.

Example: Find the cosine of $45°$ using the co-function identity $\sin(90° - x) = \cos(x)$.

Solution: Substitute $x = 45°$ into the equation:

$$\sin(90° - 45°) = \cos(45°).$$

Hence, $\cos 45° = \sin 45°$, which equals $\frac{\sqrt{2}}{2}$.

Example: Given $\tan(38°) \approx 0.7813$, find $\cot(90° - 38°)$.

Solution: Using the co-function identity $\cot(90° - x) = \tan(x)$, substitute $x = 38°$:

$$\cot(90° - 38°) = \tan(38°).$$

Thus, $\cot(90° - 38°) \approx 0.7813$.

12.9   Function Values from the Calculator

To obtain trigonometric function values using a scientific calculator, first select the correct mode (degree or radian) based on the angle's measurement. For example, on a Texas Instruments calculator, press the MODE key to toggle between DEGREE and RADIAN modes, indicated on the display's third line.

Key Point

Ensure you correctly select the mode (Degree or Radian), as per the angle you are dealing with, on your calculator.

After setting the correct mode, you can now evaluate the function. You do achieve this by pressing the button for the trigonometric function, i.e., sin, cos, or tan, you wish to compute. You then enter the angle measurement and press 'Enter' to get the result.

Key Point

It is important to remember that calculator outputs are typically approximations, not exact values.

Example: Compute $\cos(130°)$ in degree mode.

Solution: Set your calculator to degree mode. Then press the cos button, type in $130°$, and press 'Enter'. The output you get should be approximately -0.6428.

Example: Let's find the value of $\sin(\frac{\pi}{4})$ in radian mode and check it using its exact value.

Solution: Set your calculator to radian mode. Press the sin button, then type in $\frac{\pi}{4}$ and press 'Enter'. The output should be approximately 0.7071. Now, we know that the exact value of $\sin(\frac{\pi}{4})$ is $\frac{\sqrt{2}}{2}$ which is roughly 0.7071, verifying our computed result.

12.10 Reference Angles and the Calculator

Using reference angles with a calculator simplifies finding trigonometric values for any angle. Trigonometric function signs vary across the four quadrants:

Key Point

Quadrant characteristics:

1. First Quadrant ($0°$ to $90°$): All functions positive.

2. Second Quadrant ($90°$ to $180°$): sin positive, cos and tan negative.

3. Third Quadrant ($180°$ to $270°$): sin and cos negative, tan positive.

4. Fourth Quadrant ($270°$ to $360°$): cos positive, sin and tan negative.

Reference angles simplify trigonometric functions across quadrants by converting them to first-quadrant operations.

Key Point

For reference angles:

1. First Quadrant: Same as the given angle.

2. Second Quadrant: $180° - \theta$.

3. Third Quadrant: $\theta - 180°$.

4. Fourth Quadrant: $360° - \theta$.

Normalize angles outside $0°$ to $360°$ by adding/subtracting $360°$.

If θ is the measure of an angle with $90° < \theta < 360°$, the reference angle and trigonometric functions in each quadrant are:

Quadrant	Reference Angle	sin(Ref)	cos(Ref)	tan(Ref)
Second	$180° - \theta$	$\sin(180° - \theta)$	$-\cos(180° - \theta)$	$-\tan(180° - \theta)$
Third	$\theta - 180°$	$-\sin(\theta - 180°)$	$-\cos(\theta - 180°)$	$\tan(\theta - 180°)$
Fourth	$360° - \theta$	$-\sin(360° - \theta)$	$\cos(360° - \theta)$	$-\tan(360° - \theta)$

Example: Suppose we have $\sin(\theta) = 0.7547$, and we want to find two positive values of θ that are less than $360°$.

Solution: To solve this, we can use calculator to calculate θ, and we get $\theta \simeq 48.9°$. The measure of the reference angle is $48.9°$. The sine is positive in the first and second quadrants. So, one solution is $\theta = 48.9°$. To find the value of θ in the second and quadrant, we apply our knowledge of reference angles:

$$48.9° = 180° - \theta \implies \theta = 180° - 48.9° = 131.1°.$$

So, the solution is $\theta = 48.9°, 131.1°$.

12.11 Coterminal Angles and Reference Angles

Conterminal angles are angles that measure the same, and to find a coterminal angle, add or subtract $360°$ (or 2π radians) to the given angle. The reference angle is the smallest angle formed between the terminal side of an angle and the x-axis.

🔔 **Key Point**

An angle is said to be Coterminal with another if they have the same terminal side.

🔔 **Key Point**

The Reference Angle is the smallest angle that you can make from the terminal side of an angle with the x-axis.

Example: Find a positive and a negative coterminal angle to angle $65°$.

Solution: By definition, by adding or subtracting 360 degrees from the given angle we can find coterminal angles: $65° - 360° = -295°$, and $65° + 360° = 425°$. So, $-295°$ and $425°$ are coterminal with $65°$.

12.12 Evaluating Trigonometric Function

In evaluating trigonometric functions, follow this three-step approach:

Step 1: Draw the terminal side of the angle in standard position, rotating from the positive x-axis to fall in one of the four quadrants. The trigonometric function sign is quadrant-dependent.

Step 2: Find the reference angle, the smallest positive angle less than or equal to $90°$ or $\frac{\pi}{2}$ radians made with the x-axis.

Step 3: Compute the trigonometric function of the reference angle, noting that basic angle values simplify this step.

🔔 **Key Point**

Evaluating Trigonometric Functions:

1. Draw the terminal side of the angle.

2. Find the reference angle, the smallest angle from the terminal side to the x-axis.

3. Calculate the trigonometric function of the reference angle.

Example: Evaluate $\sin(135°)$.

Solution: First, draw the terminal side of the given angle. $135°$ lies in the second quadrant. The reference angle can be found by subtracting $135°$ from $180°$ which gives us $45°$. We know that $\sin(45°) = \frac{\sqrt{2}}{2}$.

Because $135°$ is in the second quadrant where the y-values are positive, $\sin(135°)$ is also positive. Therefore, $\sin(135°) = \frac{\sqrt{2}}{2}$.

12.13 Pythagorean Identities

Pythagorean identities in trigonometry, crucial for solving complex problems, include the fundamental identity $\sin^2 \theta + \cos^2 \theta = 1$ for any angle θ.

🔔 Key Point

The Pythagorean identity, $\sin^2 \theta + \cos^2 \theta = 1$, is essential in trigonometry and leads to two derived identities:

- Dividing by $\sin^2 \theta$: $1 + \cot^2 \theta = \csc^2 \theta$.
- Dividing by $\cos^2 \theta$: $\tan^2 \theta + 1 = \sec^2 \theta$.

Example: Verify the identity $\frac{\sin^2 \theta}{\frac{1}{2}} + \frac{\cos^2 \theta}{\frac{1}{2}} = 2$.

Solution: To verify this identity, we multiply both sides of the Pythagorean identity $\sin^2 \theta + \cos^2 \theta = 1$ by 2, which is equivalent to dividing by $\frac{1}{2}$

$$\frac{\sin^2 \theta}{\frac{1}{2}} + \frac{\cos^2 \theta}{\frac{1}{2}} = 2(\sin^2 \theta + \cos^2 \theta) = 2(1) = 2.$$

Hence, the identity $\frac{\sin^2 \theta}{\frac{1}{2}} + \frac{\cos^2 \theta}{\frac{1}{2}} = 2$ is verified.

12.14 The Unit Circle, Sine, and Cosine

The unit circle serves as an invaluable tool in mathematics, particularly for comprehending the trigonometric functions sine and cosine. Centered at the origin $(0,0)$ of the coordinate plane with a radius of 1 unit, it is represented by the equation $x^2 + y^2 = 1$.

The unit circle is instrumental for understanding the sine and cosine functions. The y-coordinate of a point on the unit circle provides the value of $\sin\theta$, and the x-coordinate yields the value of $\cos\theta$.

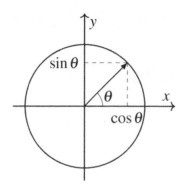

Figure 12.2: Sine and Cosine in a Unit Circle.

Example: Let $P\left(\frac{\sqrt{3}}{2}, -\frac{1}{2}\right)$ be a point on the unit circle corresponding to an angle θ in standard position. Determine $\sin\theta$ and $\cos\theta$.

Solution: A point $P(x,y)$ on the unit circle corresponds to $\sin\theta = y$ and $\cos\theta = x$. Therefore, for $P\left(\frac{\sqrt{3}}{2}, -\frac{1}{2}\right)$:

$$\sin\theta = y\text{-coordinate of } P = -\frac{1}{2}, \quad \text{and} \quad \cos\theta = x\text{-coordinate of } P = \frac{\sqrt{3}}{2}.$$

12.15 Arc Length and Sector Area

A circle is a set of points equidistant from a central point. This distance is known as the radius r. When we consider a fraction of the circle defined by a central angle θ (in degrees), we call that portion a sector. The perimeter of a sector is called the arc of the sector.

Area of a sector with a central angle θ (in degrees) $= \pi r^2 \left(\frac{\theta}{360}\right)$.

Arc length of a sector with a central angle θ (in degrees) $= \pi r \left(\frac{\theta}{180}\right)$.

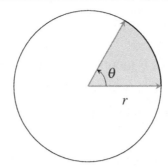

Figure 12.3: A circle with a sector marked.

Example: For a circle with a radius $r = 12$ cm and a central angle $\theta = 75°$, find the area of the sector and length of the arc.

 Solution: Starting with the area of the sector:

$$\text{Area of the sector} = \pi(12)^2 \left(\frac{75}{360} \right) = 30\pi \text{ cm}^2.$$

Next, the length of the arc:

$$\text{Arc of the sector} = \pi(12) \left(\frac{75}{180} \right) = 5\pi \text{ cm}.$$

Hence, the sector of the circle has an area of 30π cm^2 and an arc length of 5π cm.

12.16 Practices

 Solve:

1) Find the exact value for $\cos\left(150°\right)$.

2) Find the exact value for $\sin\left(225°\right)$.

3) Compute $\sin\left(300°\right)$.

4) Solve for $\cos\left(420°\right)$.

 True/False:

5) For any angle ϕ in a right triangle, $\tan(\phi) = \frac{1}{\cot(\phi)}$.

6) The value of $\cos(\theta)$ always decreases as θ increases in a right triangle.

7) The cosecant of an angle is always larger than 1.

8) The value of $\sin(\alpha)$ cannot exceed 1.

9) For any angle β in a right triangle, $\cos(\beta) = \sqrt{1 - \sin^2(\beta)}$.

Fill in the Blank:

10) $1 + \underline{\hspace{2cm}} = \csc^2\theta$.

11) $\underline{\hspace{2cm}} + 1 = \sec^2\theta$.

12) $\sin^2\theta + \cos^2\theta = \underline{\hspace{2cm}}$.

13) $\sin^2\theta + \underline{\hspace{2cm}} = 1$.

14) $\underline{\hspace{2cm}} + \cot^2\theta = \csc^2\theta$.

Fill in the Blank:

15) The equation of a unit circle in coordinate plane is $\underline{\hspace{2cm}}$.

16) An angle in standard position has its initial side along the $\underline{\hspace{2cm}}$.

17) For a point $P(x, y)$ on the unit circle, $\sin\theta = \underline{\hspace{2cm}}$ and $\cos\theta = \underline{\hspace{2cm}}$.

18) The radius of the unit circle is $\underline{\hspace{2cm}}$.

19) The center of the unit circle in the coordinate plane is at $\underline{\hspace{2cm}}$.

Solve:

20) Compute the value of $\sin(300°)$ using your calculator in degree mode.

21) Assume you are in degree mode, compute the value of $\cos(210°)$.

22) Compute the value of $\tan(\frac{\pi}{6})$ using your calculator in radian mode.

23) You are in radian mode, compute the value of $\sin(\frac{7\pi}{6})$.

24) Compute the value of $\tan(225°)$ using your calculator in degree mode.

Convert between degrees and radians:

25) Convert 60 degrees to radians.

26) Convert $\frac{7\pi}{6}$ radians to degrees.

27) Convert 225 degrees to radians.

28) Convert $\frac{2\pi}{3}$ radians to degrees.

29) Convert 330 degrees to radians.

Solve:

30) Evaluate $\sin(-225°)$.

31) Evaluate $\cos(300°)$.

32) Evaluate $\tan(210°)$.

33) Evaluate $\cot(-60°)$.

34) Evaluate $\csc(150°)$.

True/False:

35) The area of a sector can be determined even without knowing the radius of the circle.

36) The arc length formula does not depend on the central angle.

37) The area of a sector is a portion of the area of the entire circle, based on the central angle.

38) The arc length is always half the radius of the circle.

39) An arc length can never be larger than the circumference of the circle.

Answer Keys

1) $-\frac{\sqrt{3}}{2}$

2) $-\frac{\sqrt{2}}{2}$

3) $-\frac{\sqrt{3}}{2}$

4) $\frac{1}{2}$

5) True

6) False

7) False

8) True

9) True

10) $\cot^2\theta$

11) $\tan^2\theta$

12) 1

13) $\cos^2\theta$

14) 1

15) $x^2 + y^2 = 1$

16) positive x-axis

17) y, x

18) 1

19) $(0,0)$

20) -0.8660

21) -0.8660

22) 0.5774

23) -0.5

24) 1

25) $\frac{\pi}{3}$ radians

26) 210 degrees

27) $\frac{5\pi}{4}$ radians

28) 120 degrees

29) $\frac{11\pi}{6}$ radians

30) $\frac{\sqrt{2}}{2}$

31) $\frac{1}{2}$

32) $\frac{\sqrt{3}}{3}$

33) $-\frac{\sqrt{3}}{3}$

34) 2

35) False

36) False

37) True

38) False

39) True

Answers with Explanation

1) Using the property $\cos(x) = \sin\left(90^\circ - x\right)$, we get

$$\cos\left(150^\circ\right) = \sin\left(90^\circ - 150^\circ\right) = \sin\left(-60^\circ\right).$$

Since the sine function is negative in the fourth quadrant, $\sin\left(-60^\circ\right) = -\frac{\sqrt{3}}{2}$.

2) Using the property $\sin(x) = \cos\left(90^\circ - x\right)$, we get

$$\sin\left(225^\circ\right) = \cos\left(90^\circ - 225^\circ\right) = \cos\left(-135^\circ\right).$$

Now use this property: $\cos(-x) = \cos(x)$. Therefore:

$$\cos\left(-135^\circ\right) = \cos\left(135^\circ\right).$$

Using $\cos(x) = \sin\left(90^\circ - x\right)$,

$$\cos\left(135^\circ\right) = \sin\left(90^\circ - 135\right) = \sin\left(-45^\circ\right) = -\sin\left(45^\circ\right) = -\frac{\sqrt{2}}{2}.$$

3) Using the property $\sin(x) = \cos\left(90^\circ - x\right)$, we get

$$\sin\left(300^\circ\right) = \cos\left(90^\circ - 300^\circ\right) = \cos\left(-210^\circ\right).$$

Now use this property: $\cos(-x) = \cos(x)$. Therefore:

$$\cos\left(-210^\circ\right) = \cos\left(210^\circ\right) = \sin(90^\circ - 210^\circ) = -\sin(120^\circ)$$
$$= -\cos(90^\circ - 120^\circ) = -\cos(30^\circ) = -\frac{\sqrt{3}}{2}.$$

4) Using the property $\cos(x) = \cos\left(360^\circ - x\right)$, we get

$$\cos\left(420^\circ\right) = \cos\left(360^\circ - 420^\circ\right) = \cos\left(-60^\circ\right)$$

Now use this property: $\cos\left(-x\right) = \cos\left(x\right)$. Therefore:

$$\cos\left(420^\circ\right) = \cos\left(60^\circ\right) = \frac{1}{2}.$$

5) By definition, $\cot(\phi)$ is the reciprocal of $\tan(\phi)$. So, it is true that $\tan(\phi) = \frac{1}{\cot(\phi)}$.

6) In a right triangle, as θ increases from 0° to 90°, the value of $\cos\theta$ decreases from 1 to 0. However, it is not accurate to say it "always" decreases because once θ surpasses 90°, it is no longer an angle in a right triangle.

7) Not always. The cosecant of an angle can be less than or equal to 1 depending on the size of the angle.

8) This is true because in a right angled triangle, the side opposite to angle α cannot be longer than hypotenuse. Hence $\sin(\alpha)$ which is the ratio of opposite side to hypotenuse cannot exceed 1.

9) This is true due to the Pythagorean identity $\sin^2(\beta) + \cos^2(\beta) = 1$, which implies that $\cos(\beta) = \sqrt{1 - \sin^2(\beta)}$.

10) Dividing the Pythagorean identity by $\sin^2\theta$ gives $1 + \cot^2\theta = \csc^2\theta$.

11) Dividing the Pythagorean identity by $\cos^2\theta$ gives $\tan^2\theta + 1 = \sec^2\theta$.

12) The fundamental Pythagorean identity is $\sin^2\theta + \cos^2\theta = 1$.

13) The fundamental Pythagorean identity is $\sin^2\theta + \cos^2\theta = 1$.

14) Dividing the Pythagorean identity by $\sin^2\theta$ gives $1 + \cot^2\theta = \csc^2\theta$.

15) The equation $x^2 + y^2 = 1$ represents a circle of radius 1 centered at the origin.

16) In standard position, an angle's initial side is always along the positive x-axis.

17) For any point $P(x,y)$ on the unit circle, the y-coordinate gives the value of $\sin\theta$ and the x-coordinate gives the value of $\cos\theta$.

18) As its name suggests, the unit circle has a radius of 1 unit.

19) The unit circle is centered at the origin of the coordinate plane, which is the point $(0,0)$.

20) If you type $\sin(300°)$ into a calculator set to degree mode, the output will be approximately -0.8660.

21) If you type $\cos(210°)$ into a calculator in degree mode, the output will be approximately -0.8660.

22) If you calculate $\tan(\frac{\pi}{6})$ on a calculator set to radian mode, the output will be approximately 0.5774.

23) If you type $\sin(\frac{7\pi}{6})$ into a calculator in radian mode, you will receive -0.5.

24) If you calculate $\tan(225°)$ on a calculator set to degree mode, the output will be 1.

25) Using the formula $Radian = Degree \times \frac{\pi}{180}$, we substitute 60 for Degree and find that the radian measure is $\frac{\pi}{3}$.

26) Using $Degrees = Radian \times \frac{180}{\pi}$ and substituting $\frac{7\pi}{6}$ for Radian, we find that the degree measure is 210.

27) Using $Radian = Degree \times \frac{\pi}{180}$, we substitute 225 for Degree and find that the radian measure is $\frac{5\pi}{4}$.

28) Using $Degrees = Radian \times \frac{180}{\pi}$ and substituting $\frac{2\pi}{3}$ for Radian, we find that the degree measure is 120.

29) Using $Radian = Degree \times \frac{\pi}{180}$, we substitute 330 for Degree and find that the radian measure is $\frac{11\pi}{6}$.

30) First, we add 360° to $-225°$ to obtain a coterminal angle within the range 0 to 360° which results in 135°. The angle 135° lies in quadrant II, where the y-values are positve. The reference angle for 135° can be found by subtracting it from 180°, which yields 45°. Therefore, $\sin(-225°) = \sin(45°) = \frac{\sqrt{2}}{2}$.

31) The angle 300° lies in quadrant IV, where the x-values are positive. The reference angle can be found by subtracting 360° from 300°, which gives us 60°. Therefore, $\cos(300°) = \cos(60°) = \frac{1}{2}$.

32) The angle 210° lies in quadrant III, where both the x- and y-values are negative. Therefore, its tan is positive. The reference angle can be found by subtracting 180° from 210°, which gives us 30°. Therefore, $\tan(210°) = \tan(30°) = \frac{\sqrt{3}}{3}$.

33) The angle $-60°$ lies in quadrant IV, where the x-values are positive and y-values are negative. Therefore, $\cot(-60°) = -\cot(60°) = -\frac{\sqrt{3}}{3}$.

34) The angle $150°$ lies in quadrant II, where the y-values are positive. The reference angle can be found by subtracting $180°$ from $150°$, which gives us $30°$. Therefore, $\csc(150°) = \csc(30°) = 2$.

35) The area of a sector cannot be determined without knowing the radius of the circle, as the radius is a part of the formula for finding the area of a sector.

36) The central angle is a key part of the arc length formula. A larger central angle will result in a larger arc length, assuming the radius is the same.

37) Yes, the area of a sector is indeed a portion of the area of the entire circle. The portion is determined by the ratio of the central angle to 360 degrees.

38) The arc length is not always half the radius of the circle. Instead, it depends on the both radius and the central angle of the sector.

39) Yes, an arc length can never be larger than the circumference of the circle because the arc length is a part of the circle's circumference.

13. Sequences and Series

13.1 Arithmetic Sequences

In mathematics, an arithmetic sequence is a list of numbers where the difference between consecutive terms, known as the *common difference d*, is constant. For example, in the sequence $6, 8, 10, 12, 14, \cdots$, the common difference is 2. The general form of an arithmetic sequence is $a, a+d, a+2d, a+3d, \cdots$, with a as the first term. The n-th term, x_n, is found using $x_n = a + (n-1)d$.

🔔 Key Point

To find any term in an arithmetic sequence, use the formula:

$$x_n = a + (n-1)d,$$

where a is the first term, d is the common difference, and n is the term number.

Example: Find the first five terms of an arithmetic sequence with $x_8 = 38$ and $d = 3$.

Solution: First, in order to determine the first five terms of the sequence, we need to find the value of x_1 or a. We can use the arithmetic sequence formula: $x_n = a + d(n-1)$. Given that $x_8 = 38$, we know that $n = 8$. We substitute these values into the formula:

$$38 = a + 3(8-1) = a + 21 \Rightarrow a = 38 - 21 = 17.$$

Therefore, the first five terms of the sequence are: 17, 20, 23, 26, and 29.

13.2 Geometric Sequences

In geometric sequences, each term (excluding the first) is the result of multiplying the previous term by a fixed, non-zero common ratio r. For example, in the sequence $2, 4, 8, 16, 32, \ldots$, the common ratio r is 2. Geometric sequences are characterized by this common ratio, and to find a specific term without listing all preceding ones, use the formula $x_n = ar^{(n-1)}$ with n as the term number, x_n as the n-th term, a as the first term, and r as the common ratio.

Key Point

To find any term in a geometric sequence, use the formula:

$$x_n = ar^{(n-1)},$$

where n is the term number, x_n is the n-th term, a is the first term, and r is the common ratio.

This can be seen in the following example:

Example: Given the first term and the common ratio of a geometric sequence, find the first five terms of the sequence; $a = 3$ and $r = -2$.

Solution: We will use the geometric sequence formula:

$$x_n = ar^{(n-1)} \Rightarrow x_n = 3(-2)^{(n-1)}.$$

For $n = 1$, we get $x_1 = 3(-2)^{(1-1)} = 3(1) = 3$. The full series is then: 3, -6, 12, -24, and 48.

13.3 Finite Arithmetic Series

The sum of the members of a finite arithmetic sequence, known as an arithmetic series, can be calculated using the formula:

$$S_n = \frac{1}{2}n(2a + d(n-1)),$$

where n is the number of terms, S_n is the sum of the first n terms, a is the first term, and d is the common difference. An even more concise form of this formula is:

$$S_n = \frac{1}{2}n(a + x_n),$$

where x_n is the n-th term. This formula is particularly useful for practical calculations in arithmetic series.

🔔 **Key Point**

The sum of an arithmetic series is given by the formula:

$$S_n = \frac{1}{2}n(2a + d(n-1)),$$

where n is the number of terms, a is the first term, and d is the common difference. A more concise form of the formula is: $S_n = \frac{1}{2}n(a + x_n)$, where x_n is the n-th term.

Example: In the arithmetic series 4, 11, 18, $\cdots$ find the sum of the first 10 terms.

Solution: To start off, we identify a as 4, our constant difference d as $11 - 4 = 7$, and the number of terms n as 10. We can then use the arithmetic series formula $S_n = \frac{1}{2}n[2a + d(n-1)]$ to find our answer:

$$S_{10} = \frac{10}{2}[2(4) + 7(10-1)] = 5(8 + 63) = 355.$$

13.4   Finite Geometric Series

The finite geometric series formula is given as:

$$S_n = \sum_{k=1}^{n} x_k = \sum_{k=1}^{n} ar^{(k-1)} = a\left(\frac{1-r^n}{1-r}\right).$$

where n is the number of terms in the series, S_n is the sum of the first n terms of the geometric series, a is the first term, and r is the common ratio.

Key Point

The formula for the sum S_n of a finite geometric series is: $S_n = a\left(\frac{1-r^n}{1-r}\right)$, where n is the term count, a is the initial term, and r is the common ratio.

Example: Consider a geometric series given by the expression $3^{(n-1)}$. Find the sum of the first 4 terms.

  Solution: To find the sum of the first 4 terms, we apply the Finite Geometric Series formula with $a = 1$, $r = 3$, and $n = 4$.

$$S_4 = a\left(\frac{1-r^n}{1-r}\right) = 1\left(\frac{1-3^4}{1-3}\right) = 40.$$

So, the sum of the first 4 terms is 40.

13.5   Infinite Geometric Series

A geometric series is said to be infinite when there are unlimited terms (i.e., it goes on indefinitely). For an Infinite Geometric Series, the sum can be finite or infinite. It all depends on the common ratio, r. Its sum is finite when $|r| < 1$ and infinite when $|r| \geq 1$. The formula for the sum of an infinite geometric series with first term a and common ratio r ($|r| < 1$) is: $S = \frac{a}{1-r}$.

Key Point

Infinite Geometric Series:

- The sum is infinite when the absolute value of the ratio is greater than 1.
- Formula: $S = \frac{a}{1-r}$ with first term a and common ratio r where $|r| < 1$.

Example: Consider the Infinite Geometric Series $S = 1 - \frac{1}{2} + \frac{1}{4} - \frac{1}{8} + \cdots$. Find S.

  Solution: This series has a first term $a = 1$ and a common ratio $r = -\frac{1}{2}$. Since $|r| = \frac{1}{2} < 1$, the sum of the series will be finite. We want to calculate the sum. Let's substitute the values of a and r into the Infinite Geometric Series formula, we have:

$$S = \frac{1}{1-(-\frac{1}{2})} = \frac{1}{1+\frac{1}{2}} = \frac{1}{\frac{3}{2}} = \frac{2}{3}.$$

Therefore, the sum of the Infinite Geometric Series is $\frac{2}{3}$.

Example: Find the infinite sum of geometric series given by $\left(-\frac{2}{3}\right)^{(n-1)}$.

Solution: From the formula, we can deduce that the first term a is 1 and the common ratio r is $-\frac{2}{3}$, hence $|r| < 1$ and the sum of the series is finite. We can therefore calculate the sum using the Infinite Geometric Series formula as follows:

$$S = \frac{a}{1-r} = \frac{1}{1-\left(-\frac{2}{3}\right)} = \frac{1}{\frac{5}{3}} = \frac{3}{5}.$$

So, the sum of the Infinite Geometric Series with the given description is $\frac{3}{5}$.

13.6   Pascal's Triangle

Pascal's Triangle is a triangular array of numbers with the top element as 1. Rows are constructed by adding the two diagonal numbers above, with 1s on the edges. Rows start from 0 at the top, and entries are numbered from left, beginning with 0, staggered relative to adjacent rows.

Now, let us create an image of Pascal's Triangle with 8 rows:

```
                    1
                 1     1
              1     2     1
           1     3     3     1
        1     4     6     4     1
     1     5    10    10     5     1
  1     6    15    20    15     6     1
1     7    21    35    35    21     7     1
1  8   28   56   70   56   28   8   1
```

Key Point

In Pascal's Triangle, the n-th row (starting from 0) has $n+1$ entries. The k-th entry of this row is equal to $\binom{n}{k} = \dfrac{n!}{k!(n-k)!}$, where n is the row number, and k is the position of the entry within that row, starting from 0.

Example: Build the third row of Pascal's Triangle.

Solution: The third row starts and ends with 1. The other numbers must be derived from the second row. Hence, $1+2=3$ and $2+1=3$. So, the third row (starting from 0) of Pascal's Triangle is $1,3,3,1$.

Example: What is the fifth entry (starting from 0) of the 7-th row of Pascal's Triangle?

Solution: According to the key point above, the k-th entry of the n-th row is equal to $\binom{n}{k}$. So, the fifth entry of the 7-th row corresponds to $\binom{7}{5} = \frac{7!}{5!2!}$, which equals 21.

13.7 Binomial Theorem

The Binomial Theorem for positive integer n is given by:

$$(x+y)^n = \sum_{k=0}^{n} \binom{n}{k} x^{n-k} y^k,$$

where $\binom{n}{k} = \dfrac{n!}{k!(n-k)!}$ is the binomial coefficient. This formula has $n+1$ terms, corresponding to the entries in the n-th row of Pascal's Triangle. Each term can be determined as $\binom{n}{k-1} x^{n-k+1} y^{k-1}$.

🔔 Key Point

In the expansion of $(x+y)^n$, the exponents on x start with n and decrease, while the exponents on y start with 0 and increase. The powers on x and y always add up to n in each term.

Example: Expand the expression $(x+y)^4$.

Solution: We have $n = 4$, therefore:

$$(x+y)^4 = \binom{4}{0} x^4 + \binom{4}{1} x^3 y + \binom{4}{2} x^2 y^2 + \binom{4}{3} x^1 y^3 + \binom{4}{4} x^0 y^4.$$

This reduces to:

$$x^4 + 4x^3 y + 6x^2 y^2 + 4xy^3 + y^4.$$

Notice how each term involves a power of x and a power of y, and these always add up to 4. Additionally, the coefficients match with the 4-th row from Pascal's triangle.

Example: Determine the 3rd term in the expansion of $(a-1)^5$.

Solution: We will use the formula for the k-th term. The third term is

$$\binom{5}{3-1}(a)^{(5-3+1)}(-1)^{(3-1)} = \binom{5}{2}(a)^3(-1)^2.$$

This gives us $10a^3$.

Example: Use the binomial theorem to expand the expression $(2b+2)^3$.

Solution: We can use the binomial theorem to expand $(2b+2)^3$ by substituting $x=2b$ and $y=2$, with $n=3$. So, we get:

$$(2b+2)^3 = \binom{3}{0}(2b)^3 + \binom{3}{1}(2b)^2(2)$$

$$+ \binom{3}{2}(2b)(2)^2 + \binom{3}{3}(2)^3 = 8b^3 + 24b^2 + 24b + 8.$$

13.8   Sigma Notation (Summation Notation)

The Greek letter Σ (Sigma) is used in mathematics to represent the sum of a sequence of numbers. It is particularly helpful when dealing with sequences where each term is a function of its term number. The sum notation is expressed as: $\sum_{i=m}^{n} f(i)$. In this notation, i is the indexing variable that varies from m to n, and $f(i)$ represents the expression to be summed.

🔔 **Key Point**

Summation notation is a powerful tool for working with sequences and series and makes calculations much easier.

Example: Find the sum of the series $\sum_{i=1}^{5} i^2$.

Solution: In the sum $\sum_{i=1}^{5} i^2$, our function is $f(i) = i^2$. To find the sum:

For $i=1$, we have $1^2 = 1$.

For $i=2$, we have $2^2 = 4$.

For $i=3$, we have $3^2 = 9$.

For $i = 4$, we have $4^2 = 16$.

For $i = 5$, we have $5^2 = 25$.

Adding these terms together, we get the total sum 55.

The Sigma notation can also be applied to sequences described by a formula.

Example: Find the sum of the series for $n = 1, 2, 3, 4$ represented by the function $f(n) = \frac{n^2}{2}$ using summation notation.

Solution: Here, the sum becomes $\sum_{n=1}^{4} \frac{n^2}{2}$.

For $n = 1$, we have $\frac{1^2}{2} = \frac{1}{2}$.

For $n = 2$, we have $\frac{2^2}{2} = 2$.

For $n = 3$, we have $\frac{3^2}{2} = \frac{9}{2}$.

For $n = 4$, we have $\frac{4^2}{2} = 8$.

We add these terms to get the total sum $\frac{30}{2} = 15$.

13.9 Alternate Series

An alternate series is a special type of mathematical series. In its general form, it can be written as follows:

$$\sum_{k=1}^{\infty} (-1)^k a_k.$$

Where $a_k \geq 0$ and the starting index is arbitrary. This means that the term, with which the series starts, can be either positive or negative.

🔔 Key Point

The first term of an alternating series can be either positive or negative, depending on the index used to start the series.

An alternating series $\{a_n\}$ is termed convergent if it satisfies these conditions:

1. $0 \leq a_{n+1} \leq a_n$ for all $n \geq 1$, indicating non-increasing terms.

2. $a_n \to 0$ as $n \to \infty$, meaning the terms approach zero as the index approaches infinity.

🔔 **Key Point**

An alternating series is convergent if its terms approach 0, and each term is equal to or less than the preceding term.

Example: Determine whether the following series converge or diverge: $\sum_{i=1}^{\infty} (-1)^i \frac{2}{i+5}$.

    Solution: Let us check the two conditions for the series to be convergent: First, we consider $a_i = \frac{2}{i+5}$ and check if it approaches zero or not. As i approaches infinity, the denominator $i+5$ also approaches infinity. When you divide a constant 2 by an increasingly large number, the result approaches zero. Next, we compare the consecutive terms to see if each term is less than or equal to the preceding term: $0 \leq a_{k+1} \leq a_k$ implies $0 \leq \frac{2}{(i+1)+5} \leq \frac{2}{i+5}$ which simplifies to $0 \leq \frac{2}{i+6} \leq \frac{2}{i+5}$, leading us to the inequality $i+6 \geq i+5$ or $6 \geq 5$, which is true. Therefore, the given series is convergent.

13.10 Practices

🪑 **Fill in the Blank:**

1) An arithmetic sequence can be defined in the general form $a, a+\_, a+2\_, a+3\_, \cdots$.

2) In an arithmetic sequence, every term is obtained by adding the _____ to the preceding term.

3) The formula to find any term in an arithmetic sequence is $x_n = a + $_____.

4) When $a_5 = 20$ and $d = 3$ in an arithmetic sequence, then $a_3 = $_____.

5) An arithmetic sequence $2, 4, 6, 8, \ldots$, has common difference _____.

🪑 **Solve:**

6) The first term and the sum of first three terms of a geometric sequence are 2 and 14 respectively. Find the common ratio.

7) For a geometric sequence with positive common ratio, the second term is 8 and the fourth term is 2. Determine the first term and common ratio.

8) Find the 10th term of a geometric sequence whose first term is 1 and the sum of the first 10 terms is 1023.

9) If the fifth term of a geometric sequence is 10 and the eighth term is 80, calculate the second term.

10) For a geometric sequence with a positive common ratio, the 3rd term is 27 and the 5th term is 243. Identify the common ratio.

Solve:

11) Find the sum of the first 15 terms of the arithmetic series 2, 6, 10, $\cdots$.

12) In an arithmetic series where the first term is 7, the common difference is 3, and the number of terms is 9, what is the sum of these terms?

13) An arithmetic series has 10 terms with a first term of 5 and a last term of 23. Calculate the sum of the series.

14) In the arithmetic sequence 3, 7, 11, $\cdots$, find the sum of the first 20 terms.

15) An arithmetic series has 12 terms. The first term is 4 and the last term is 25. What is the sum of the series?

True/False:

16) Is it true that for a geometric series with $a = 3$ and $r = -2$, the sum of the first 5 terms is finite?

17) True or False? A geometric series with $a = 1$ and $r = 0.5$ will have an infinite sum if we try to add up an infinite number of terms.

18) True or False? For a geometric series where $a = 2$ and $r = 2$, the sum of the first 8 terms is finite.

19) Is it true that if $a = 0.1$ and $r = 2$, the sum of all terms in the geometric series will be finite?

20) True or False? For a geometric series with $a = -0.3$ and $r = -0.75$, the sum of all terms will be finite.

Solve:

21) Calculate the sum of the series: $5 + 2.5 + 1.25 + 0.625 + \ldots$.

22) Determine the sum of the following series: $3 - 1.5 + 0.75 - 0.375 + \ldots$.

23) Compute the sum of the series: $\left(-\frac{2}{3}\right) + \left(\frac{4}{9}\right) - \left(\frac{8}{27}\right) + \left(\frac{16}{81}\right) + \ldots$.

24) Find the sum of this series: $1 + \left(\frac{1}{2}\right) + \left(\frac{1}{4}\right) + \left(\frac{1}{8}\right) + \ldots$.

25) Determine the sum of the series: $-4 + 2 - 1 + \frac{1}{2} - \frac{1}{4} + \ldots$.

True/False:

26) The k-th entry of the n-th row of Pascal's Triangle is $\binom{k}{n}$. True/False?

27) Every row of Pascal's Triangle sums up to 2^n. True/False?

28) Pascal's Triangle can be used to calculate coefficients in polynomials' expansions. True/False?

29) The first row of Pascal's triangle is 2. True/False?

30) The nth row of Pascal's Triangle (starting from 0) has exactly n entries. True/False?

Solve:

31) Find the value of $\sum_{i=1}^{5} i$.

32) Find the value of $\sum_{i=1}^{4} 2i$.

33) Compute the value of $\sum_{i=2}^{6} 4$.

34) Find the value of $\sum_{i=1}^{5} (2i + 1)$.

35) Find the value of $\sum_{i=1}^{4} (3i^2 - 2i + 1)$.

Fill in the Blank:

36) For an alternating series $\sum_{k=1}^{\infty} (-1)^k a_k$ to be convergent, the terms must approach _____ as the index goes to ∞.

37) The first term of an alternating series can be either _____ or _____, depending on the index used to start the series.

38) If _____ $\leq a_{k+1} \leq a_k$ for all $k \geq 1$, this implies the terms of the series are either constant or _____ in magnitude.

39) An alternating sum would _____ if terms of the series do not approach 0 as k approaches ∞.

40) The general form of an alternating series is _____, where $a_k \geq 0$.

Answer Keys

1) d

2) common difference

3) $d(n-1)$

4) 14

5) 2

6) 2 or -3

7) 16, 0.5

8) 512

9) 1.25

10) 3

11) 450

12) 171

13) 140

14) 820

15) 174

16) True

17) False

18) True

19) False

20) True

21) 10

22) 2

23) $-\frac{2}{5}$

24) 2

25) $-\frac{8}{3}$

26) False

27) True

28) True

29) False

30) False

31) 15

32) 20

33) 20

34) 35

35) 74

36) 0

37) positive, negative

38) 0, decreasing

39) Diverge

40) $\sum_{k=1}^{\infty} (-1)^k a_k$

Answers with Explanation

1) The common difference d is the value by which each succeeding term increases in an arithmetic sequence.

2) Every term in an arithmetic sequence is obtained by adding the common difference to the preceding term.

3) The formula to find the nth term in an arithmetic sequence is $x_n = a + d(n-1)$.

4) From the given $x_5 = 20$ and $d = 3$, we can calculate $x_3 = x_5 - 2d = 20 - 2(3) = 14$.

5) The common difference can found by subtracting the first term from the second term in the sequence. In this case, $4 - 2 = 2$.

6) The sum of first three terms in a geometric series is given by $S_3 = \dfrac{a(r^3 - 1)}{r - 1}$, substituting given values and solving for r, we get $r = 2$ or $r = -3$.

7) We have $x_2 = ar$ and $x_4 = ar^3$. By dividing $\frac{x_4}{x_2}$ and canceling a, we find $r^2 = \frac{1}{4}$. Since r is positive, we get $r = 0.5$. Substituting r into $x_2 = ar$ gives $a = 16$.

8) The sum of the first ten terms gives $S_{10} = \dfrac{a(r^{10} - 1)}{r - 1} = 1023$, so $r = 2$. The tenth term is then $x_{10} = ar^{(10-1)} = 1 \times 2^9 = 512$.

9) From $x_5 = ar^4 = 10$ and $x_8 = ar^7 = 80$, we can get that $r = 2$ and $a = 0.625$. So the second term is $x_2 = ar = 0.625 \times 2 = 1.25$.

10) By writing $x_3 = ar^2 = 27$ and $x_5 = ar^4 = 243$ and dividing, we get $r^2 = 9$, so $r = 3$.

11) To find the sum, we first identify $a_1 = 2$, $d = 4$, and $n = 15$. Using the formula

$$S_n = \frac{1}{2}n(2a + d(n-1)),$$

we get $S_{15} = \frac{15}{2}(2(2) + 4(15 - 1)) = 450$.

12) Using the formula $S_n = \frac{1}{2}n(2a+d(n-1))$, we substitute $n=9$, $a=7$, and $d=3$ to get $S_9 = \frac{9}{2}(2(7) + 3(9-1)) = 171$.

13) Using the formula $S_n = \frac{1}{2}n(a+x_n)$, with $n=10$, $a=5$, and $x_{10} = 23$, we get

$$S_{10} = \frac{1}{2}(10)(5+23) = 140.$$

14) Here, $a=3$, $n=20$, $d=7-3=4$, using the formula $S_n = \frac{1}{2}n(2a+d(n-1))$, we calculate the sum

$$S_{20} = \frac{20}{2}(2(3)+4(20-1)) = 820.$$

15) Here, $a=4$, $x_{12} = 25$, and $n=12$, plug these into the formula $S_n = \frac{1}{2}n(a+x_n)$ to get

$$S_{12} = \frac{12}{2}(4+25) = 174.$$

16) The absolute value of r is 2, which is greater than 1. However, the sum of a finite number of terms in a geometric series is always finite, irrespective of the ratio.

17) The absolute value of r is 0.5, which is less than 1. Thus, the sum of an infinite number of terms in this series will be finite.

18) Irrespective of the value of r, the sum of a finite number of terms in a geometric series is always finite.

19) The absolute value of r is 2, which is greater than 1. Thus, if we attempt to sum up an infinite number of terms in this series, we would get an infinite sum.

20) The absolute value of r is 0.75, which is less than 1. Thus, the sum of an infinite number of terms in this series will be finite.

21) Here, the first term a is 5 and the common ratio r is $\frac{1}{2}$. The sum of the series, S, can be calculated as $S = \frac{5}{1-\frac{1}{2}} = 10$.

22) Here, $a=3$ and $r=-\frac{1}{2}$. Hence, the sum of the series, S, can be obtained as $S = \frac{3}{1-(-\frac{1}{2})} = 2$.

23) Here, $a = -\frac{2}{3}$ and $r = -\frac{2}{3}$. Therefore, the sum of the series, S, is $S = \frac{-\frac{2}{3}}{1-(-\frac{2}{3})} = -\frac{2}{5}$.

24) Here, $a = 1$ and $r = \frac{1}{2}$. Thus, the sum of the series, S, is $S = \frac{1}{1-\frac{1}{2}} = 2$.

25) Here, $a = -4$ and $r = -\frac{1}{2}$. Hence, the sum of the series, S, can be found as $S = \frac{-4}{1-(-\frac{1}{2})} = -\frac{8}{3}$.

26) This is false. The k-th entry of the n-th row of Pascal's Triangle is $\binom{n}{k}$, not $\binom{k}{n}$.

27) This is true. The sum of the entries of the nth row of Pascal's Triangle is indeed 2^n.

28) This is true. Pascal's triangle gives the coefficients in binomial expansions, which are polynomials.

29) This is false. The first row of Pascal's Triangle is $1, 1$, not 2.

30) This is false. The nth row of Pascal's Triangle has $n+1$ entries when numbering starts at row 0.

31) The sum goes from $i = 1$ to $i = 5$, and we add each value of i: $1+2+3+4+5 = 15$.

32) The sum goes from $i = 1$ to $i = 4$, and for each i, we add $2i$:

$$(2 \times 1) + (2 \times 2) + (2 \times 3) + (2 \times 4) = 2+4+6+8 = 20.$$

33) The sum goes from $i = 2$ to $i = 6$, and for each i, we add the value 4. So, this is simply $4 \times 5 = 20$, because there are 5 terms between 2 and 6 (inclusive).

34) The sum goes from $i = 1$ to $i = 5$, and for each i, we add $2i + 1$:

$$(2 \times 1 + 1) + (2 \times 2 + 1) + (2 \times 3 + 1) + (2 \times 4 + 1) + (2 \times 5 + 1) = 3+5+7+9+11 = 35.$$

35) The sum goes from $i = 1$ to $i = 4$, and for each i, we add $3i^2 - 2i + 1$:

$$(3(1)^2 - 2(1) + 1) + (3(2)^2 - 2(2) + 1) + (3(3)^2 - 2(3) + 1) + (3(4)^2 - 2(4) + 1) = 74.$$

36) For an alternating series to be convergent, the terms of the series must approach 0 as the index goes to ∞.

37) The first term of an alternating series can be either positive or negative, depending on the index used to start the series.

38) If $0 \leq a_{k+1} \leq a_k$ for all $k \geq 1$, this implies the terms of the series are either constant or decreasing in magnitude.

39) An alternating series will diverge if the terms of the series do not approach 0 as the index goes to ∞.

40) The general form of an alternating series is $\sum_{k=1}^{\infty} (-1)^k a_k$, where $a_k \geq 0$.

It is Time to Test Yourself

In the following, there are two complete College Algebra Tests. Once you've completed them, evaluate your performance by using the provided answer key.

- **Gather your supplies:** Ensure you have a pencil and a calculator ready before starting the test.

- **Question types:** There are two types of questions you'll encounter:

  1) **Multiple choice** questions where have four or more answer choices for these questions.

  2) **Grid-ins questions**: You'll need to write your answer in the provided box.

- **Don't be afraid to guess:** It's perfectly fine to make educated guesses. Remember, there are no penalties for wrong answers.

- **Review your work:** After completing the test, take some time to go over the answer key. It will help you identify where you made mistakes and areas that need improvement.

- **Stay calm and confident:** Believe in yourself and your abilities. You've got this!

14. Practice Test 1

College Algebra Practice Test

Total number of questions: 60

Time: 90 Minutes

Calculator is permitted for College Algebra Test.

14.1 Practices

1) Which of the following points lies on the line $3x - 6y = 9$?

☐ A. $(3, 1)$

☐ B. $(1, 1)$

☐ C. $(0, -1.5)$

☐ D. $(2, -2)$

☐ E. $(3, -2)$

2) What is the equation of the graph depicted below?

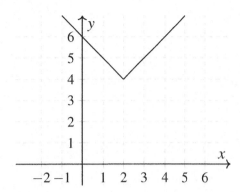

☐ A. $y = |x - 2| + 4$

☐ B. $y = |x + 3| + 1$

☐ C. $y = |x| + 2$

☐ D. $y = |x - 1| - 3$

☐ E. $y = |x + 4| - 2$

3) Solve for m, where $m \in \mathbb{N}$: $\frac{(m+3)!}{(m)!} = 120$. (Write the answer in the following box) ☐

4) The ratio of girls to boys in a class is $3 : 4$. If there are 420 students in the class, how many girls are in the class?

☐ A. 240

☐ B. 180

☐ C. 210

☐ D. 280

☐ E. 150

5) Simplify the expression: $(6x - 3y)(4x + 5y) = ?$

☐ A. $24x^2 - 7xy - 15y^2$

☐ B. $24x^2 + 18xy - 15y^2$

☐ C. $24x^2 + 30xy - 15y^2$

☐ D. $24x^2 + 12xy + 15y^2$

☐ E. $24x^2 + 33xy + 15y^2$

6) Which of the following expressions is equivalent to $4x(5 + 3y)$?

☐ A. $20x + 12xy$

☐ B. $4x + 12xy$

☐ C. $20x + 7xy$

☐ D. $9x + 12xy$

☐ E. $20x + 3xy$

7) Simplify $2 - \frac{1}{3-i}$ (Note: i is the complex number $\sqrt{-1}$).

☐ A. $\frac{1}{10}(17-i)$

☐ B. $\frac{1}{10}(5-3i)$

☐ C. $\frac{1}{10}(7+3i)$

☐ D. $2+\frac{3}{10}-\frac{i}{10}$

☐ E. $\frac{1}{5}(11-i)$

8) What is the 30th term of the arithmetic sequence $2, 7, 12, \cdots$?

☐ A. 145

☐ B. 147

☐ C. 149

☐ D. 151

☐ E. 153

9) What is the solution of the following inequality?

$$|x+5| \leq 4$$

☐ A. $x \geq -1$ or $x \leq -9$

☐ B. $-9 \leq x \leq -1$

☐ C. $-1 \leq x \leq 9$

☐ D. $x \geq -1$

☐ E. $x \leq -9$

10) Two fifths of 25 is equal to $\frac{1}{3}$ of what number?

☐ A. 15

☐ B. 30

☐ C. 45

☐ D. 75

☐ E. 90

11) The marked price of a smartphone is P dollars. Its price increased by 15% in March and later decreased by 10% in April. What is the final price of the smartphone in P dollars?

☐ A. $1.035\,P$

☐ B. $0.945\,P$

☐ C. $1.05\,P$

☐ D. $0.90\,P$

☐ E. $1.10\,P$

12) If $X = \{3, 6, 9, 12\}$, $Y = \{2, 3, 4, 5, 6, 7\}$, and $Z = \{6, 8, 10, 12, 14\}$, then which of the following sets is $(X \cup Y) \cap Z$?

☐ A. $\{2, 3, 4, 5, 6, 7, 8, 10, 12, 14\}$

☐ B. $\{2, 3, 4, 5, 6, 9, 12\}$

☐ C. $\{6, 8, 10, 12, 14\}$

☐ D. $\{6, 12\}$

☐ E. $\{12\}$

13) The first three terms in an arithmetic sequence are 7, 13, and 19. What is the 25th term in the sequence? (Write the answer in the following box)

14) The table shows the linear relationship between the balance of Mrs. Smith's savings account and the number of months she has been saving. Based on the table, what was the rate of change of the balance of her savings account in dollars per month?

week	0	2	5	7	10	12	15
Balance (dollars)	110	125	147.5	162.5	185	200	222.5

☐ A. 7.5

☐ B. 8.5

☐ C. 9

☐ D. 10

☐ E. 12.5

15) What are the solutions to the equation $3x^2 - 4x = 8$?

☐ A. $\frac{2 + 2\sqrt{7}}{3}$ and $\frac{2 - 2\sqrt{7}}{3}$

☐ B. $\frac{2 + \sqrt{7}}{3}$ and $\frac{2 - \sqrt{7}}{3}$

☐ C. 4 and $-\frac{2}{3}$

☐ D. -2 and 3

☐ E. −3 and 2

16) For what value of x is $|x+2|-2$ equal to 0?

☐ A. −4

☐ B. 0

☐ C. 2

☐ D. 4

☐ E. A and B

17) In 2005, the average company's revenue increased by $3,000$ per year starting from a base of $30,000$. Which equation represents a revenue greater than the average?

☐ A. $R > 3,000y + 30,000$

☐ B. $R > -3,000y + 30,000$

☐ C. $R < -3,000y + 30,000$

☐ D. $R < 3,000y - 30,000$

☐ E. $R < 28,000y + 30,000$

18) Given that 2 and 0 are zeros of $p(x) = x^4 + 2x^3 - 4x^2 - 8x$, what are the factors of $p(x)$?

☐ A. $\{x, x-2, x+2\}$

☐ B. $\{x, x^2 - 2\}$

☐ C. $\{x, x-2, x+3, x^2-2\}$

☐ D. $\{x+2, x-3, x^2+1\}$

☐ E. $\{x, x+2, x-3, x^2+1\}$

19) Which option correctly define the domain of $f(x) = 3 - \frac{2}{x+3}$?

☐ A. All real numbers

☐ B. $\mathbb{R} - \{3, -3\}$

☐ C. $\mathbb{R} - \{-3\}$

☐ D. $\mathbb{R} - \{3\}$

☐ E. $(-\infty, +\infty)$

20) The score of Leo was one third that of Mia, and the score of Zoe was twice that of Mia. If the score of Zoe was 60, what is the score of Leo?

  ☐ A. 10

  ☐ B. 20

  ☐ C. 30

  ☐ D. 40

  ☐ E. 50

21) If $C = \{2,4,6,8,10,12\}$ and $D = \{3,6,9,12,15,18\}$, how many elements are in $C \cup D$?

  ☐ A. 4

  ☐ B. 6

  ☐ C. 8

  ☐ D. 10

  ☐ E. 12

22) Which function does this graph represent?

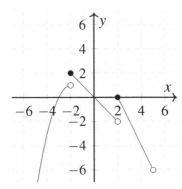

  ☐ A. $f(x) = \begin{cases} -(x+2)^2 + 1, & -\infty < x < -2 \\ |x-2| - 2, & -2 \leq x < 2 \\ -2x + 4, & 2 \leq x < 5 \end{cases}$

  ☐ B. $f(x) = x^3 - 3x^2 + 2x$

  ☐ C. $f(x) = \frac{x^2 + 2}{x - 1}$

  ☐ D. $f(x) = \begin{cases} x+1, & -\infty < x < -2 \\ |x-2| - 2, & -2 \leq x < 2 \\ -2x + 4, & 2 \leq x < 5 \end{cases}$

  ☐ E. $f(x) = x^2 - 4x + 4$

23) Which of the following inequality statements represents the set of possible values for the variable "v" that satisfies the inequality $3v + 5w \leq 39$, where $w = -3$?

☐ A. $v \leq 18$

☐ B. $v \leq -18$

☐ C. $v \leq 10$

☐ D. $v \geq 12$

☐ E. $v \geq -12$

24) Write in terms of $\log(x)$, $\log(y)$:

$$\log \frac{y^{\frac{1}{2}}}{5x^3y^2}$$

☐ A. $-\frac{3}{2}\log y - 3\log x - \log 5$

☐ B. $\log y + 3\log x - \log 5$

☐ C. $-\frac{1}{2}\log y - 3\log x - \log 5$

☐ D. $\frac{1}{2}\log y - 3\log x + \log 5$

☐ E. $-\frac{3}{2}\log y - 3\log x + \log 5$

25) If $\sqrt{3m-2} = m$, what is (are) the value(s) of m?

☐ A. 0

☐ B. 1

☐ C. 1, 2

☐ D. -1, 2

☐ E. -1, -2

26) When a number is added to 14 and the sum is divided by that number, the result is 4. What is the value of the number?

☐ A. 4

☐ B. $\frac{14}{3}$

☐ C. $\frac{7}{3}$

☐ D. $\frac{16}{3}$

☐ E. 7

27) Consider the expansion of $\left(2x^3 - 3\right)^3$. How many terms are there in this expansion? What is the coefficient of x^3?

☐ A. -27

☐ B. -54

☐ C. 18

☐ D. 54

☐ E. 27

28) The exponential growth function $f(x) = 2(4)^x$ is shown in the following table. Find the average rate of change over the interval $2 \leq x \leq 4$.

x	1	2	3	4	5
$f(x)$	8	32	128	512	2048

☐ A. 240

☐ B. 120

☐ C. 60

☐ D. 8

☐ E. 4

29) Find $\sum_{i=1}^{m}(2i+3)$.

☐ A. m

☐ B. $m+3$

☐ C. $m(m+3)$

☐ D. $\frac{m(m+1)}{2} + 3m$

☐ E. $m^2 + 4m$

30) Find the zeros of the following function: $g(x) = x^3 - 9x$. (Write the answer in the following box) ☐

31) If $y = mx + 3$, where m is a constant, and when $x = 8$, $y = 19$, what is the value of y when $x = 12$?

☐ A. 15

☐ B. 23

☐ C. 27

☐ D. 31

☐ E. 35

32) A chemical solution contains 8% sugar. If there is 32 *ml* of sugar, what is the volume of the solution?

☐ A. 300 *ml*

☐ B. 400 *ml*

☐ C. 800 *ml*

☐ D. 1,000 *ml*

☐ E. 4,000 *ml*

33) According to the graph, what is the minimum number of degrees of the function $h(x)$?

☐ A. 0

☐ B. 1

☐ C. 2

☐ D. 3

☐ E. 5

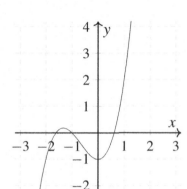

34) If the function $f(x)$ has three distinct zeros, which of the following could represent the graph of $f(x)$?

☐ A.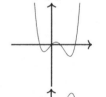

☐ B.

☐ C.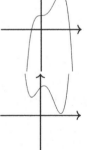

☐ D.

☐ E.

35) If 50% of y is equal to 25% of 40, then what is the value of $(y+4)^2$?

☐ A. 36

☐ B. 64

☐ C. 100

☐ D. 144

☐ E. 576

36) Multiply and write the product in scientific notation:

$$(3.2 \times 10^4) \times (2.5 \times 10^3)$$

☐ A. 8×10^6

☐ B. 8.0×10^7

☐ C. 7.5×10^7

☐ D. 8.0×10^8

☐ E. 7.5×10^8

37) If $2a + 3b = d$ and $abd = 24$. What is the value of $8a^3 + 27b^3 - d^3$?

☐ A. 216

☐ B. 72

☐ C. 24

☐ D. -144

☐ E. -432

38) 10 less than three times a positive integer is 83. What is the integer?

☐ A. 31

☐ B. 33

☐ C. 35

☐ D. 37

☐ E. 39

39) A laptop costing $1200 is discounted by 10%. After a week, the laptop is discounted by another 10%. Which of the following expressions can be used to find the selling price of the laptop?

☐ A. $(1200)(0.80)$

☐ B. $(1200) - 1200(0.20)$

☐ C. $(1200)(0.80) - (1200)(0.10)$

☐ D. $(1200)(0.90)(0.90)$

☐ E. $(1200)(0.90)(0.90) - (1200)(0.10)$

40) If $f(x) = x^3 - 3x^2 + 2x$, which of the following statements is correct?

I. The domain of $f(x)$ is all real numbers.

II. $f(x)$ has three real roots.

III. When $x \to +\infty$, $f(x) \to -\infty$.

IV. $f(x)$ is an odd function.

V. $f(x)$ has no real roots.

- ☐ A. I
- ☐ B. II
- ☐ C. I and II
- ☐ D. II and IV
- ☐ E. All of the statements are correct

41) Which of the following is the smallest?

- ☐ A. $|3-7|-|4|$
- ☐ B. $|2|+|-6|$
- ☐ C. $3|-1-4|$
- ☐ D. $|3-7|-|2-3|$
- ☐ E. $|4-5|+|5-4|$

42) If $g(x) = 4x + 3(x+2) + 1$, then $g(3x) =$?

- ☐ A. $21x+7$
- ☐ B. $18x+5$
- ☐ C. $15x-4$
- ☐ D. $13x+2$
- ☐ E. $12x-2$

43) A line in the $xy-$plane passes through the origin and has a slope of $\frac{2}{5}$. Which of the following points lies on the line?

- ☐ A. $(6,2)$
- ☐ B. $(10,4)$
- ☐ C. $(11,6)$
- ☐ D.$(24,10)$
- ☐ E. $(5,4)$

44) Which of the following is equivalent to $2m(m-2)+(7-3m^2+2m)$?

- ☐ A. $m+3$
- ☐ B. $m-5$
- ☐ C. m^2+7
- ☐ D. $m-4m^2$
- ☐ E. $-m^2-2m+7$

45) Given the table below for the polynomial function $g(x)$, determine the minimum degree of the function.

(Write the answer in the following box) ☐

x	$g(x)$
-3	4
-2	3
-1	-2
1	2
3	-5
5	-7

46) If $x \neq -3$ and $x \neq 4$, which of the following is equivalent to $\dfrac{1}{\frac{1}{x-4}+\frac{1}{x+3}}$?

- ☐ A. $\dfrac{(x-4)(x+3)}{(x-4)+(x+3)}$
- ☐ B. $\dfrac{(x+3)+(x-4)}{(x+3)(x-4)}$
- ☐ C. $\dfrac{(x+3)(x-4)}{(x+3)-(x-4)}$
- ☐ D. $\dfrac{(x+3)+(x-4)}{(x+3)-(x+4)}$
- ☐ E. $\dfrac{(x-3)+(x-4)}{(x+3)-(x-4)}$

47) The monthly cost of a membership at a wellness center can be found using the function $y=60x+20$, where x is the number of sessions a customer attends and y is the cost in dollars. The cost includes a flat fee for equipment use. If the fee for equipment use is not included, which statement is true?

- ☐ A. The cost is 20 dollars less per session.
- ☐ B. The cost is 20 dollars less.
- ☐ C. The cost is 20 dollars more per session.
- ☐ D. The cost is 20 dollars more.
- ☐ E. The cost is 60 dollars more per session.

48) After a ball is dropped from a height of 4.05 meters, it bounces several times, with each bounce reaching $\frac{3}{5}$ the height of the previous bounce. For example, after the first bounce, the ball bounces to a height of $4.05 \times \frac{3}{5}$ meters. Which of the following represents the total number of meters the ball travels up to the fifth bounce?

☐ A. $4.05 + \sum_{k=1}^{\infty} 4.05 \left(\frac{3}{5}\right)^k$

☐ B. $\sum_{k=1}^{5} 8.1 \left(\frac{3}{5}\right)^k$

☐ C. $4.05 + \sum_{k=1}^{\infty} 8.1 \left(\frac{3}{5}\right)^k$

☐ D. $4.05 + \sum_{k=1}^{4} 8.1 \left(\frac{3}{5}\right)^k$

☐ E. $4.05 + \sum_{k=1}^{5} 8.1 \left(\frac{3}{5}\right)^k$

49) Which statement about the quadratic equation below is true.

$$-2y^2 + 8y = 0$$

☐ A. The equation has $y = 0$ as its only solution.

☐ B. The equation has no real solutions.

☐ C. The equation has $y = 0$ and $y = 4$ as its only solutions.

☐ D. The equation has an infinite number of solutions.

☐ E. The equation has $y = -4$ as its only solution.

50) In the xy-plane, the graph of the function $f(x) = x^2 - 6x + 8$ has two x-intercepts. What is the distance between the x-intercepts?

☐ A. -3

☐ B. 2

☐ C. 3

☐ D. 6

☐ E. 12

51) Which of the points in the below figure represents the complex number $2i - 1$?

☐ A. A

☐ B. B

☐ C. C

☐ D. D

☐ E. E

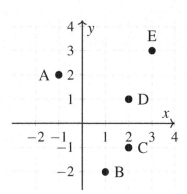

52) What is the value of $\log_5 \frac{\sqrt{125}\sqrt[4]{25}}{5}$?

☐ A. 8

☐ B. $\frac{1}{8}$

☐ C. $-\frac{1}{16}$

☐ D. $-\frac{1}{2}$

☐ E. 1

53) Determine the intervals where the function is decreasing. Write your answer in interval notation. (Write the answer in the following box) [   ]

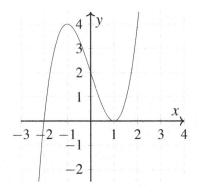

54) Which of the following is the expanded form of $(2-d)(3a-c+2)^2$?

☐ A. $18a^2 + 2c^2 - 12ac + 24a - 8c + 8 - 9da^2 - dc^2 + 6dac - 12da + 4dc - 4d$

☐ B. $18a^2 + c^2 + 6a - 3c - 6ac + 6da^2 - 7dc^2 + 6dac + 3dc - 6da - d + 4$

☐ C. $6a^2 + c^2 + 6a - 2c - 6ac - 6da^2 - dc^2 + 6dac + 3dc - 6da - d + 4$

☐ D. $9a^2 + c^2 + 12a - 4c - 6ac - 6da^2 - dc^2 + dac + 8dc - 6da - d + 4$

☐ E. $6a^2 + c^2 + 12a - 3c - 6ac - 6da^2 - 7dc^2 + 6dac + 3dc + 6da - 3d - 4$

55) The Greenfield Library is ordering new chairs. If y is the number of chairs the library wants to order, and each costs \$150 and there is a one-time delivery charge of \$450, which of the following represents the total cost, in dollars, per chair?

☐ A. $\frac{150y+450}{y}$

☐ B. $\frac{150y+450}{150}$

☐ C. $450y+450$

☐ D. $150+450y$

☐ E. $150y+450$

56) For functions h and j we have: $h(4) = 3$, $h(6) = 2$, $j(6) = 7$, and $j(2) = 5$. What is the value of $(j \circ h)(6)$?(Write the answer in the following box) ☐

57) Which function does the following graph represent?

☐ A. $f(x) = e^{x-3} + 1$

☐ B. $f(x) = e^{x+2}$

☐ C. $f(x) = e^{x-3} - 1$

☐ D. $f(x) = e^x - 2$

☐ E. $f(x) = \left(\frac{1}{3}\right)^{x-3} - 2$

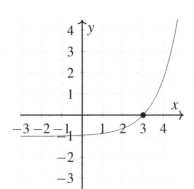

58) What is the coefficient of x^8 of $3x^2 \sum_{k=0}^{n} \frac{k+1}{3k+2} x^k$?

☐ A. $\frac{21}{9}$

☐ B. $\frac{21}{20}$

☐ C. $\frac{3}{4}$

☐ D. $\frac{4}{3}$

☐ E. $\frac{9}{20}$

59) Which graph could be used to find the solution of the system of equations $2x^2 - 8x = 12 - 4y$ and $4y + 6x = x^2 + 12$?

□ A.

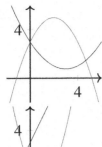

□ B.

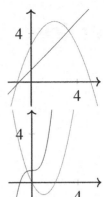

□ C.

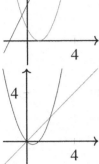

□ D.

□ E.

60) What is the inverse of the function $f(x) = (x+2)^2 - 2;$ $(x \leq -2)$?

□ A. $f^{-1}(x) = \sqrt{x+2} + 2$

□ B. $f^{-1}(x) = \sqrt{x+4} - 2$

□ C. $f^{-1}(x) = -\sqrt{x+2} - 2$

□ D. $f^{-1}(x) = \sqrt{x-2} + 2$

□ E. $f^{-1}(x) = \pm\sqrt{x-2} + 2$

14.2 Answer Keys

1) C. $(0, -1.5)$

2) A. $y = |x - 2| + 4$

3) $m = 2$

4) B. 180

5) B. $24x^2 + 18xy - 15y^2$

6) A. $20x + 12xy$

7) A. $\frac{1}{10}(17 - i)$

8) B. 147

9) B. $-9 \le x \le -1$

10) B. 30

11) A. $1.035 P$

12) D. $\{6, 12\}$

13) 151

14) A. 7.5

15) A. $\frac{2 + 2\sqrt{7}}{3}$ and $\frac{2 - 2\sqrt{7}}{3}$

16) E. A and B

17) A. $R > 3,000y + 30,000$

18) A. $\{x, x - 2, x + 2\}$

19) C. $\mathbb{R} - \{-3\}$

20) A. 10

21) D. 10

22) A. $f(x) = \begin{cases} -(x+2)^2 + 1, & -\infty < x < -2 \\ |x - 2| - 2, & -2 \le x < 2 \\ -2x + 4, & 2 \le x < 5 \end{cases}$

23) A. $v \le 18$

24) A. $-\frac{3}{2}\log y - 3\log x - \log 5$

25) C. 1, 2

26) B. $\frac{14}{3}$

27) D. 54

28) A. 240

29) E. $m^2 + 4m$

30) $0, \pm 3$

31) C. 27

32) B. 400 ml

33) D. 3

34) B.

35) E. 576

36) B. 8.0×10^7

37) E. -432

38) A. 31

39) D. $(1200)(0.90)(0.90)$

40) C. I and II

41) A. $|3 - 7| - |4|$

42) A. $21x + 7$

43) B. $(10, 4)$

44) E. $-m^2 - 2m + 7$

45) 3

46) A. $\frac{(x-4)(x+3)}{(x-4)+(x+3)}$

47) B. The cost is 20 dollars less.

48) E. $4.05 + \sum_{k=1}^{5} 8.1 \left(\frac{3}{5}\right)^k$

49) C.

50) B. 2

51) A. A

52) E. 1

53) $(-1, 1)$

54) A.

55) A. $\frac{150y+450}{y}$

56) 5

57) C. $f(x) = e^{x-3} - 1$

58) B. $\frac{21}{20}$

59) A.

60) C. $f^{-1}(x) = -\sqrt{x+2} - 2$

14.3   Answers with Explanation

1) To find which point lies on the line, substitute the x and y values from each option into the equation $3x - 6y = 9$. The only point that satisfies the equation is C:

$$(3 \times 0) - (6 \times -1.5) = 9.$$

Therefore, option C is the correct answer.

2) The equation $y = |x - 2| + 4$ represents a V-shaped graph with the vertex at $(2, 4)$. This is characteristic of an absolute value function, where the graph shifts 2 units to the right and 4 units up from the origin, matching the described graph. Thus, A is the correct equation.

3) Simplify the expression:

$$\frac{(m+3)!}{m!} = \frac{(m+3)(m+2)(m+1)m!}{m!} = (m+3)(m+2)(m+1) = 120.$$

Factoring 120, we find $120 = 5 \times 4 \times 3$, which corresponds to $m+3 = 5, m+2 = 4, m+1 = 3$. Therefore, $m = 2$, satisfying the condition for $m \in \mathbb{N}$.

4) The total ratio parts are $3 + 4 = 7$. Girls have 3 parts of this ratio. Therefore, to find the number of girls, multiply the total number of students by the fraction representing girls: $\frac{3}{7} \times 420 = 180$. Thus, there are 180 girls in the class.

5) Multiply the expressions: $(6x - 3y)(4x + 5y) = 24x^2 + 30xy - 12xy - 15y^2 = 24x^2 + 18xy - 15y^2$.

6) To simplify $4x(5 + 3y)$, distribute $4x$ across the terms inside the parentheses: $4x \times 5 + 4x \times 3y = 20x + 12xy$, making A the correct answer.

7) To simplify $2 - \frac{1}{3-i}$, first multiply the numerator and denominator by the conjugate of the denominator: $(3 + i)$. This gives $\frac{(3+i)}{(3-i)(3+i)} = \frac{3+i}{10}$. Subtracting this from 2 gives $2 - \frac{3}{10} - \frac{i}{10} = \frac{1}{10}(20 - 3 - i) = \frac{1}{10}(17 - i)$, making option A the correct answer.

8) The common difference in this sequence is 5. The nth term of an arithmetic sequence is given by

$a_n = a_1 + (n-1)d$. Substituting $a_1 = 2$, $d = 5$, and $n = 30$, we get $a_{30} = 2 + (30-1) \times 5 = 2 + 145 = 147$.

9) This gives two cases: $x + 5 \leq 4$ and $x + 5 \geq -4$. Solving these gives $x \leq -1$ and $x \geq -9$, respectively. Therefore, $-9 \leq x \leq -1$ is the correct answer.

10) Two fifths of 25 is $25 \times \frac{2}{5} = 10$. To find the number that 10 is $\frac{1}{3}$ of, set up the equation $10 = \frac{1}{3}x$. Solving for x gives $x = 30$, making B the correct answer.

11) First, the price increases by 15%, making it $P \times 1.15$. Then, it decreases by 10%, making the final price $P \times 1.15 \times 0.9 = 1.035P$, indicating that A is the correct answer.

12) First, form the union of X and Y: $\{2,3,4,5,6,7,9,12\}$. Next, find the intersection of this set with Z: $\{6,12\}$. Therefore, D is the correct answer.

13) The common difference in this sequence is 6. The nth term of an arithmetic sequence is given by $a_n = a_1 + (n-1)d$. Substituting $a_1 = 7$, $d = 6$, and $n = 25$, we get $a_{25} = 7 + (25-1) \times 6 = 7 + 144 = 151$.

14) In a linear relationship between two variables, the rate of change is equal to the slope of the line that passes through these given points. Therefore, to evaluate the rate of change, we calculate the slope of the line passing through (any) two points such as $(2, 125)$ and $(5, 147.5)$. So, $m = \frac{147.5 - 125}{5 - 2} = 7.5$.

15) First, rearrange the equation to $3x^2 - 4x - 8 = 0$. Using the quadratic formula, $x = \frac{-b \pm \sqrt{b^2 - 4ac}}{2a}$, where $a = 3$, $b = -4$, and $c = -8$. Substituting these values gives $x = \frac{4 \pm \sqrt{(-4)^2 - 4 \times 3 \times (-8)}}{2 \times 3}$. This simplifies to $x = \frac{4 \pm \sqrt{16 + 96}}{6} = \frac{4 \pm \sqrt{112}}{6}$, which simplifies further to the roots $\frac{2 + 2\sqrt{7}}{3}$ and $\frac{2 - 2\sqrt{7}}{3}$, which is option B.

16) The expression $|x + 2| - 2 = 0$ simplifies to $|x + 2| = 2$. The absolute value of $x + 2$ can be 2, leading to $x + 2 = 2$ or $x + 2 = -2$. Solving these gives $x = 0$ or $x = -4$, Hence, option E is correct.

17) The equation for revenue, R, the average after y years from 2005 would be $R = 3,000y + 30,000$. This represents a linear increase in revenue, where y is the number of years after 2005, and $30,000$ is the starting revenue. Any revenue more than that is $R > 3,000y + 30,000$.

18) Performing synthetic division by $x - 2$:

$$\begin{array}{r|rrrr} 2 & 1 & 2 & -4 & -8 \\ \hline & 1 & 4 & 4 & 0 \end{array}$$

So, $p(x) = (x-2)(x^3 + 4x^2 + 4x)$, Now, performing synthetic division by x:

$$\begin{array}{r|rrrr} 0 & 1 & 4 & 4 & 0 \\ \hline & 1 & 4 & 4 & 0 \end{array}$$

So, $p(x) = (x-2)(x)(x^2 + 4x + 4) = (x-2)(x)(x+2)^2$, Therefore, the factors of $p(x)$ are $(x-2),(x)$ and $(x+2)$.

19) The function $f(x) = 3 - \frac{2}{x+3}$ is undefined when the denominator is 0, which occurs when $x = -3$. Therefore, the domain of $f(x)$ is all real numbers except -3, making C the correct answer.

20) Given that Zoe's score is twice Mia's, and Mia's score is $\frac{60}{2} = 30$. Leo's score is one third of Mia's, which is $\frac{30}{3} = 10$. Therefore, Leo's score is 10, making A the correct answer.

21) Combining sets C and D and removing duplicates gives $\{2, 3, 4, 6, 8, 9, 10, 12, 15, 18\}$, which contains 10 unique elements. Therefore, D is the correct answer.

22) This piecewise function represents segments of a parabola, an absolute value function, and a linear function, which could correspond to the given graph's features such as curvature, vertex, and slope changes at specified intervals, making A the most likely match.

23) Substituting $w = -3$ into the inequality $3v + 5(-3) \leq 39$ gives $3v - 15 \leq 39$, which simplifies to $3v \leq 54$. Dividing by 3 gives $v \leq 18$.

24) Using the logarithm properties, the expression simplifies to $\frac{1}{2}\log y - 3\log x - 2\log y - \log 5$, which can be further simplified to $-\frac{3}{2}\log y - 3\log x - \log 5$, correctly representing the logarithmic expression in terms of $\log(x)$ and $\log(y)$.

25) Squaring both sides of the equation $\sqrt{3m-2} = m$ gives $3m - 2 = m^2$. Rearranging, we get $m^2 - 3m + 2 = 0$, which factors to $(m-1)(m-2) = 0$. Thus, the values of m that satisfy the equation are 1 and 2, making C the correct answer.

26) Let the number be n. The equation based on the problem statement is $\frac{14+n}{n} = 4$. Solving for n, we get $14 + n = 4n$, which simplifies to $3n = 14$. Dividing both sides by 3 gives $n = \frac{14}{3}$.

27) In the expansion of $\left(2x^3 - 3\right)^3$, there are 4 terms due to the binomial theorem. The coefficient of x^3 comes from the term where the exponent of x^3 is 1 in the expansion, which is part of the term $3(2x^3)(-3)^2 = 54x^3$. Therefore, the coefficient of x^3 is 54, making D the correct answer.

28) To find the average rate of change, calculate the function values at $x = 4$ and $x = 2$, then subtract and divide by the interval length. The average rate of change is $\frac{512-32}{4-2} = \frac{480}{2} = 240$, making A the correct answer.

29) The sum can be split into two parts: the sum of $2i$, which is $2\frac{m(m+1)}{2} = m(m+1)$, and the sum of 3 repeated m times, which is $3m$. Combining these gives $m(m+1) + 3m = m^2 + m + 3m = m^2 + 4m$.

30) Factor $g(x)$ to find its zeros: $g(x) = x(x^2 - 9) = x(x-3)(x+3)$. Setting each factor equal to zero gives the zeros of $g(x)$ as $0, 3, -3$. Therefore, the zeros of $g(x)$ are $0, \pm 3$.

31) First, find the value of m using the given point $(8, 19)$: $19 = m \cdot 8 + 3$. Solving for m gives $m = 2$. Then, to find y when $x = 12$: $y = 2 \cdot 12 + 3 = 24 + 3 = 27$.

32) To find the total volume of the solution, use the proportion $\frac{32\ ml}{x\ ml} = \frac{8}{100}$. Solving for x gives $x = \frac{32 \times 100}{8} = 400\ ml$, meaning the total volume of the solution is $400\ ml$, making B the correct answer.

33) According to the given graph, the value of the function is zero for three inputs. It means that the degree of the function is equal or greater than 3.

34) A zero of a function corresponds to an x-intercept of the graph of the function in the xy-plane. Therefore, the graph of the function $f(x)$, which has three distinct zeros, must have three x-intercepts. Only the graph in choice B has three x-intercepts.

35) First, solve the equation $0.5y = 0.25 \times 40$ to find y. This gives $y = 20$. Then, calculate $(y+4)^2 = (20+4)^2 = 24^2 = 576$.

36) Multiplying the given numbers: $(3.2 \times 2.5) \times 10^{4+3} = 8.0 \times 10^7$. This puts the product in scientific notation correctly, making B the right choice.

37) We have: $x^3 + y^3 + z^3 - 3xyz = (x+y+z)(x^2+y^2+z^2-xy-yz-zx)$. So, if $x+y+z=0$ then: $x^3 + y^3 + z^3 = 3xyz$. Since, $2a + 3b = d$, so $2a + 3b - d = 0 \rightarrow (2a) + (3b) + (-d) = 0$. Therefore, $(2a)^3 + (3b)^3 + (-d)^3 = 3(2a)(3b)(-d) = -18abd$. Finally, $8a^3 + 27b^3 - d^3 = -18 \times 24 = -432$.

38) Let the integer be n. The equation formed is $3n - 10 = 83$. Solving for n, we get $3n = 93$, and $n = 31$. Therefore, the integer is 31, making A the correct answer.

39) To find the discount, multiply the number by (100%- rate of discount). Therefore, for the first discount, we get $1200(100\% - 10\%) = (1200)(0.9)$. For the next 10% discount: $(1200)(0.90)(0.90)$.

40) Evaluate each expression for the function $f(x)$:

I. The domain of a polynomial function is all real numbers.

II. To find the roots of $f(x)$, we solve $f(x) = 0$. So, we have: $x^3 - 3x^2 + 2x = 0 \rightarrow x(x^2 - 3x + 2) = 0 \rightarrow x(x-1)(x-2) = 0$, This equation has three real roots at $x = 0$, $x = 1$, and $x = 2$.

II. As x tends towards positive infinity, the dominant term in $f(x)$ is x^3. Since x^3 becomes very large as x increases, $f(x)$ will also become very large and positive.

IV. For a function to be odd, it must satisfy $f(-x) = -f(x)$ for all x in its domain. Let's check: $f(-x) = (-x)^3 - 3(-x)^2 + 2(-x) = -x^3 - 3x^2 - 2x$, and $-f(x) = -(x^3 - 3x^2 + 2x) = -x^3 + 3x^2 - 2x$, Since $f(-x)$ is not equal to $-f(x)$, the function is not odd.

V. As we found in statement II, $f(x)$ has three real roots at $x = 0$, $x = 1$, and $x = 2$.

So, the correct statements are I and II.

41) Evaluate each option: A results in $|3 - 7| - |4| = 4 - 4 = 0$, B gives $|2| + |-6| = 2 + 6 = 8$, C is $3|-1 - 4| = 3 \times 5 = 15$, D results in $|3 - 7| - |2 - 3| = 4 - 1 = 3$, and E equals $|4 - 5| + |5 - 4| = 1 + 1 = 2$. Therefore, A is the smallest.

42) Substitute $3x$ into $g(x)$: $g(3x) = 4(3x) + 3(3x + 2) + 1 = 12x + 9x + 6 + 1 = 21x + 7$.

43) First, find the equation of the line. All lines through the origin are of the form $y = mx$, so the equation is $y = \frac{2}{5}x$. Of the given choices, only choice $B(10,4)$, satisfies this equation: $y = \frac{2}{5}x \rightarrow 4 = \frac{2}{5}(10) = 4$.

44) Simplify the expression: $2m(m-2) + (7 - 3m^2 + 2m) = 2m^2 - 4m + 7 - 3m^2 + 2m = -m^2 - 2m + 7$.

45) Since the polynomial functions are continuous, the function has at least one root every time it changes sign. According to the table, in the intervals of $(-2,-1)$, $(-1,1)$ and $(1,3)$, the values of the function change from positive to negative and vice versa. Therefore, the function $g(x)$ has at least three zero values. So, the minimum degree is 3.

46) Simplify the given expression: $\frac{1}{\frac{1}{x-4}+\frac{1}{x+3}} = \frac{1}{\frac{x+3+x-4}{(x-4)(x+3)}} = \frac{(x-4)(x+3)}{x+3+x-4}$, making A the correct equivalence.

47) Removing the flat fee for equipment use (20 dollars) from the total cost does not affect the per session cost of 60 dollars. It simply reduces the total cost by 20 dollars, making B the correct statement.

48) Considering the initial drop and the subsequent bounces, the total distance includes the descent and ascent for each bounce, doubling the distance for each bounce except the first descent. The correct formula accounting for the initial drop and bounces up to the fifth bounce is $4.05 + \sum_{k=1}^{5} (2 \times 4.05) \times \left(\frac{3}{5}\right)^k = 4.05 + \sum_{k=1}^{5} 8.1 \left(\frac{3}{5}\right)^k$, making E the correct choice.

49) Factoring the given equation $-2y^2 + 8y = 0$ gives $-2y(y-4) = 0$. Setting each factor equal to zero yields $y = 0$ and $y = 4$ as solutions, confirming that C is correct.

50) The x-intercepts of the graph of $f(x) = x^2 - 6x + 8$ are the points $(x, f(x))$ on the graph where $f(x) = 0$. Substituting 0 for $f(x)$ in the function equation yields $0 = x^2 - 6x + 8$. Factoring the equation yields $0 = (x-2)(x-4)$. If $0 = (x-2)(x-4)$, then $0 = (x-2)$ or $0 = (x-4)$. Solving both of these equations for x yields $x = 2$ and $x = 4$. Therefore, the x-intercepts of the graph of $f(x) = x^2 - 6x + 8$ are $(2,0)$ and $(4,0)$. Since both points lie on the x-axis, the distance between $(2,0)$ and $(4,0)$ is equivalent to the number of unit spaces between 2 and 4 on the x-axis, which is 2.

51) The real part of the complex number is -1, and the imaginary part is 2. We plot the ordered pair $(-1,2)$, in which the real number (-1) is plotted on the x-axis, and the imaginary part (2) is plotted on the y-axis. Point A represents the complex number $-1 + 2i$.

52) Simplify the argument of the logarithm: $\frac{\sqrt{125}\sqrt[4]{25}}{5} = \frac{(5^{\frac{3}{2}})(5^{\frac{2}{4}})}{5} = \frac{5^2}{5} = 5$. Then, $\log_5 5 = 1$.

53) To solve Here, you can see that for any two arbitrary numbers a and b in the interval $(-\infty, -1)$ such that $a < b$, then the value of the function at a is less than at b. That is, the function is increasing in this interval. Similarly, for the interval $(1, +\infty)$, the graph is increasing. The graph is decreasing in the interval $(-1,1)$. Since for every a and b in the interval $(-1,1)$ such that $a < b$, the value of the function at a is greater than b.

54) Considering that $(x+y+z)^2 = x^2+y^2+z^2+2xy+2yz+2zx$, then: $(3a-c+2)^2 = (3a)^2 + (-c)^2 + 2^2 + 2(3a)(-c)+2(3a)2+2(-c)2$. Simplified, this would be: $(3a-c+2)^2 = 9a^2 + c^2 + 4 - 6ac + 12a - 4c$. Now, multiply the above by $(2-d)$: $(2-d)(9a^2 + c^2 - 6ac + 12a - 4c + 4) = 18a^2 + 2c^2 - 12ac + 24a - 8c + 8 - 9da^2 - dc^2 + 6dac - 12da + 4dc - 4d$.

55) The total cost includes the cost of the chairs plus a one-time delivery charge. Dividing the total cost by the number of chairs gives the cost per chair, which is $\frac{150y+450}{y}$.

56) Since $h(6) = 2$, we find $(j \circ h)(6) = j(h(6)) = j(2)$. Given that $j(2) = 5$, Therefore, $(j \circ h)(6) = 5$.

57) According to the graph, you can see 3 is the x-intercept. By putting $(3,0)$ in the choices:

A. $f(3) = e^{(3-3)} + 1 = e^0 + 1 = 2 \neq 0$

B. $f(3) = e^{(3+2)} = e^5 \neq 0$

C. $f(3) = e^{(3-3)} - 1 = e^0 - 1 = 0$

D. $f(3) = e^3 - 2 \neq 0$

E. $f(3) = (\frac{1}{2})^{(3-3)} - 2 = -1 \neq 0$

Therefore, the choice $f(x) = e^{x-3} - 1$ is correct.

58) To find the coefficient of x^8, you must multiply $3x^2$ by the coefficient of the explicit formula. So, $3x^2 \times \frac{(k+1)}{(3k+2)}x^k = \frac{3(k+1)}{(3k+2)}x^{(k+2)}$. Then, let $x^8 = x^{(k+2)} \to k+2 = 8 \to k = 6$. Substitute $k = 6$ in $\frac{3(k+1)}{(3k+2)}$. Therefore: $\frac{3(6+1)}{(3(6)+2)} = \frac{21}{20}$.

59) First, rewrite the system of equation in the standard form.

$$\begin{cases} y = -\frac{1}{2}x^2 + 2x + 3 \\ y = \frac{1}{4}x^2 - \frac{3}{2}x + 3 \end{cases}$$

This system consists of two quadratic equations. Choices B, C, and E are incorrect because their graphs depict a combination of a linear equation and a quadratic equation. Option D shows a cubic equation and a quadratic equation, which does not match the system's requirements. Option A displays two quadratic equations, making it the correct answer.

60) To find the inverse, solve for x in terms of y: $y = (x+2)^2 - 2 \Rightarrow x = \pm\sqrt{y+2} - 2$. Since $x \leq -2$, the inverse function $f^{-1}(x)$ is $-\sqrt{x+2}-2$.

15. Practice Test 2

College Algebra Practice Test

Total number of questions: 60

Time: 90 Minutes

Calculator is permitted for College Algebra Test.

15.1 Practices

1) If $h(x) = 3x - 1$ and $j(x) = x^2 + 2x - 3$, then find $\left(\frac{h}{j}\right)(x)$.

☐ A. $\frac{3x-1}{x^2+2x-3}$

☐ B. $\frac{3x-1}{x^2+5x-3}$

☐ C. $\frac{x-1}{x^2+3x-1}$

☐ D. $\frac{3x-1}{x^2+x-3}$

☐ E. $\frac{x^2+2x-3}{3x-1}$

2) In the standard (x,y) coordinate plane, which of the following lines contains the points $(1,2)$ and $(5,14)$?

☐ A. $y = \frac{3}{4}x + \frac{5}{2}$

☐ B. $y = 3x - 1$

☐ C. $y = 3x + 1$

☐ D. $y = \frac{1}{2}x + \frac{3}{2}$

☐ E. $y = 4x - 2$

3) Which expression is equivalent to $3x\left(\frac{1}{3}y - 6\right) + 4(2x - 3) + 2y(x - 2)$?

☐ A. $3xy - 10x - 4y - 12$

☐ B. $3xy - 22x - 4y + 12$

☐ C. $xy - 10x - 4y + 12$

☐ D. $5xy - 10x - 6y + 12$

☐ E. $5xy - 18x + 2y - 12$

4) What is the product of all possible values of x in the following equation? $|x - 5| = 3$

☐ A. 2

☐ B. 16

☐ C. 10

☐ D. 15

☐ E. 20

5) According to the following graph, which of the statements is correct?

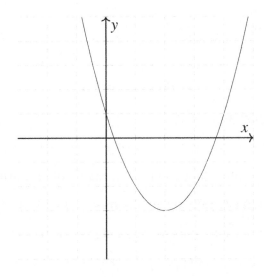

☐ A. $\{-2\}$ is an absolute maximum.

☐ B. $\{3\}$ is an absolute maximum.

☐ C. $(2, -3)$ is an absolute minimum.

☐ D. $\{2\}$ is an absolute maximum.

☐ E. There is not a absolute minimum value.

6) In an arithmetic sequence starting with 5 and ending with 205, how many integers are divisible by 5?

☐ A. 41

☐ B. 40

☐ C. 39

☐ D. 38

☐ E. 37

7) The graph illustrates how the number of presentations made by a convention presenter relates to the number of Cookies she had left to give away.

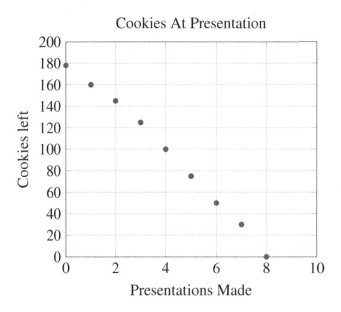

What does the x-intercept of the graph represent?

☐ A. The initial number of Cookies the presenter had before making any presentations.

☐ B. The point at which the presenter stopped giving away Cookies during the presentations.

☐ C. The rate at which the presenter made presentations per unit of time.

☐ D. The maximum number of presentations the presenter made before running out of Cookies.

☐ E. The number of remaining Cookies the presenter had at the end of any presentation.

8) The graph of $y = g(x)$ in the $xy-$plane is shown below. What is the value of $g(4)$?

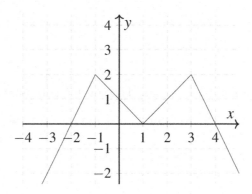

☐ A. -5

☐ B. -3

☐ C. 0

☐ D. 3

☐ E. 5

9) Which point is a solution to the system of equations displayed in the graph below?

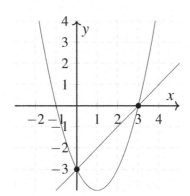

☐ A. $(0, -3)$

☐ B. $(2, 0)$

☐ C. $\left(\frac{5}{2}, -\frac{1}{2}\right)$

☐ D. $(-4, 5)$

☐ E. $(0, -2)$

10) What is the domain of the function $g(x) = \frac{x^2 - 9}{x^2 - 5x + 6}$?

☐ A. $\{x : x \neq 2\}$

☐ B. $\{x : x \neq 3\}$

□ C. $\{x : x \neq -3, 3\}$

□ D. $\{x : x \notin \mathbb{Z}\}$

□ E. $\{x : x \neq 2, 3\}$

11) A gardening service is planting a row of bushes. The service can plant 20 *cm* of the row per minute. After 60 minutes, $\frac{2}{3}$ of the row is completed. How many meters long is the row?

□ A. 9

□ B. 12

□ C. 15

□ D. 18

□ E. 24

12) What is the solution of the following inequality?

$$|x+3| \leq 4$$

□ A. $x \leq -7 \cup x \geq 1$

□ B. $-7 \leq x \leq 1$

□ C. $-1 \leq x \leq 7$

□ D. $x \geq 7$

□ E. $x \leq -1$

13) What is the set of $y-$values of the local minimum and maximum of the graphed function $g(x)$?

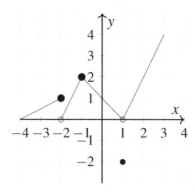

□ A. $\{-1, 2\}$

□ B. $\{-2, 1, 2\}$

□ C. $\{-2,0,2,-4\}$

□ D. $\{-4,-1.5,0,1.5,4\}$

□ E. The function has no local maximum/minimum point.

14) If $4j+k=9j-1$, what is k in terms of j?

□ A. $j=5k+1$

□ B. $k=5j-1$

□ C. $j=4k$

□ D. $k=j-2$

□ E. $k=5j-2$

15) Solve for y in the equation: $\log_4(3y-2)=-\log_4 y$.

□ A. 1

□ B. -1

□ C. 1 and $\frac{-1}{3}$

□ D. no solution

□ E. Infinite solutions

16) A bank is offering 3.5% simple interest on a savings account. If you deposit $15,000$, how much interest will you earn in three years?

□ A. $1,575$

□ B. $1,050$

□ C. $3,150$

□ D. $4,725$

□ E. $5,250$

17) What is the domain of the function: $f(x)=\frac{1}{x^2-4}$.

□ A. $\{-2,2\}$

□ B. $\mathbb{R}$

□ C. $\mathbb{R}-\{0\}$

□ D. $\mathbb{R}-\{-2,2\}$

□ E. $\mathbb{R}-(-2,2)$

18) A farmer needs to calculate the amount of seed required to plant in a circular field. If the field has a diameter of d meters, and the farmer adds 15 square meters to the area for buffer, which function can be used to find the total area, $S(d)$, for seed calculation?

☐ A. $S(d) = \pi \left(\frac{d}{2}\right)^2 + 15$

☐ B. $S(d) = 2\pi \left(\frac{d}{2}\right)^2 + 15$

☐ C. $S(d) = \pi(d+15)^2$

☐ D. $S(d) = \pi \left(\frac{d^2}{4} + 15\right)$

☐ E. $S(d) = \pi \left(\left(\frac{d}{2}\right)^2 - 15\right)$

19) For which values of m does the equation $x^3 - mx^2 + 4x = 0$ have exactly one real root?

☐ A. $-4 < m < 4$

☐ B. $m > 2\sqrt{2}$

☐ C. $m > 2\sqrt{2} \cup -2\sqrt{2} > m$

☐ D. $-2\sqrt{2} > m$

☐ E. No real number.

20) What is the inverse of the function $f(x) = \ln(x+3)$?

☐ A. $\frac{1}{\log(x+3)}$

☐ B. $e^x - 3$

☐ C. $10^x - 3$

☐ D. $e^x + 3$

☐ E. $2e^x - 3$

21) If $h(x) = 3x^3 - 2x^2 - x + 1$ and $j(x) = 3$, what is the value of $h(j(x))$?

☐ A. 61

☐ B. 59

☐ C. 40

☐ D. 27

☐ E. 19

22) The first five terms in row 20 of Pascal's triangle are 1, 20, 190, 1140, and 4845. Find the first five terms in row 21. (Write the answer in the following box) [   ]

23) What is the equivalent temperature of $131°F$ in Celsius?

☐ A. 50.5

☐ B. 52

☐ C. 53.5

☐ D. 55

☐ E. 59

24) Find the coefficient of x^4 in the expansion of $(2-x)^2 \sum_{n=0}^{N}(-1)^n x^n$.

☐ A. -9

☐ B. -4

☐ C. 0

☐ D. 4

☐ E. 9

25) The following table shows some of the values of a 5rd degree polynomial $g(x)$. Based on the values shown, what is the minimum number of real roots of the equation $g(x) = 0$?

x	$g(x)$
-5	2
-3	-4
-1	6
2	-8
3	1
5	2
7	5

☐ A. Zero

☐ B. One

☐ C. Two

☐ D. Three

☐ E. Four

26) If 125% of a number is 50, then what is 75% of that number?

☐ A. 30

☐ B. 35

☐ C. 40

☐ D. 45

☐ E. 60

27) What is the value $f(1)$ of the following function?

$$f(x) = \begin{cases} 2x+1, & -\infty < x \le -1 \\ x^2+2x+1, & -1 < x < 1 \\ x+3, & 1 \le x < 4 \end{cases}$$

☐ A. Undefined

☐ B. 1

☐ C. 4

☐ D. 3

☐ E. 5

28) In two successive years, the population of a city increased by 5% and then 15%. What percent of the population increase is approximately observed after two years?

☐ A. 20%

☐ B. 21%

☐ C. 22%

☐ D. 30%

☐ E. 40%

29) Assuming water flows into a bathtub at a rate of 100 liters per hour and the bathtub already contains 200 liters of water with a capacity of 800 liters, at what time will the bathtub be full if the water starts flowing at $14:00$? (Write the answer in the following box) ☐

30) The telephone number of a location consists of ten digits chosen from the set of numeric numbers between 0 and 9, as shown as follows: $V = \{0,1,2,3,4,5,6,7,8,9\}$.

The set X represents the digits in the telephone number for Springfield: $X = \{9,8,2,3,1,3,5,1,1,3,2\}$.

The set Y represents the digits in the telephone number for Rivertown: $Y = \{8,8,2,1,7,3,2,1,1,9,3\}$.

How many numbers are in the set $(X \cap Y)$?

☐ A. 5

☐ B. 6

☐ C. 8

☐ D. 12

☐ E. 24

31) What is the value of x in the following system of equations?

$$5x + 2y = 3$$

$$y = x$$

☐ A. $x = \frac{1}{3}$

☐ B. $x = \frac{3}{7}$

☐ C. $x = \frac{2}{3}$

☐ D. $x = \frac{4}{3}$

☐ E. $x = \frac{5}{3}$

32) In a hotel, there are 5 floors and x rooms on each floor. If each room has exactly y chairs, which of the following gives the total number of chairs in the hotel?

☐ A. $2xy$

☐ B. $5xy$

☐ C. $x + y$

☐ D. $x + 5y$

☐ E. $2x + 5y$

33) If $\alpha = 2\beta$ and $\beta = 3\gamma$, how many α units are equal to 36γ?

☐ A. 1

☐ B. 2

☐ C. 4

☐ D. 6

☐ E. 12

34) How many solutions are there for the following system of equations?

$$y = 2x^2 + 3x - 5$$
$$2x - y = 2$$

- ☐ A. 0
- ☐ B. 1
- ☐ C. 2
- ☐ D. 3
- ☐ E. 4

35) Which of the following are the solutions of the equation $2x - 1 = x - 3x^2$?

- ☐ A. -2 and 3
- ☐ B. $\frac{1-\sqrt{13}}{3}$ and $\frac{-1-\sqrt{13}}{3}$
- ☐ C. $\frac{1-\sqrt{13}}{3}$ and $\frac{1+\sqrt{13}}{3}$
- ☐ D. $\frac{-1-\sqrt{13}}{6}$ and $\frac{-1+\sqrt{13}}{6}$
- ☐ E. $\frac{1-\sqrt{13}}{6}$ and $\frac{-1+\sqrt{13}}{6}$

36) Consider the points $(2, \frac{4}{9})$ and $(6, 35)$. Both a linear and an exponential growth model pass through these points. Determine the range of values for which the linear growth is less than the exponential growth. (Write the answer in the following box) ☐

37) If $h(x) = 3x^3 - 1$ and $j(x) = \frac{2}{x}$, what is the value of $h(j(x))$?

- ☐ A. $\frac{3}{2x}$
- ☐ B. $\frac{6}{x^3} - 1$
- ☐ C. $\frac{3}{2x-1}$
- ☐ D. $\frac{3}{2x^3-1}$
- ☐ E. $\frac{24}{x^3} - 1$

38) What are the coordinates of the x-intercept in the graph provided below?

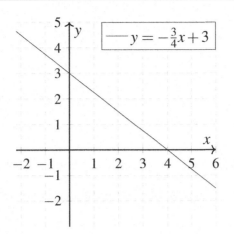

☐ A. (0,4)

☐ B. (4,0)

☐ C. (-3,4)

☐ D. (-4,0)

☐ E. (-4,3)

39) If the ratio of $3c$ to $4d$ is $\frac{3}{8}$, what is the ratio of c to d?

☐ A. $\frac{1}{2}$

☐ B. $\frac{1}{4}$

☐ C. $\frac{3}{8}$

☐ D. $\frac{8}{3}$

☐ E. $\frac{4}{3}$

40) Given the condition $(y < -2)$, which of the following is a possible value of y?

☐ A. -3

☐ B. 0

☐ C. $\sqrt{9}$

☐ D. 9

☐ E. 18

41) If $\frac{x-2}{3} = P$ and $P = 4$, what is the value of x? (Write the answer in the following box) ☐

42) If $c^{\frac{-4}{3}} = y$, where $c > 0, y > 0$, which of the following equations gives c in terms of y?

☐ A. $\sqrt[3]{y}$

- ☐ B. $\sqrt[4]{\frac{1}{y^3}}$
- ☐ C. $\frac{1}{y^3}$
- ☐ D. $\sqrt{y^3}$
- ☐ E. $\sqrt[3]{y^{-4}}$

43) On Sunday, Tom read O pages of a book each hour for 2 hours, and Jerry read J pages of a book each hour for 5 hours. Which of the following represents the total number of pages of the book read by Tom and Jerry on Sunday?

- ☐ A. $7OJ$
- ☐ B. $10OJ$
- ☐ C. $2O+5J$
- ☐ D. $5O+2J$
- ☐ E. $5O-2J$

44) If 35 wooden planks were stacked on top of each other in a column, the column would be approximately $70\frac{7}{10}$ centimeters tall. At this rate, which of the following is closest to the number of wooden planks it would take to make a 141-centimeter-tall column?

- ☐ A. 35
- ☐ B. 50
- ☐ C. 70
- ☐ D. 100
- ☐ E. 140

45) Which of the following represents the graph of the line with the equation $3x+4y=12$?

- ☐ A.

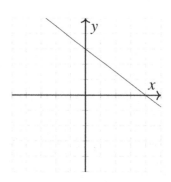

☐ B.

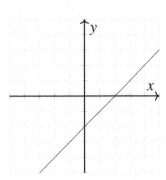

☐ C.

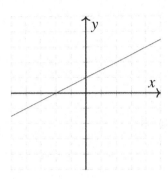

☐ D.

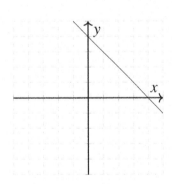

☐ E.

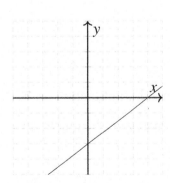

46) If $x + \frac{1}{x} = 3$, find the value of $x^2 + \frac{1}{x^2}$.

☐ A. 5

☐ B. 7

☐ C. 8

☐ D. 9

☐ E. 10

47) Which of the following inequalities is true?

☐ A. $\frac{4}{5} > \frac{3}{4}$

☐ B. $\frac{3}{8} < \frac{2}{7}$

☐ C. $\frac{6}{9} > \frac{8}{11}$

☐ D. $\frac{4}{7} > \frac{7}{10}$

☐ E. $\frac{3}{5} < \frac{4}{9}$

48) Which of the following is the smallest?

☐ A. $|3 - 1|$

☐ B. $|1 - 3|$

☐ C. $|-1 - 3|$

☐ D. $|1 - 3| - |3 - 1|$

☐ E. $|1 - 3| + |3 - 1|$

49) Simplify $\frac{2+4i}{-2i} + 4$.

☐ A. $2i$

☐ B. $i + 2$

☐ C. $4 - 4i$

☐ D. $2i - 8$

☐ E. $-2i$

50) The equation below represents a quadratic function in the $xy-$plane. Which of the following equivalent forms of the equation shows the $x-$intercepts of the quadratic as constants or coefficients?

$$y = x^2 - 6x + 9$$

☐ A. $y = x - 3$

☐ B. $y = x(x - 6)$

☐ C. $y = (x-3)^2$

☐ D. $y = (x-2)(x-4)$

☐ E. $y = (x-3)(x-2)$

51) A worker's total income from a project consists of a fixed sum plus an amount that depends on the number of hours worked. The table below shows the linear relationship between the number of hours worked and the worker's total income in dollars. What is the rate of change of the worker's total income in dollars with respect to the number of hours worked?

Number of Hours Worked	Total Income
2	$47
5	$80
8	$113
11	$146
14	$179
17	$212

☐ A. 8.5

☐ B. 10.5

☐ C. 11

☐ D. 12

☐ E. 33

52) What is the value of $\frac{5c}{d}$ when $\frac{d}{c} = 3$? (Write the answer in the following box) ☐

53) Given $x+4 = 7$, and $3y-2 = 4$, what is the value of $xy+14$?

☐ A. 23

☐ B. 21

☐ C. 19

☐ D. 20

☐ E. 16

54) Given $\frac{a-c}{c} = \frac{9}{14}$, then which of the following must be true?

☐ A. $\frac{a}{c} = \frac{9}{14}$

☐ B. $\frac{a}{c} = \frac{9}{23}$

☐ C. $\frac{a}{c} = \frac{14}{23}$

☐ D. $\frac{a}{c} = \frac{23}{14}$

☐ E. $\frac{a}{c} = \frac{14}{9}$

55) Which of the following lines is perpendicular to $4y + 3x = 12$?

☐ A. $y = -\frac{3}{4}x + 2$

☐ B. $y = \frac{3}{4}x - 1$

☐ C. $y = -\frac{4}{3}x + 3$

☐ D. $y = \frac{4}{3}x + 4$

☐ E. $y = \frac{1}{3}x - 4$

56) If $x = -2$ is a solution to the equation $3x^5 - ax^2 + x + 8 = 0$, what is the value of a?

☐ A. -25

☐ B. -2

☐ C. 0

☐ D. 4

☐ E. -22.5

57) Which of the following equations best represents the following graph?

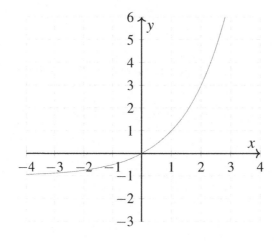

☐ A. 2^x

☐ B. 2^{x+1}

☐ C. 2^{1-x}

☐ D. $2^x - 1$

☐ E. 2^{x-1}

58) What is the constant term in the expansion of $\left(2x^2+1\right)\left(1-\frac{2}{x}\right)^3$? (Write the answer in the following box)

$\boxed{}$

59) Sara orders a box of pens for \$3 per box. A tax of 8.5% is added to the cost of the pens before a flat shipping fee of \$6 closes out the transaction. Which of the following represents the total cost of p boxes of pens in dollars?

☐ A. $3p+6$

☐ B. $6p+3$

☐ C. $6p+6$

☐ D. $1.085(6p)+3$

☐ E. $1.085(3p)+6$

60) A plant grows at a linear rate. After five weeks, the plant is 40 *cm* tall. Assuming the plant was 0 *cm* tall at week 0, which of the following functions represents the relationship between the height (y) of the plant and the number of weeks of growth (x)?

☐ A. $y(x)=40x+8$

☐ B. $y(x)=8x+40$

☐ C. $y(x)=40x$

☐ D. $y(x)=8x$

☐ E. $y(x)=4x$

15.2   Answer Keys

1) A. $\frac{3x-1}{x^2+2x-3}$

2) B. $y = 3x - 1$

3) A. $3xy - 10x - 4y - 12$

4) B. 16

5) C. $(2, -3)$ is a absolute minimum.

6) B. 40

7) D.

8) C. 0

9) A. $(0, -3)$

10) E. $\{x : x \neq 2, 3\}$

11) D. 18

12) B. $-7 \leq x \leq 1$

13) B. $\{-2, 1, 2\}$

14) B. $k = 5j - 1$

15) A. 1

16) A. $\$1,575$

17) D. $\mathbb{R} - \{-2, 2\}$

18) A. $S(d) = \pi \left(\frac{d}{2}\right)^2 + 15$

19) A. $-4 < m < 4$

20) B. $e^x - 3$

21) A. 61

22) 1, 21, 210, 1330 and 5985

23) D. 55

24) E. 9

25) E. Four

26) A. 30

27) C. 4

28) B. 21%

29) The bathtub will be full at $20 : 00$.

30) A. 5

31) B. $x = \frac{3}{7}$

32) B. $5xy$

33) D. 6

34) C. 2

35) D. $\frac{-1-\sqrt{13}}{6}$ and $\frac{-1+\sqrt{13}}{6}$

36) $(6, +\infty)$

37) E. $\frac{24}{x^3} - 1$

38) B. $(4, 0)$

39) A. $\frac{1}{2}$

40) A. -3

41) 14

42) B. $\sqrt[4]{\frac{1}{y^3}}$

43) C. $2O + 5J$

44) C. 70

45) A.

46) B. 7

47) A. $\frac{4}{5} > \frac{3}{4}$

48) D. $|1 - 3| - |3 - 1|$

49) B. $i + 2$

50) C. $y = (x - 3)^2$

51) C. 11

52) $\frac{5}{3}$

53) D. 20

54) D. $\frac{a}{c} = \frac{23}{14}$

55) D. $y = \frac{4}{3}x + 4$

56) E. -22.5

57) D. $2^x - 1$

58) The constant term is 25.

59) E. $1.085(3p) + 6$

60) D. $y(x) = 8x$

15.3   Answers with Explanation

1) To find $(\frac{h}{j})(x)$, simply place $h(x)$ over $j(x)$. Therefore, $(\frac{h}{j})(x) = \frac{3x-1}{x^2+2x-3}$. This form directly follows from the definitions of $h(x)$ and $j(x)$ without any need for simplification, making A the correct choice.

2) To find the slope (m) of the line through $(1,2)$ and $(5,14)$, use $m = \frac{y_2-y_1}{x_2-x_1} = \frac{14-2}{5-1} = \frac{12}{4} = 3$. To find the y-intercept (b), use one of the points: $2 = 3(1)+b$, solving for b gives $b = -1$. Thus, the equation of the line is $y = 3x - 1$, making B the correct answer.

3) Simplifying the expression, $3x(\frac{1}{3}y - 6) + 4(2x - 3) + 2y(x - 2) = xy - 18x + 8x - 12 + 2xy - 4y = 3xy - 10x - 4y - 12$, thus A is the correct equivalent expression.

4) The equation $|x - 5| = 3$ leads to two cases: $x - 5 = 3$ and $x - 5 = -3$. Solving the first gives $x = 8$, and the second gives $x = 2$. The product of 8 and 2 is 16.

5) Given the quadratic function opening upwards with a vertex at $(2, -3)$, the vertex represents the lowest point on the graph, making it a absolute minimum. Therefore, C is the correct choice.

6) The arithmetic sequence is defined by starting at 5 and ending at 205, with each term being divisible by 5. The first term divisible by 5 is 5 itself, and the last term is 205. To find the total number of terms divisible by 5, we use the formula for the number of terms in an arithmetic sequence: $N = \frac{\text{last term}-\text{first term}}{\text{common difference}} + 1 = \frac{205-5}{5} + 1 = 40 + 1 = 41$. However, since both the first and last terms are included, we do not need to add 1 for this specific scenario, making the correct count 40.

7) The x-intercept of a graph is the point where the line or curve intersects the x-axis. In this context, the x-axis represents the number of presentations made by the convention presenter, and the y-axis represents the number of Cookies she had left to give away. Therefore, the y-intercept represents the point at which the number of presentations made by the presenter is zero, i.e., the initial state before any presentations were made. At this point, the presenter had all the Cookies she started with and had not given away any yet. Hence, the x-intercept of the graph represents the maximum number of presentations the presenter made before running out of Cookies.

8) The value of $g(4)$ is equal to the value of $g(x)$, or y, when $x = 4$. The graph indicates that when $x = 4$,

$y = 0$. It follows that the value of $g(4) = 0$.

9) The answer to a system of equations is the intersection of the equations. Therefore, find the points where the two graphs intersect. Clearly, you can see that the points $(0, -3)$ and $(3, 0)$ are the solutions of this system.

10) To find the domain of $g(x)$, we set the denominator $x^2 - 5x + 6$ equal to zero and solve for x. Factoring the denominator gives $(x - 2)(x - 3) = 0$, so the values of x that make the denominator zero are $x = 2$ and $x = 3$. These values are excluded from the domain, making the domain $\{x : x \neq 2, 3\}$.

11) After 60 minutes, $\frac{2}{3}$ of the row is planted. Since 20 *cm* is planted per minute, 60×20 *cm* $= 1200$ *cm* or 12 *m* represents $\frac{2}{3}$ of the total length. To find the full length, set up the proportion $\frac{2}{3} = \frac{12}{x}$, solving for x gives $x = 18$ *m*.

12) The inequality $|x + 3| \leq 4$ can be split into two conditions: $x + 3 \leq 4$ and $x + 3 \geq -4$. Solving the first gives $x \leq 1$, and solving the second gives $x \geq -7$. Thus, the solution is $-7 \leq x \leq 1$.

13) To find the set of y-values corresponding to the local minimum and maximum of the graphed function $g(x)$, we need to identify the lowest and highest points on the graph.
A local minimum occurs at a point where the function reaches its lowest value within a small interval around that point. Looking at the graph, we see that the lowest point occurs at $(1, -2)$. This means that around this point, there are no other points with lower y-values nearby. Similarly, a local maximum occurs at a point where the function reaches its highest value within a small interval around that point. From the graph, we can identify two local maximum points: One occurs at $(-2, 1)$, where the function reaches its highest value. Another occurs at $(-1, 2)$, which is also a local maximum. Around both of these points, there are no other nearby points with highest y-values. So, the set of y-values corresponding to the local minimum and maximum of the graphed function $g(x)$ is $\{-2, 1, 2\}$. These values represent the y-coordinates of the points where the function either reaches its highest or lowest values within small intervals around those points.

14) To find k in terms of j, rearrange the equation $4j + k = 9j - 1$ to get $k = 9j - 4j - 1 = 5j - 1$.

15) To solve the equation $\log_4(3y - 2) = -\log_4 y$, we'll use properties of logarithms to manipulate the equation and isolate y. First, we'll move the $\log_4 y$ term to the left side of the equation by adding it to both sides: $\log_4(3y - 2) + \log_4 y = 0$. Using the property that $\log_a b + \log_a c = \log_a(bc)$, we can combine the logarithms on the left side: $\log_4(y(3y - 2)) = 0$. Simplifying inside the logarithm: $\log_4(3y^2 - 2y) = 0$. Now, we'll use the property that if $\log_a b = c$, then $a^c = b$: $4^0 = 3y^2 - 2y$. Rearranging the equation into standard quadratic form: $3y^2 - 2y - 1 = 0$. Now, we can solve this quadratic equation for y. Let's use the quadratic formula: $y = \frac{-b \pm \sqrt{b^2 - 4ac}}{2a}$. For our equation $3y^2 - 2y - 1 = 0$, $a = 3$, $b = -2$, and $c = -1$. Substituting these values into the quadratic formula: $y = \frac{-(-2) \pm \sqrt{(-2)^2 - 4(3)(-1)}}{2(3)} \rightarrow y = \frac{2 \pm \sqrt{4+12}}{6}$ $y = \frac{2 \pm \sqrt{16}}{6} \rightarrow y = \frac{2 \pm 4}{6} \rightarrow y = \frac{-1}{3}, y = 1$ So, the solutions to the equation $\log_4(3y - 2) = -\log_4 y$ are $y = \frac{-1}{3}$ and $y = 1$. To verify the solutions: Substitute $y = \frac{-1}{3}$:

$$\log_4\left(3\left(\frac{-1}{3}\right) - 2\right) = -\log_4\left(\frac{-1}{3}\right)$$

Since logarithms are not defined for negative numbers, the solution $y = \frac{-1}{3}$ is extraneous. Substitute $y = 1$:

$$\log_4(3(1) - 2) = -\log_4(1)$$

$$\log_4(1) = -\log_4(1)$$

Since $\log_4(1) = 0$, the equation holds true. Therefore, the only valid solution to the equation $\log_4(3y - 2) = -\log_4 y$ is $y = 1$.

16) Simple interest is calculated as $I = P \times r \times t$ where P is the principal amount ($\$15,000$), r is the annual interest rate (3.5% or 0.035), and t is the time in years (3 years). Thus, $I = 15000 \times 0.035 \times 3 = \$1,575$. Therefore, the interest earned in three years is $\$1,575$, making A the correct choice.

17) The function $f(x) = \frac{1}{x^2 - 4}$ is undefined when the denominator equals zero. Factoring the denominator gives $(x + 2)(x - 2) = 0$, so the function is undefined for $x = -2$ and $x = 2$. Thus, the domain is all real numbers except -2 and 2, written as $\mathbb{R} - \{-2, 2\}$, making D the correct choice.

18) The area of a circle is πr^2, where r is the radius. Given a diameter d, the radius is $\frac{d}{2}$. Thus, the total area the farmer will use for seed calculation, including the buffer, is $A = \pi\left(\frac{d}{2}\right)^2 + 15$. This accounts for the area of the circular field plus an additional 15 square meters, making A the correct formula.

19) The equation $x^3 - mx^2 + 4x = 0$ can be factored to $x(x^2 - mx + 4) = 0$, indicating one real root at $x = 0$. For the quadratic part to have no real roots, its discriminant must be negative: $m^2 - 4(1)(4) < 0$. So the equation $x^3 - mx^2 + 4x = 0$ has one real roots for $-4 < m < 4$. So, option A is correct.

20) To find the inverse of $f(x) = \ln(x + 3)$, swap x and y and solve for y: $x = \ln(y + 3)$. Converting to exponential form gives $y + 3 = e^x$, thus $y = e^x - 3$. Therefore, the inverse function is $e^x - 3$, making B the correct choice.

21) Substitute $j(x) = 3$ into $h(x)$: $h(j(x)) = h(3) = 3(3)^3 - 2(3)^2 - 3 + 1 = 27(3) - 18 - 3 + 1 = 81 - 18 - 3 + 1 = 61$.

22) Given the property: $_nC_{k-1} +_n C_k =_{n+1} C_k$ .Let's use this property to find the first five terms in row 21 of Pascal's triangle: Given the first five terms in row 20 are 1, 20, 190, 1140, and 4845. Using the property:

$$_{21}C_0 = \frac{21!}{0!(21-0)!} = \frac{21!}{21!} = 1$$

$$_{21}C_1 =_{20} C_0 +_{20} C_1 = 1 + 20 = 21$$

$$_{21}C_2 =_{20} C_1 +_{20} C_2 = 20 + 190 = 210$$

$$_{21}C_3 =_{20} C_2 +_{20} C_3 = 190 + 1140 = 1330$$

$$_{21}C_4 =_{20} C_3 +_{20} C_4 = 1140 + 4845 = 5985$$

Therefore, the first five terms in row 21 of Pascal's triangle are 1, 21, 210, 1330 and 5985

23) Using the formula $C = \frac{5}{9}(F - 32)$, substitute $F = 131$: $C = \frac{5}{9}(131 - 32) = \frac{5}{9} \times 99 = 55°C$.

24) To find the coefficient of x^4 in the expansion of $(2 - x)^2 \sum_{n=0}^{N}(-1)^n x^n$, we first expand $(2 - x)^2$:

$$(2 - x)^2 = (2 - x)(2 - x) = 4 - 2x - 2x + x^2 = 4 - 4x + x^2$$

Now, we multiply this expression by the series $\sum_{n=0}^{N}(-1)^n x^n$:

$$(4 - 4x + x^2) \sum_{n=0}^{N}(-1)^n x^n = \sum_{n=0}^{N} 4(-1)^n x^n + (-4)(-1)^n x^{n+1} + (-1)^n x^{n+2}$$

To find the coefficient of x^4, we need to find all the terms in the expansions of x^4 in each of these series and then sum up the coefficients. Therefore, to find the coefficient of x^4 in this term $4(-1)^n x^n + (-4)(-1)^n x^{n+1} + (-1)^n x^{n+2}$, we find that the coefficient of x^4 in $4(-1)^n x^n$ is: $x^4 = x^n \rightarrow n = 4 \rightarrow 4(-1)^4 = 4$, and the coefficient of x^4 in $(-4)(-1)^n x^{n+1}$ is: $x^4 = x^{n+1} \rightarrow n = 3 \rightarrow (-4)(-1)^3 = 4$, and the coefficient of x^4 in $(-1)^n x^{n+2}$ is:

$x^4 = x^{n+2} \rightarrow n = 2 \rightarrow (-1)^2 = 1$, Thus, the coefficient of x^4 in the expansion of $(2-x)^2 \sum_{n=0}^{N}(-1)^n x^n$ is $4+4+1 = 9$.

25) To determine the minimum number of real roots of $g(x) = 0$, we examine the sign changes in $g(x)$ values from the table. A change in sign of $g(x)$ between two consecutive x-values indicates a root exists within that interval (by the Intermediate Value Theorem). Observing the table:

- From $x = -5$ to $x = -3$, $g(x)$ changes from positive to negative (2 to -4), indicating at least one root.
- From $x = -3$ to $x = -1$, $g(x)$ changes from negative to positive (-4 to 6), indicating at least one more root.
- From $x = -1$ to $x = 2$, $g(x)$ changes from positive to negative (6 to -8), indicating at least one more root.
- From $x = 2$ to $x = 3$, $g(x)$ changes from negative to positive (-8 to 1), indicating at least one more root.

The function is a fifth-degree polynomial. So, it can have a maximum of five roots. Because the value of the function has changed sign four times, it has at least four roots.

26) First, find the number. 125% of the number is 50, so the number is $50 \div 1.25 = 40$. Then, find 75% of 40: $40 \times 0.75 = 30$. Therefore, 75% of that number is 30, making A the correct choice.

27) For $x = 1$, we use the interval $1 \leq x < 4$ where $f(x) = x + 3$. Substituting 1 for x gives $f(1) = 1 + 3 = 4$. Therefore, the value of $f(1)$ is 4, making C the correct answer.

28) Let the original population be P. After a 5% increase, the population is $P \times 1.05$. After a 15% increase the following year, the population is $P \times 1.05 \times 1.15$. This results in a total multiplier of 1.2075, or a 20.75% increase, rounded to 21%. Therefore, the total population increase after two years is approximately 21%, making B the correct choice.

29) The capacity left is $800 - 200 = 600$ liters. At 100 liters per hour, it takes $600 \div 100 = 6$ hours to fill. Starting at $14:00$, adding 6 hours brings us to $20:00$. Thus, the bathtub will be full at $20:00$.

30) To find the intersection of sets X and Y, we list the unique numbers present in both sets: $X = \{1,2,3,5,8,9\}$ and $Y = \{1,2,3,7,8,9\}$. Counting the unique numbers that appear in both sets gives us a total of 5 numbers in the set $(X \cap Y) = \{1,2,3,8,9\}$, thus the correct answer is A.

31) Substitute y with x in the first equation: $5x + 2x = 3$, which simplifies to $7x = 3$. Thus, $x = \frac{3}{7}$, making B the correct answer.

32) The total number of rooms in the hotel is $5x$ (since there are x rooms on each of the 5 floors), and if each room has y chairs, then the total number of chairs is $5x \times y = 5xy$, making B the correct choice.

33) Given $\alpha = 2\beta$ and $\beta = 3\gamma$, then $\alpha = 2(3\gamma) = 6\gamma$. Thus, 36γ is equal to $36\gamma \div 6\gamma = 6$ units of α, making D the correct choice.

34) To find the solutions, substitute y from the first equation into the second: $2x - (2x^2 + 3x - 5) = 2$, which simplifies to a quadratic equation in terms of x. Solving this quadratic equation typically yields two solutions, indicating that there are 2 intersections between the parabola and the line, making C the correct answer.

35) Rearrange the equation to form a quadratic: $3x^2 + x - 1 = 0$. Using the quadratic formula, $x = \frac{-b \pm \sqrt{b^2 - 4ac}}{2a}$, with $a = 3$, $b = 1$, and $c = -1$, yields $x = \frac{-1 \pm \sqrt{(1)^2 - 4(3)(-1)}}{2(3)} = \frac{-1 \pm \sqrt{1+12}}{6} = \frac{-1 \pm \sqrt{13}}{6}$. Thus providing solutions $\frac{-1 - \sqrt{13}}{6}$ and $\frac{-1 + \sqrt{13}}{6}$, making D the correct choice.

36) Since exponential growth is faster than linear growth, and both exponential and linear growth passes through the points $(1, \frac{4}{9})$ and $(6, 35)$. Therefore, from point 6 onwards, exponential growth is greater than linear growth. That is, for the interval $(6, +\infty)$.

37) Substitute $j(x) = \frac{2}{x}$ into $h(x)$: $h(j(x)) = h\left(\frac{2}{x}\right) = 3\left(\frac{2}{x}\right)^3 - 1 = \frac{24}{x^3} - 1$.

38) To find the x-intercept of the equation $y = -\frac{3}{4}x + 3$, set $y = 0$ and solve for x. Thus, $0 = -\frac{3}{4}x + 3$. Solving for x gives $x = 4$, which indicates that the x-intercept is at $(4, 0)$, aligning with option B.

39) Write the ratio of $3c$ to $4d$. $\frac{3c}{4d} = \frac{3}{8}$. Use cross multiplication and then simplify.

$$\frac{3c}{4d} = \frac{3}{8} \rightarrow 3c \times 8 = 4d \times 3 \rightarrow 24c = 12d \rightarrow c = \frac{1}{2}d$$

Now, find the ratio of c to d:

$$\frac{c}{d} = \frac{\frac{1}{2}d}{d} = \frac{1}{2}$$

40) Given the condition $(y < -2)$, all values smaller than -2 are possible values of y. Options B, C, D, and E are all greater than -2. Therefore, -3 is a possible value for y.

41) Solve for x using the given equation: $\frac{x-2}{3} = P$. Since $P = 4$, substitute P with 4 to get $\frac{x-2}{3} = 4$. Multiply both sides by 3 to get $x - 2 = 12$. Adding 2 to both sides gives $x = 14$.

42) To solve for c in terms of y when $c^{\frac{-4}{3}} = y$, take both sides to the power of $-\frac{3}{4}$ to invert the exponent on c. This results in $c = y^{-\frac{3}{4}}$, which simplifies to $c = \sqrt[4]{\frac{1}{y^3}}$, showing how to isolate c based on the given condition.

43) The total number of pages read by Tom and Jerry on Sunday can be found by adding the product of the number of hours each spent reading and the number of pages they read per hour. Tom read for 2 hours and Jerry read for 5 hours, so the total pages read is $2O + 5J$.

44) To determine the number of wooden planks needed for a 141-centimeter-tall column, use the ratio from the given height and number of planks. If 35 planks make $70\frac{7}{10}cm$, then 1 plank is approximately $2cm$ tall. For a 141-cm tall column, divide 141 by 2 to find the approximate number of planks needed, which gives 70.5. The closest option to 70.5 is 70.

45) To graph the equation $3x + 4y = 12$, we first solve for y in terms of x, obtaining $y = -\frac{3}{4}x + 3$. This equation indicates a slope of $-\frac{3}{4}$ and a y-intercept of 3. Among the options provided, option A correctly shows a line with a negative slope that, if extended, would intersect the y-axis at 3. The other options either depict lines with incorrect slopes, incorrect y-intercepts, or incorrect orientations relative to the x and y axes. Therefore, A is the correct representation of the given line equation.

46) Given $x + \frac{1}{x} = 3$, to find $x^2 + \frac{1}{x^2}$, square both sides of the equation to get $\left(x + \frac{1}{x}\right)^2 = 3^2$. This simplifies to $x^2 + 2\left(x \cdot \frac{1}{x}\right) + \frac{1}{x^2} = 9$, which simplifies further to $x^2 + \frac{1}{x^2} + 2 = 9$. Subtracting 2 from both sides gives $x^2 + \frac{1}{x^2} = 7$.

47) Evaluate each inequality after taking common denominators:

- A. $\frac{4}{5} > \frac{3}{4}$: Taking common denominators: $\frac{16}{20} > \frac{15}{20}$, Since $16 > 15$, A is true.
- B. $\frac{3}{8} < \frac{2}{7}$: Taking common denominators: $\frac{21}{56} < \frac{16}{56}$, Since $21 < 16$, B is false.
- C. $\frac{6}{9} > \frac{8}{11}$: Taking common denominators: $\frac{66}{99} > \frac{72}{99}$, Since $66 < 72$, C is false.
- D. $\frac{4}{7} > \frac{7}{10}$: Taking common denominators: $\frac{40}{70} > \frac{49}{70}$, Since $40 < 49$, D is false.
- E. $\frac{3}{5} < \frac{4}{9}$: Taking common denominators: $\frac{27}{45} < \frac{20}{45}$, Since $27 > 20$, E is false.

To compare $\frac{4}{5}$ and $\frac{3}{4}$, convert them to equivalent fractions with a common denominator or compare their decimal forms. $\frac{4}{5} = 0.8$ and $\frac{3}{4} = 0.75$, so $\frac{4}{5} > \frac{3}{4}$.

48) Evaluating each option: A and B both equal 2, C equals 4, D is 0 since $|1-3|-|3-1|$ equals $2-2=0$, and E equals 4 because it is the sum of 2 and 2. Therefore, D is the smallest value.

49) To simplify the fraction, multiply both the numerator and denominator of $\frac{2+4i}{-2i}$ by i:

$$\frac{2+4i}{-2i} \times \frac{i}{i} = \frac{2i+4i^2}{-2i^2} = \frac{2i-4}{2} = i-2$$

Now, we have: $\frac{2+4i}{-2i}+4 = i-2+4 = i+2$

50) Factoring the given quadratic equation $y = x^2 - 6x + 9$ results in $y = (x-3)^2$. This form clearly shows the x−intercept, which in this case, is 3. The squared term indicates that the x−intercept is a double root, occurring at $x = 3$.

51) To find the rate of change of the worker's total income with respect to the number of hours worked, we can use any two points from the table. For example, using the first and last points, (2, \$47) and (17, \$212), we calculate the rate of change as $\frac{\$212-\$47}{17-2} = \frac{\$165}{15} = \$11$ per hour. This rate represents the worker's hourly wage in addition to the fixed sum, indicating that for each hour worked, the total income increases by \$11.

52) Given $\frac{d}{c} = 3$, invert the ratio for $\frac{c}{d}$, which becomes $\frac{1}{3}$. Multiplying by 5 gives $\frac{5c}{d} = \frac{5}{3}$.

53) First, solve the given equations for x and y. From $x+4 = 7$, we find $x = 3$. From $3y-2 = 4$, we find $3y = 6$, hence $y = 2$. Next, substitute $x = 3$ and $y = 2$ into the expression $xy + 14$. This yields $3 \times 2 + 14 = 6 + 14 = 20$. Therefore, the value of $xy + 14$ is 20.

54) Start with the given equation $\frac{a-c}{c} = \frac{9}{14}$. To find $\frac{a}{c}$, add 1 to both sides of the equation (since $\frac{a-c}{c} + \frac{c}{c} = \frac{a}{c}$). This gives $\frac{a-c}{c}+1 = \frac{9}{14} + \frac{14}{14} = \frac{23}{14}$.

55) A line perpendicular to $4y+3x = 12$ would have a slope that is the negative reciprocal of the original line's slope. The original line, $4y+3x = 12$, simplifies to $y = -\frac{3}{4}x+3$. Therefore, the slope of the perpendicular line is $\frac{4}{3}$, and the line with this slope is $y = \frac{4}{3}x+4$.

56) Substitute $x = -2$ into the equation: $3(-2)^5 - a(-2)^2 + (-2) + 8 = 0$. This simplifies to $-96 - 4a - 2 + 8 = 0$. Solving for a, $-90 - 4a = 0$, so $-4a = 90$ and $a = -\frac{90}{4} = -22.5$.

57) A vertical shift downward by one unit would actually be represented by subtracting. Thus, the correct representation for a vertical shift downward by one unit from the base function 2^x would be $2^x - 1$.

58) Expand $\left(1 - \frac{2}{x}\right)^3$ to get $1 - \frac{6}{x} + \frac{12}{x^2} - \frac{8}{x^3}$. Now, multiply by $(2x^2 + 1)$ to find the constant term in the expression $(2x^2 + 1)\left(1 - \frac{2}{x}\right)^3$. So,

$$(2x^2 + 1)\left(1 - \frac{6}{x} + \frac{12}{x^2} - \frac{8}{x^3}\right) = 2x^2 - 12x + 24 - \frac{16}{x} + 1 - \frac{6}{x} + \frac{12}{x^2} - \frac{8}{x^3}$$

Simplified,

$$(2x^2 + 1)\left(1 - \frac{6}{x} + \frac{12}{x^2} - \frac{8}{x^3}\right) = 2x^2 - 12x + 25 - \frac{22}{x} + \frac{12}{x^2} - \frac{8}{x^3}$$

Finally, you find that the constant term of $(2x^2 + 1)\left(1 - \frac{2}{x}\right)^3$ is 25.

59) The total cost before shipping is the cost of the pens plus tax: $3p \times 1.085$. Adding the flat shipping fee of $6 gives $1.085(3p) + 6$, making E the correct formula for calculating the total cost.

60) Since the plant grows linearly and was 0 *cm* tall at week 0, reaching 40 *cm* at week 5, the rate of growth per week is $\frac{40\ cm}{5\ weeks} = 8\ cm/week$. Therefore, the height of the plant after x weeks is given by $y(x) = 8x$, making D the correct representation.

Author's Final Note

I hope you enjoyed this book as much as I enjoyed writing it. I have tried to make it as easy to understand as possible. I have also tried to make it fun. I hope I have succeeded. If you have any suggestions for improvement, please let me know. I would love to hear from you.

The accuracy of examples and practice is very important to me. We have done our best. But I also expect that I have made some minor errors. Constant improvement is the name of the game. If you find any errors, please let me know. I will fix them in the next edition.

Your learning journey does not end here. I have written a series of books to help you learn math. Make sure you browse through them. I especially recommend workbooks and practice tests to help you prepare for your exams.

I also enjoy reading your reviews. If you have a moment, please leave a review on Amazon. It will help other students find this book.

If you have any questions or comments, please feel free to contact me at drNazari@effortlessmath.com.

And one last thing: Remember to use online resources for additional help. I recommend using the resources on https://effortlessmath.com. There are many great videos on YouTube.

Good luck with your studies!

Dr. Abolfazl Nazari

Made in the USA
Las Vegas, NV
06 June 2024

90803941R00168